Methods and Materials in
SCHOOL HEALTH EDUCATION

Methods and Materials

in

SCHOOL HEALTH EDUCATION

by

LESLIE W. IRWIN, Ph.D.
Professor of Health Education
School of Education
Boston University

JAMES H. HUMPHREY, Ed.D.
Associate Professor in Charge of Teacher Education Curriculum in Elementary Health and Physical Education
University of Maryland

WARREN R. JOHNSON, Ed.D.
Professor and Curriculum Coordinator
of Health Education
University of Maryland

ST. LOUIS *1956* THE C. V. MOSBY COMPANY

COPYRIGHT, 1956, BY THE C. V. MOSBY COMPANY

(All rights reserved)

Printed in the
United States of America

Press of
The C. V. Mosby Company
St. Louis

PREFACE

The recent rapid growth and development of health education in both elementary and secondary schools throughout the country has emphasized the need for acceptable methods of teaching health. During the period between World War I and World War II the growth of health education in the schools was marked by more or less trial and error and haphazard methods of teaching health. It was learned, largely through experience with these trial and error methods of teaching health, that there must be proper education and training in methods on the part of teachers if health teaching is to be most successful. It was also learned that health teaching can result in more harm than good if it is not done properly. Therefore, it has become luminously clear, particularly during the past few years, that the first step in preparing to teach health successfully is that the teachers become thoroughly grounded in the proper methods, procedures and techniques of teaching in this area.

Although in past years there have been many books dealing with the school health program available for teachers and special students, they have not been very satisfactory as texts or reference books in the area of methods of teaching in health. Practically all books available, even at the present time, deal with all phases of the school health program including school health services, healthful school environment, healthful school living and organization, administration and conduct of health. Most of these health texts place little or no emphasis on *methods of teaching* health. One of the main reasons, apparently, why this is true is that most of the authors of these books are specialists in the field of health education and they are lacking in background, training, and experience in actually teaching health in elementary and secondary schools. Therefore, they are not particularly prepared nor qualified to approach the problem from the actual teaching of health materials. Furthermore, in preparing both health specialists and elementary school classroom teachers in the present day, usually each phase of the school health program is dealt with separately. That is, college courses in health are usually set up and organized so that separate courses are given in areas such as school health services, organization and administration of health, health guidance and methods of teaching health or methods and materials in health education. Consequently, a book that covers all areas of the school health program such as those typically available today is not suitable for the special courses in health education. There has been a need, for many years, for a text dealing primarily with methods and materials in health education.

This book, *Methods and Materials in School Health Education,* is designed as a text for use in courses dealing with health teaching of both graduate and undergraduate students in professional courses. It is particularly adapted to courses preparing health educators and in preparing elementary school classroom teachers to teach health to their children. Also, it should be very valuable to school administrators, supervisors and teachers in-service.

The materials presented herein are the results of many years of study, research, experimentation, and experience by the authors at all levels including the elementary, junior high school, senior high school, and college levels. The material and information are not merely opinions but carefully recorded results of actual experimentation and experience which was conducted under circumstances making it possible to determine with a high degree of objectivity the practices, methods, and procedures necessary to make the greatest contribution to the health teaching of children. The combined experience and training of the authors represents study and experience not only in teaching children but in preparing teachers.

The senior author experimented for over twelve years in teaching elementary school, junior and senior high school students in finding ways, means and methods to make health teaching successful. In that this extended experimentation was conducted in a laboratory school under controlled conditions, the results have been particularly fruitful when applied to teaching health in the schools.

Although Part I of the book deals briefly with school health services, health guidance, and the healthful school environment, it is intended only for orientation of elementary school classroom teachers and professional students in health education. The orientation presented is for the purpose of giving a common background for understanding the methods and materials presented in Part II of the book. It should be kept in mind that Part I is not intended to give either elementary school classroom teacher, school administrator or the professional student in health education the knowledge needed in the area of healthful school environment, health guidance or school health services. These areas must be studied and considered in courses primarily set up for the purpose.

Part II of the book, which is the major portion of the volume, is concerned specifically with methods and materials in teaching health in both elementary and secondary schools. It is in Part II that the research, experimentation, and experience of the authors is fully presented. The most recent and modern methods of teaching which have proved successful through measurements of results are included.

The authors are indebted to many people including students, colleagues, and publishers in the preparation and completion of the manuscript.

Boston, Massachusetts
College Park, Maryland
College Park, Maryland

Leslie W. Irwin
James H. Humphrey
Warren R. Johnson

CONTENTS

PART I. ORIENTATION IN SCHOOL HEALTH EDUCATION

CHAPTER   *Page*

1. INTRODUCTION 17
    Development of School Health Programs Prior to 1900 17
    School Health Between 1900 and World War I 18
    School Health Following World War I 18
    School Health Since World War II 20
    Terminology In School Health 21
    School Health Program 21
    School Health Services 22
    Healthful School Living 22
    School Health Education 22
    Healthful School Environment 22
    School Health Appraisal 23
    Health Counseling 23

2. ORGANIZATION AND ADMINISTRATION
   OF THE SCHOOL HEALTH PROGRAM 24
    Responsibility for Education Through the Public Schools 24
    Responsibility for Health Programs in the Schools 25
    Administration of the School Health Program Under an
        Official Community Health Organization 26
    The Administration of the School Health Program Under a
        Board of Education or a School Committee 31
    The Administration of the School Health Programs as a Joint Responsibility of the Schools and the Community Health Department .. 34
    Organization and Administration of the Health Program
        Within the Schools 36
    Fundamental Policies, Procedures, and Essentials in the Organization
        and Administration of the School Health Program 37

3. TEACHER OBSERVATION OF THE HEALTH OF CHILDREN .. 40
    The General Appearance of Health 40
    The Daily Health Observation 40
    Detecting Illnesses and Making Referrals 41

CHAPTER	Page
The Bases of Good Health	43
Health in Relation to Growth	43
Heredity and Health	44
The Health Record Card	45
Common Signs, Symptoms and Warning Signals	45
Facial Appearance	46
The Respiratory System	46
The Eyes	46
The Ears	47
The Neck	48
The Teeth	48
The Hair and Scalp	49
Posture	49
Speech Difficulties	50
Mental and Emotional Health	50
4. HEALTH GUIDANCE IN SCHOOLS	**54**
The Meaning of Health Guidance	54
Need for Health Guidance in Schools	55
Purpose of Health Guidance	56
Problems in Which Children and Youth Need Health Guidance	57
Bases for Determining Problems in Which Children and Youth Need Health Guidance	58
Health Appraisal	58
Teacher Observations	59
School Records	59
Devices for Gathering Information from Pupils	59
Surveys of Student Health Interests	60
Organization and Administration of the School Health Guidance Program	60
Desirable Principles of Operation	61
Media for Health Guidance	62
Responsibilities of Various School Personnel	62
School Administrative Officers	62
Health Service Personnel	63
Health Coordinator	63
Guidance Personnel	63
School Psychologist	63
Elementary School Teachers	64
Secondary School Teachers	64

CHAPTER	Page
Special Teachers	64
Extra-class Sponsors	64
Methods and Techniques of Health Guidance	65
Health Counseling	65
Group Health Guidance	66
Evaluation and Appraisal of the Health Guidance Program	67

PART II. METHODS AND MATERIALS IN TEACHING HEALTH

5. THE HEALTH TEACHING PROGRAM 70
   - The Need for Health Teaching in the Schools 70
   - The Place of Health Education in the School 88
   - The Value of Health Teaching 91
   - The Scope of the School Health Teaching Program 92
   - Plans for Health Teaching 93
   - Health Teaching in the Elementary School 96
   - Health Teaching in the Junior High School Grades 98
   - Health Teaching in the High School 101
   - The Use of Courses of Study and Curriculum Guides 105
   - Teaching Health Through Correlation 105
   - Teaching Health Through Integration 106

6. THE RELATIONSHIP OF HEALTH AND SAFETY IN THE SCHOOL PROGRAM 110
   - Deaths and Injuries from Accidents 110
   - Safety Prior to Modern Times 112
   - Safety in the World Today 112
   - Classification of Accidents 113
   - Risk and Exposure to Accidents 114
   - Mental, Emotional and Physical Factors Involved in Safety and Accident Prevention 115
   - Some Basic Causes of Child Accidents 117
   - Habit Formation in Safety 118
   - The Probable Value of Safety Education 118
   - Organization and Supervision of School Safety Programs 119
   - Home Accidents 120
   - Motor Vehicle Accidents 123
   - Occupational Accidents 125
   - Public Non-Motor Vehicle Accidents 126
   - School Accidents 126

CHAPTER	Page
Liability and Responsibility for School Accidents	128
Responsibility for Safety Education in the School Program	130
Safety Teaching at the Elementary School Level	132
Some Safety Topics Suggested for the Primary Grades	134
Some Safety Topics Suggested for Grades Four, Five and Six	137
Safety Education in the Junior High School Grades	140
Safety Topics for the Junior High School or Advanced Elementary Grades	141
Safety Education in the High School	145
Community Cooperation for Child Safety	149
7. CONCEPTS OF METHODOLOGY IN HEALTH EDUCATION	**153**
The Meaning of Method	153
Importance of Methods of Teaching	153
Early Methods of Health Education	154
Changing Concepts in Health Teaching Methods	155
Some Factors Affecting Methods in Health Education	156
The Individual Teacher	156
Time Allotment	157
Equipment and Materials	157
Classification of Pupils	157
Sources for the Selection of Methods	158
Some Principles of Learning Applied to Health Education	158
Some General Methods of Teaching Health	163
The Lecture Method	164
The Textbook Method	165
The Recitation Method	166
The Individual Method	166
The Small Group Method	167
The Problem Solving Method	167
8. THE UNIT METHOD IN HEALTH EDUCATION	**170**
The Meaning of Unit in Health Education	170
Development of the Unit Method	170
Types of Units	172
Resource Units	172
Teaching Units	173
Unit Patterns	173
Unit Construction	176

CHAPTER	Page
Length of Units	183
Lesson Planning	184

9. ORAL PRESENTATION IN HEALTH EDUCATION ... 194
The Role of Oral Presentation	194
Questions and Answers	195
Some Considerations in Developing and Utilizing Questions	196
Types of Questions to Avoid	197
Oral Presentation as an Introductory Activity	198
Oral Presentation by Students	199
The Discussion Leader	200
A Typical Class Discussion	201
The Lecture	202
Oral Comprehension	203
Critical Listening	203
Evaluation	204

10. MATERIAL AIDS TO LEARNING IN HEALTH EDUCATION .. 206
The General Nature, Purpose and Use of Material Aids to Learning in Health Education	207
Bulletin Boards	209
Cartoons	210
Charts	210
Flash Cards	212
Flat or Still Pictures	213
Graphs	214
Maps	217
Objects, Specimens and Models	217
Posters	219
Scrapbooks	219
Study and Activity Guides	220
Workbooks	222
Evaluation of Material Aids to Learning in Health Education	223

11. THE PLACE OF AUDIO-VISUAL MATERIALS IN HEALTH EDUCATION ... 226
The Place of Audio-Visual Aids in Health Education	226
The Purpose of Audio-Visual Aids in Health Education	227
How Audio-Visual Aids Contribute to Motivation and Interest in Health Education	229

CHAPTER   Page

    Basic Factors Involved in the Efficient and Effective Use of
        Audio-Visual Materials in Health Education 230
    Selection of Audio-Visual Aids 230
    Adequate Preparation in the Use of Audio-Visual Materials 231
    The Program of Sensory Aids In Health Education 234
    Evaluation of the Audio-Visual Aids in Health Education 235

12. MOTION PICTURES, RADIO, AND TELEVISION
    IN HEALTH EDUCATION 237
    Silent and Sound Motion Pictures 239
    Motion Pictures in Health Education 239
        State Departments of Education as Film Sources 240
        Departments of Health as Film Sources 241
        Voluntary Agencies, Industrial and Commercial
            Organizations as Source of Films 242
    Standards for Selecting Health Education Films 243
    Using Films 244
    Previewing and Scheduling the Film 245
    Showing the Film 246
    Radio as a Teaching Aid in Health Education 247
    The Use of Television in Health and Safety Education 249

13. DEMONSTRATIONS IN HEALTH EDUCATION 255
    Comparison of Individual Laboratory Work and Demonstrations ... 255
    The Role of the Demonstration 257
    Teacher Demonstrations 257
    Pupil Demonstrations 258
    Preparation for Demonstrations 259
    Utilizing Pupil Ingenuity 260
    Assigning Demonstrations 261
    Examples of Demonstrations 262
    Animal Experiments as Demonstrations 267
    Some Possible Safety Demonstrations 271
    Presentation of Demonstrations 272
    Preserving Demonstration Materials 274

14. FIELD TRIPS IN HEALTH EDUCATION 276
    The Purposes and Values of Field Trips
        in Health and Safety Education 278
    Kinds of School Health and Safety Trips 280
    Correlation and Integration Through School Trips 283

CHAPTER   Page

    Organization for Health and Safety Field Trips 284
    Plans, Procedures and Arrangements for Health
       and Safety Field Trips 285
    Evaluation and Appraisal of Health and Safety Field Trips 286
    Suggestions for Field Trips in Health and Safety 287
    Health and Safety Trips, Studies and Objectives
       Within the School 288
    Health and Safety Trips, Studies and Objectives in the
       Community and Surrounding Area 289

15. EXHIBITS AND MUSEUMS IN HEALTH EDUCATION 292
    Uses of Exhibits 293
    Principles of Exhibit Construction and Preparation 295
    School and Classroom Exhibits 295
    Museums in Health Education 298

16. DRAMATIZATION IN HEALTH EDUCATION 302
    The Meaning of Dramatization in Health Education 302
    Characteristics of Children as a Basis for Dramatics 303
    General Characteristics of the Dramatic Method 303
    Amateur Shows 305
    Health Plays 305
    Pageants 306
    Pantomime 307
    Puppets 307
    Quiz Programs 308
    Radio Broadcasts 308
    Role-Playing and Socio-drama 309
    Story Telling and Story Playing 310
    Grade Placement of Health Dramatic Activities 311

17. SOURCES OF HEALTH EDUCATION MATERIALS
    AND INFORMATION 313
    Textbooks 314
    Library Sources 315
    The Department of Education and Health 316
    The Federal Government 317
    Professional Organizations 317
    Business and Commercial Groups 318
        Free and Inexpensive Materials 319
        Some Major Sources of Free and Inexpensive Materials 319
        Survey of Sources **324**

CHAPTER

18. EVALUATION AND APPRAISAL IN HEALTH EDUCATION ... 333
    The Meaning of Evaluation in Health Education 333
    Why Evaluation is Necessary in Health Education 333
    General and Specific Evaluation in Health Education 334
        General Evaluation 334
        Specific Evaluation 336
    Some Evaluative Techniques for Health Education 337
        Data Gathering Devices Originating With the Teacher 338
        Standardized Tests 338
        Pupil Records 338
        Pupil Evaluation 338
    Evaluating for Health Knowledge 339
        Teacher-Prepared Paper and Pencil Tests 339
        Oral Questioning 342
        Demonstrations 343
        Flash Cards 344
        Examination of Work Done By Pupils 344
        Dramatization 344
    Evaluating for Health Attitudes 345
    Evaluating for Health Practices 346
    Necessary Abilities for Successful Evaluation and
        Appraisal of Learning in Health Education 347

19. IN-SERVICE EDUCATION IN HEALTH EDUCATION 350
    Need for In-Service Education in Health and Safety Education 350
    Scope of In-Service Education in Health 351
    Supervision in Health Education 352
        Visitation 352
        Meetings and Conferences 352
        Bulletins 353
        Demonstrations 353
    Health Education Workshops 353
    School System In-Service Courses 355
    Advanced Study 356
        Institutional Education 356
        Independent Study 357
    Professional Literature 357
    Professional Associations 358

PART I
ORIENTATION IN SCHOOL HEALTH EDUCATION

CHAPTER 1
INTRODUCTION

The rapid development of school health education during the past decade has created an urgent need for reexamination and reevaluation of policies, means and methods of dealing with the health of children and youth of school age. The school health program in the United States is rapidly emerging from a more or less trial and error period of attempting to provide and contribute in the most efficient and effective way to the optimum growth and development of the school child. Crystalization of the results of experience and experimentation with school health during the past few years has made it luminously clear that a new approach is needed to numerous phases of the program if parents, teachers and the schools are to contribute optimally to the physical, mental and emotional growth and development of children.

In order to understand the present status of school health in the United States, as well as to be prepared to take advantage of past experience in improving programs for school children, it may be helpful to briefly consider the stages of growth and development of our school health programs as they exist today.

Development of School Health Programs Prior to 1900.— Although there was some emphasis on the health of the school child in the United States prior to the year 1900, the greatest efforts to establish what is today recognized as modern and acceptable school health programs is a comparatively new development.

The main efforts in school health before 1900 centered largely in the more or less unorganized and haphazard attempts to control communicable diseases and in teaching physiology and hygiene with special reference to alcohol and narcotics.

The first public schools in America gave practically no attention whatever to the health of the school population. Beginning about the year 1880, most states passed laws requiring the schools to give instruction concerning the ill effects of alcohol and narcotics. In many cases, the state law required that instruction in alcohol and narcotics be a part of a broader program of instruction in physiology and hygiene.

As the year 1900 approached, the program for controlling communicable diseases among school children was gaining wider attention than ever before. Medical inspections were developed as a major means of attempting to control communicable diseases. This procedure in one form or another became a routine part of most school programs.

School Health Between 1900 and World War I.—Experience with school medical inspections following 1900 gradually showed that, although helpful to some extent in controlling communicable diseases, they were wholly inadequate as a school health program. Thus, there began a slow but gradual development of school health service programs.

The physiology and hygiene courses developed prior to 1900 were almost completely discontinued because of a lack of agreement concerning needs, results and methods of teaching. Furthermore, it was never fully established and agreed upon among educators that responsibility for the health of the school population was a function of the schools.

Although the period between 1900 and World War I was not particularly fruitful from the viewpoint of school health, the rapidly developing public health work in the United States gave considerable impetus to the formation of various groups and organizations interested in the study, development and promotion of child health.

School Health Following World War I.—Great emphasis was placed on the health of the school child following World War I. Revelation of the adverse physical, mental and emotional condition of a substantial percentage of the draftees in World War I was a main factor in awakening a realization on the part of educators and the American public of an urgent need for better school health programs. Educators in particular, became highly conscious of the need for progress designed to improve and maintain the health of school children. The emphasis upon health was so strong following World War I that national education groups placed the health of the school child as one of the major objectives of education.

Even though health was listed as one of the most important objectives of education the development of acceptable school health programs was comparatively slow. One of the reasons for this somewhat slow development immediately following World War I was that major emphasis was placed on health and physical education programs in attempting to improve and maintain child health. Physical education programs came into wide popularity and developed very rapidly. However, over the years the physical education phase of the work was emphasized almost to the exclusion of what is now recognized as acceptable and desirable school health programs. Unfortunately, a rather general impression grew that physical education was the same as health education and that a physical education program was entirely adequate. This was to be expected as a majority of the teacher education institutions preparing physical education teachers did not prepare them to deal properly with a modern school health program. Furthermore, physical education teachers, on the whole, have not had sufficient time in the school program to properly handle and develop both physical education and health education. In most schools teaching physical education is a full-time position and serious difficulties are usually encountered when the additional work of conducting a satisfactory health program is also required.

Another reason for the comparatively slow development of school health is that certain phases of the program require the assistance of many health specialists who are not ordinarily a part of the school personnel. Physicians, nurses, dentists, dental hygienists, nutritionists, health educators and psychologists are among those considered necessary in certain phases of the modern school health program. Although most schools do not as yet have the services of all these specialists, nevertheless, some of them are considered indispensable particularly to the school health service program.

A few schools have been fortunate enough to have adequate funds to employ the services of sufficient health and medical specialists to have excellent health service programs. Some schools have recognized the need for the help of many health specialists and sometimes they have had sufficient funds to employ them but they found they were not available. Other schools have recognized the need for health specialists but have not had funds to employ them even if they were available. Then, too, some schools have not had sufficient funds and neither have they recognized the need for better health services that can be provided only with the assistance of health and medical specialists. These same conditions continue to exist even today. Furthermore, they will likely exist until such time as health and medical specialists are trained in sufficient numbers to provide the proper service for school children.

The shortage of health and medical specialists was usually most acute in rural areas. Consequently, children in rural areas were most neglected so far as school health service programs were concerned.

School Health Since World War II.—The results of medical and psychological examinations of millions of people during the second World War revealed a high percentage of youth unfit for military service. Approximately 40 per cent of those examined for military service were rejected for medical reasons or for mental and emotional disorders. Because the physical, mental and emotional status of youth of military age in World War II had not seemingly improved so far as it could be directly compared with the status of military personnel in World War I, it was reasoned that little progress was made during the interim between wars, regardless of the greater emphasis placed on school health and physical education. Consequently, the schools were frequently criticized by some people for what was considered a failure of school health programs. However, such criticisms were unjustifiable because of the fact that during the time between World War I and the beginning of World War II a majority of the schools in the United States did not have even the bare minimum requirements of what is now considered modern school health programs. If any criticism is justifiable, perhaps it should be that in a majority of the schools in the United States there was almost a complete lack of what is now considered desirable and necessary for the proper improvement and maintenance of the health of children and youth.

Although the verbal emphasis on the importance of school health following World War I was great, it has been even greater during and since the end of World War II. In addition to continued interest and emphasis on the part of educators there is far greater interest than ever before on the part of local, state and national medical and public health groups as well as public and private welfare agencies and organizations. The trend in making adequate provisions for the school health services and protection programs has moved in the direction of close, cooperative planning between school and community health departments and organizations.

It is now generally recognized that physical education, the same as other areas in the school program, has certain contributions to make to the health of school children. It is also recognized that a physical education program should not be considered a health program. Neither should a physical education program be considered a substitute for a health program.

In addition to the comparatively rapid progress of school health service and protection programs since World War II, there has been very marked progress in health education programs in elementary, junior and senior high schools, particularly since 1950. School administrators in increasing numbers are recognizing the obligation of the schools to provide healthful and safe conditions for work and play, to maintain reasonable standards of appraisal of the health status of children and to provide learning experiences which will prepare children to live healthfully throughout their lives.

Terminology in School Health.—There is frequent misunderstanding concerning the exact meaning of words and terms used to describe various phases of the school health programs. Numerous individuals, groups and organizations have at times attempted to define the health terms commonly used. Although these attempts to universally clarify health terminology have been helpful, rapid progress and changing conditions and situations operate to change and alter the meaning of rigidly defined terms.

The work of the Joint Committee[1] on Terminology in School Health Education of the American Association for Health, Physical Education and Recreation and the American School Health Association has perhaps been most influential in determining the use of terminology in this area in recent times. Health terms used in this volume will follow the work of the terminology committee so far as possible in view of changing emphasis, practices, programs and needs since the committee completed the work.

School Health Program.—The school health program embodies the total school program in health. It involves all health activities

---

[1]Report of the Committee on Terminology in School Health Education, Journal of the American Association for Health, Physical Education and Recreation, Vol. XXII, No. 7, September, 1951.

which are planned, organized and conducted by the school and under the jurisdiction of the school. It includes all school activities that contribute to understanding, maintenance and improvement of the health of the school population including health services, health education, healthful school living and healthful school environment. Ordinarily, a major part of the health program is carried on within the confines of the school although highly important parts of the work may be on a community-wide basis and it may involve numerous community organizations and agencies.

School Health Services.—Health services as applied to the school program embody all efforts of the school to conserve, protect and improve the health of the school population through activities and procedure such as medical and dental examinations; follow-up of health examinations; encouragement and assistance in plans for the correction of defects; observation of pupils; control of communicable diseases; health counseling; appraisal of health status; providing emergency care for the sick and injured; provisions for the care and education of handicapped and exceptional children; and supervision and maintenance of hygienic and sanitary conditions of the school plant and facilities.

Healthful School Living.—Healthful school living is a term used to designate the plans, procedures and activities involved in the provision of conditions within the school which are most conducive to optimum physical, mental and emotional health and safety of the school population. It includes such factors as the provisions of a wholesome and favorable environment; total school organization basically designed to maintain optimum health; satisfactory relationship between teachers, pupils and administrators; satisfactory relationship between pupils; ample periods of rest, relaxation and recreation; and school buildings, facilities and activities free from unnecessary safety hazards.

School Health Education.—The term school health education has taken on new meaning in recent years. At one time health education was used to designate the total school health program. It is now commonly used to designate that part of the school health program which provides teaching and learning experiences and activities for the purpose of favorably influencing knowledge, habits, attitudes, practices, appreciations and conduct pertaining to individual and group health.

Healthful School Environment.—The terms healthful school living and healthful school environment are used more or less synonymously by many educators and in much of the literature dealing with school health. It is usually thought that healthful school living embodies all factors making up a healthful school environment. In some cases, however, the term school "environment" is used in a broader sense to indicate not only the school plant and facilities but the surrounding area in the community. An example of this is that of considering the traffic conditions particularly in the vicinity of the school as a part of the school environment.

School Health Appraisal.—The term health appraisal has been adopted in late years to indicate that phase of the school health program which attempts to determine the total health status of the child through the use of such means as health histories; observations, screenings and medical, dental and psychological examinations. The information secured through the total appraisal of the school child helps teachers, nurses, physicians and others to recognize and understand the needs of the individual. Also, it may help to provide a basis for health counseling. Also, the various appraisal procedures are frequently used as important learning experiences for pupils.

Health Counseling.—School health counseling is the process by which various members of the school personnel may help students with their problems and assist them in developing plans of action which will lead to solutions of personal problems. Teachers, physicians, guidance personnel, nurses, administrators and others may at various times, depending upon needs, assist in school health counseling. In some cases the counseling may take the form of interpretation and determination of the extent, nature and significance of health problems of children and it may involve parents in an effort to help a child. In many cases it is frequently necessary for health counseling to involve the parents of children in order to satisfactorily solve personal health problems.

CHAPTER 2

ORGANIZATION AND ADMINISTRATION OF THE SCHOOL HEALTH PROGRAM

Although there is almost universal agreement that the health of the school child is of primary importance, there is wide difference of opinion, as well as much misunderstanding, concerning the organization, administration and conduct of the modern school health program.

Responsibility for Education Through the Public Schools.— Education through the public schools in the United States is fundamentally based upon the principle of equal opportunity for all children. Although people often differ in opinion regarding the management, direction, and conduct of the educational program within the schools, they are in practically unanimous agreement that every child should have the best education possible in the tax-supported schools.

In order to determine the ultimate responsibility for the health program in the schools it is necessary to call attention to the development of public school education in the United States. The Tenth Amendment to the Constitution of the United States clarifies the power of the Federal and State Governments concerning the public education of the people. This Amendment clearly places upon each state the responsbility for the education of its people, to the extent at least that education through the public schools is not the direct responsibility of the Federal Government.

During the growth of the public schools the extent of responsibility taken for public education has varied greatly from one state to another. In most states the balance of power in establishing, conducting and operating the public tax-supported schools has remained largely in the hands of the local communities. The local communities have the power to establish any kind of education desired by its citizens within the limits of state laws and regulations pertaining to public school education and to available funds. It is true that many states have controlled education in the local communities to a certain extent, through state laws and the dispensation of financial aid through official agencies such as state departments of public instruction. Yet, in the main, it remains the power of the local community in most states to almost completely control the educational programs in the public schools.

Responsibility for Health Programs in the Schools.—As the school health program is, in all of its ramifications, a part of the total school educational program, it follows then that those responsible for education through the public schools are also directly responsible for the total school health program. If local communities are directly responsible for their public schools, limited only by existing state laws and regulations, then naturally they are directly responsible for all health activities conducted within the jurisdiction of the schools. Boards of education, school committees, or other duly elected or appointed representatives are usually vested with the power to represent the citizens within the community in the direct operation and control of the public schools. So far as existing functioning programs of health in the schools are concerned then, boards of education or school committees are directly responsible for school health activities the same as for other phases of the educational program.

The power of school boards or school committees to deal with the health program in the schools is, to some extent, limited by the power of state and community health authorities. That is, the power of school boards and school committees is limited in school health to the extent of the power of local and state health authorities to protect and conserve the health of the citizens within the community of which the school children are a part. Frequently, the power of local and state health authorities is limited largely to the protection of the public and individual health in times of emergency or in situations or circumstances in which there is an urgent need for lawfully controlled health measures. Although the actual power of local and state health groups is frequently limited largely to the protective phases of health, nevertheless, they are frequently active in health education movements within the state and community designed to improve the general health status of both school children and adults.

There has been a growing feeling among certain groups in late years that health specialists, and particularly medical specialists, should assume full and complete control of certain phases of the school health program. This feeling has come about partly because of the need for health specialists in carrying out certain phases of the school health program. In the area of health service particularly, it is necessary to use many health specialists; physicians, nurses, dentists, dental hygienists, nutritionists, health educators and others are considered necessary to the proper conduct of the most acceptable and desirable types of health service programs. It is the feeling of some medical specialists, because state and community health groups are responsible to a certain extent for the health of school children at all times, that the school health program should be considered as only one part of the community-wide child health program. Also, some medical groups feel that members of the school personnel are not qualified to organize and administer the work of health specialists.

Although there frequently exists divided opinion relative to the question of the ultimate responsibility for school health service programs and certain parts of the healthful school environment program, there is almost unanimous agreement among all groups that the schools should continue to assume full responsibility for organized health teaching programs.

The controversy surrounding the administrative control of school health programs began many years ago when the main function of the community boards of health was to assume control of and accept at least partial responsibility for communicable diseases in the school. The growth of the modern school health program has heightened the controversy as to the extent of responsibility of both boards of education and official community health agencies. Many of the differences of opinion have arisen largely because of the varying backgrounds of training and experience of school and health authorities. Diversity of needs in different communities and methods used in trying to care for the needs have added to the complexities of the problem and to misunderstandings between health and school authorities.

Administration of the School Health Program Under an Official Community Health Organization.—Some of the usual arguments postulated in favor of the administration of school health under an official community health organization are:

1. The official community health organization has the power and legal status and is organized and prepared to deal with the control of communicable diseases. The control of communicable diseases often involves the entire community of which the schools are a part.

2. Children are a community problem from the viewpoint of health a large part of the time as they attend school only four to six hours a day through six to ten months of the year.
3. Duplication of services rendered by health specialists employed by the schools and those employed by a community health department can be eliminated.
4. Mistakes made in the organization, administration, and conduct of health programs because of a lack of specialized training needed in the health field can be avoided and thereby decrease the cost and increase the efficiency of the total school and community child health program.
5. The official community health organization ordinarily has a more comprehensive knowledge of community conditions which are likely to affect the health of all including the school children.
6. Health and medical specialists should be considered authorities in selecting subject matter employed in instructing children in health and healthful living in order to avoid misunderstandings and misinterpretations of technical and specific health knowledge.

Although the arguments in favor of the administration of the school health program under an official community health organization rather than a board of education or school committee are convincing, careful consideration of the arguments shows that there are some criticisms to such a plan at least at the present time. Experience in the schools shows that the assuming of full and complete control of any regular school activity on the part of organizations or agencies outside the jurisdiction of the schools is a highly questionable procedure for a number of reasons. First, with the present legal arrangements for the direct control of the schools in local communities in most states, boards of education or school committees are directly and legally responsible to the community for all phases of education conducted in the schools, including health education. If health departments attempted to assume full and complete control of the school health program without being under the control of the school board or school committee there would be divided responsibility for the educational program within the schools. In the absence of state legislation which might legalize such an arrangement, it becomes questionable. Second, divided responsibility leads to misunderstandings and inefficiency in the conduct of the total school program. Third, personnel of health departments usually lack experience, training, and understanding of education routine and methods which are highly essential to the efficient and effective operation of an educational program for the millions of children in the schools.

The argument concerning the duplication of services of health specialists such as physicians, nurses and dentists is valid for those schools and communities where health specialists are in sufficient number to bring about a duplication of work. However, this argument does not apply to a vast majority of the schools and communities in the United States for there are not enough health specialists available to handle even a bare minimum of activities that should be included in an acceptable and desirable school health program. As a matter of fact, large numbers of schools throughout the country do not have sufficient services of school or community nurses and only a very small percentage have the services of physicians to the extent of providing what is considered a modern and acceptable health service program. Therefore, at this time at least, and likely for many years to come, the problem of the duplication of school health services on the part of school and community health specialists in a majority of the communities in the United States does not necessarily constitute a problem which would justify dividing the responsibility for the organization, administration and conduct of the schools. Furthermore, in those communities fortunate enough to have enough school and community health specialists to cause some duplication of health services, it is likely that the most advisable procedure would be to work out some kind of joint or cooperative plan to eliminate the overlapping without dividing the responsibility for the conduct of the schools.

The argument that members of community health departments should have full and complete control of school health because they are better prepared to organize and administer the program in view of their specialized training is becoming less valid as time moves forward. With the growing and widespread knowledge concerning health and healthful living school administrators and health specialists employed by the schools, as well as others of the school personnel, are becoming better prepared to organize and administer school health programs and, thereby, better able to properly coordinate all activities in the educational program without dividing the responsibility which might serve to lessen the efficiency of the total educational program. Furthermore, it is both possible and desirable particularly in the larger schools, to employ a medical specialist responsible to the school administrators and to the board of education or school committee to assume responsibility for the organization and administration of the school health service program. In such cases the school medical specialist and other members of the school personnel can work on a cooperative basis with the community health department without dividing the responsibility for the operation of the schools.

The claim that community health departments have a wider knowledge of community conditions which might affect health is convincing when considered from the point of view of protection. So far as the type of health program that should be conducted in the schools is concerned, however, it is questionable whether health departments are as well aware of conditions which affect the positive health of the child as teachers and some other members of the school personnel. For example, a classroom teacher becomes thoroughly familiar with all of her pupils. She becomes so familiar with them within a very short time after the beginning of school that she is at once able to tell whether factors within the life of a child are conductive to his health. It may be that a child's health is adversely affected through a failure to practice the proper health measures pertaining to foods, rest, sleep, and the like. It may be necessary for the teacher to contact the home in trying to establish the best health routine for the child. Or, the child's health may be affected because of an imbalance of school work and work outside the school. In such cases the classroom teacher may need to help make the proper adjustments. After consideration of the many factors involved in an educational and positive health program for school children, it is evident that members of the school personnel may be far more familiar with conditions within the community and homes of the children than the health department simply because of the nature of certain factors affecting the health of the school child. It is very true that health departments are in a position to understand general health conditions within the community far better than others. Because they are not in a position to know about most of the more intimate factors concerned with the maintenance of health, such as is learned for example, by classroom teachers in the course of their daily living with the school child, it is questionable whether the direct responsibility for the total educational program of the school should be divided on this basis.

The idea that medical specialists should be considered authorities on health subject matter used in teaching children hygiene and healthful living in order to avoid misunderstanding and misinterpretation of technical and specific knowledge can be accepted only in part. There is no question but that medical specialists are authorities upon technical and specific health matters but they cannot be considered authorities on subject matter used in teaching children. Those in the medical field who continue to insist upon authority of this kind which is, in the absence of experience and specialized preparation in teaching, beyond their capacity and training to assume successfully, are certain to create discord and a resentful attitude among teachers who are specifically and professionally trained in methods, techniques, and procedures in teaching children. Furthermore, there is not the need for such high specialization to select authoritative and technically correct health content materials for children as is often implied by those who insist upon this point. The level of maturity of school children is such that highly technical matters in the field of health and hygiene are beyond their capacity and therefore undesirable for introduction particularly at the elementary and lower secondary grade levels. Also, there are in the present day, ample health study materials written and prepared on a co-authorship basis by specialists in both the field of medicine and the field of professional education from which to select. If medical experts in health departments of communities attempted to determine the health content material a third grade teacher, for example, should offer as study materials for her pupils, the process would likely resolve itself into the selection of textbooks and reading materials prepared by authors who are both medical and professional education experts. In many instances it would be a case wherein a community physician attempting to tell a third grade teacher what to use would be far less capable of judging the health content material for third grade children than the physician and teacher who are authors of the study materials or books. Therefore, it is relatively safe to say that considering the present general level of knowledge of teachers and the public, the matter of the selection and gradation of health study materials should be left very largely to the teachers and school administrators. Then, if they feel the need of consultation and assistance in the matter of selecting health content materials for the children they are free to seek assistance from among those health authorities of their choice and in whom they have confidence rather than being compelled to abide by arbitrary decisions of individuals in whom both the teachers and the children may lack confidence. In many schools throughout the country there are health specialists such as nurses, health educators and others who are fully capable of assisting teachers in selecting health study materials if they feel the need of assistance.

The argument that medical specialists should be considered authorities in selecting subject matter employed in teaching children in health and healthful living is incompatible with the generally accepted fact that even though community health departments do assume full and complete control of the health service program within the school, they should not assume control of the health teaching program which must be left to those specifically educated and trained to teach children.

The Administration of the School Program Under a Board of Education or a School Committee.—Some of the reasons frequently given to justify the continuance of the school health program as a direct responsibility of the board of education or school committee are:

1. The board of education or school committee, in the absence of local or state legislation, is dutifully and legally obligated to the citizens within the community to assume full control of and responsibility for all phases of the educational program, including the health program conducted in the public schools.
2. School administrators and teachers, by virtue of their training in professional education methods, are better prepared to coordinate, organize, and conduct the total school program for children which requires a unique kind of preparation and experience.
3. The school plant, facilities, and equipment belong to the school. Responsibility for the sanitation and hygienic condition of school facilities should be accepted by the school authorities.
4. The organization of the total school day for the best health of the children can be done best by the school personnel.
5. The division of responsibility for the educational program which would exist if health departments assumed full and complete control of the school health program places teachers in a position of being responsible to two community authorities. It is not considered administratively sound to have two separate and distinct groups attempting to direct the work of teachers. Any friction that might develop between the board of education or the school committee and the community health department would place the teachers in the school in a difficult position.
6. Teachers are far more likely to cooperate with the board of education or school committee and school

administrators than with organizations outside the schools.
7. In many communities in the United States, the schools are less likely than health departments to be subject to political interference, particularly in matters surrounding the determination and allotment of financial support.
8. Teachers are better able to handle organized health teaching programs at all grade levels throughout the school. Medical experts and health department specialists are usually neither qualified nor prepared to assume responsibility for organized health teaching on the most successful basis.
9. When the health program is under a board of education or school committee it can be considered with and take its place alongside other phases of the school program in curriculum revision projects which are a common and constant procedure in the modern educational program.

In attempting to determine whether a board of education or a health department should administer the school health program on the basis of the arguments in favor of a board of education or school committee taking the responsibility, it must be admitted that, largely because of the background of growth and development of the present educational system, it seems that full and complete responsibility should be retained in the hands of the school. If health departments attempt to take the full responsibility for the health program, they are taking away from the schools certain prerogatives and rights which have grown and developed with the public school education system. However, as the modern school health program broadens, it becomes increasingly evident that the schools must have the aid and assistance of community health departments. It is quite possible that in the distant future the most logical and acceptable procedure will be for health departments to take full responsibility for school health programs. The present, however, does not seem to be the opportune time for a wholesale change in responsibility in this area. There are, unquestionably, many schools and communities which can function best, because of circumstances peculiar to the individual community, with the health department administering the school health program.

Under certain circumstances a majority of the arguments in favor of the administration of the health program under a board of education or school committee can be surmounted. In regard to the obligation of the local school board or school committee to assume full and complete control and responsibility for the school health program, it may be said that local and state legislation can relieve the schools of this obligation. Also, the schools can delegate authority to health departments for the organization, administration, and conduct of the program.

In answer to the argument that school administrators and teachers, by virtue of their education and experience, are better prepared to coordinate, organize, and conduct the total school program including health, it may be said that health departments can overcome this argument by requiring members of their personnel who are to work directly with schools to get sufficient training in educational methods to enable them to function more efficiently and effectively in the public school program. The argument pertaining to the division of responsibility is the most difficult to surmount because all teachers in the school program should have a part in the health program. If only the health specialists in the schools were involved it would not be so difficult, for they could be employed by a health department or perhaps they could be employed jointly by a board of education and a health department which is a common practice at present in some communities.

With respect to the health teaching program, it seems reasonably certain that this phase of the health program will remain in the hands of the school administrators and the teachers, regardless of who may finally assume the total and complete responsibility for other phases of school health. Furthermore, it is not likely that health departments will ever have final authority in the determination of subject matter and study materials to be used in educating children in health and healthful living.

In organizing the total school day on a basis conducive to the best health of the children, it may be done better finally as a joint responsibility of the school and health department. That is, when health authorities have progressed to the point of securing sufficient preparation in professional education methods to properly understand the school educational program in all of its ramifications, they can be helpful to the school personnel in arriving at the best organization of the school day.

The Administration of the School Health Program as a Joint Responsibility of the Schools and the Community Health Department.—There is an ever-growing trend and tendency for the school health program to be administered jointly by the board of education or the school committee and the community health department. In some communities such plans have been in operation for many years. The arguments ordinarily advanced in favor of the joint responsibility are:

1. Specialized health personnel can be employed jointly by the board of education and the health department.
2. Communicable diseases can be controlled better through a joint administrative responsibility.
3. Sanitation and hygienic conditions within the school plant and facilities can be more readily assured on a joint basis.
4. Jointly employed health specialists can help to secure the better cooperation of all teachers when they are recognized members of the school personnel.
5. Jointly employed health specialists are in a better position to participate in curriculum revision within the school which may have a bearing upon the health program. Also, the health specialist is in a position to take some part in the total health teaching program.

On first consideration it may seem that the joint responsibility plan is the solution to the problem of administering the school health program. As a matter of fact, it has many shortcomings. Yet, it is quite possible that this plan will emerge in the future as the one most readily accepted during the period of transition and development of more effective ways and means of capitalizing upon present knowledge in providing for and assuring the optimum health, growth, and development of the school child. The fact that neither health authorities nor educators are willing to agree unanimously on the responsibility for the administration of the school health program makes it seem more than ever likely that the joint responsibility plan will be accepted as a compromise for many years to come. The joint responsibility plan may be best in most communities, for it should tend to make both educators and health specialists more tolerant of the positions of each, as well as more likely to cooperate to the greatest extent for the best interests and welfare of the school child.

Even though the joint responsibility plan seems to be the one most likely to be adopted in the very near future, it should be pointed out that the most sensible and logical approach to the problem of deciding upon the responsibility for the administration of the school health program is in first considering the needs in the individual school and community. The circumstances peculiar to the individual community should be the determining factors in assigning final responsibility regardless of the general trends throughout the country.

Another point that should be strongly emphasized in the matter of the joint responsibility for school health is that there must be full cooperation and participation on the part of both the school personnel and health department specialists. Domination by one group and acquiesence on the part of the other does not represent true joint responsibility. Neither is it conducive to close cooperation and smooth functioning of the plan. An administrative arrangement on a joint basis between the educators and health authorities within the community in which one group or other dominates or attempts to dominate the arrangement is likely doomed to failure. It may function partially for a time but sooner or later there is likely to be friction of a nature to cause withdrawal of one group or another from the plan and thereby deprive the school child for many years to come of a desirable health program. Experience has shown that health groups are more likely to attempt to dominate the arrangements in the joint responsibility plan, although this is not always true. Apparently the tendency on the part of the health specialists to dominate in the school health program is frequently based upon the fact that they often fail to properly appreciate and understand the emphasis placed upon democracy in the modern educational process. Modern educational methods strongly emphasize the need to organize and conduct the school program on a democratic basis in the process of educating children for democracy. Health authorities, on the other hand, may not be cognizant of the usual democratic approach in the schools. A part of the lack of understanding may stem from the fact that it has often been necessary for health authorities to be more or less arbitrary in their approach and manner of dealing with the public in order to safeguard the welfare of all. In the school health program, however, an arbitrary or dictatorial attitude on the part of either educators or health specialists is likely to both jeopardize close cooperation and lead to friction, with the ultimate result of hindering and handicapping the health of the child. Both educators and health specialists should keep in mind that there are times when each must accept and act upon the advice of the other.

Organization and Administration of the Health Program Within the School.—There are many differences of opinion concerning the ways the health program should be organized and administered within the school. There may be frequent conflict among the teachers, health specialists and school departments regarding the conduct of various phases of the school health program. Perhaps most of the arguments surrounding the conduct of the school health program concern the person or department to head or direct the program. Next in order are questions relative to whether health service should be organized separately from other phases of the health program, and whether or not there should be a health director or coordinator. Plans for the best type of organization for health within the schools have not fully crystallized. It is likely to be many years before the most advantageous plans emerge to the point where it can be said with any degree of certainty which plan is best to use in the average school situation. As a matter of fact, plans for organizing school health programs may never crystallize to the point where it will not be necessary to make adaptations on the basis of existing conditions within the individual school and community. At the present time there are numerous plans of organization for health in operation in the schools throughout the country. The type of health organization to use naturally depends upon many factors such as the size and location of the school, financial conditions, local and state laws pertaining to health which may affect the school program, specific needs of the children within the particular school, availability of health specialists, and perhaps most important of all, the attitude, interest, and leadership of boards of education or school committees, school administrators, and health officials within the community.

In the larger city school systems it is often the custom to have a school health division which is primarily responsible for the health service program as well as for a large share of the healthful school living program. Ordinarily, in the large city system the organized health teaching program is not a part of the school health division. More often it is organized entirely separate and as a part of the total school instruction program. Or it may be a part of the physical education program, particularly at the secondary school level. However, it is no longer considered most desirable for the health teaching program to be organized as a part of the physical education program.

In schools between the sizes of the large city systems and what might be termed schools of average size, various kinds of organizations are evident. In some cases, the health program remains as a part of the physical education program. In other cases, there may be a separate health division under the guidance of a director of health or a health coordinator, or there may not be any clear-cut lines of organization. In the smaller schools, and a majority of the schools in the United States are small schools located in small communities, there is little need for highly organized health programs for they usually lack the personnel to conduct even a bare minimum of the health education essentials.

In many of the small schools physical education teachers remain responsible for the health program. That is, they are responsible for the health work if anything is done for they are usually the only teachers in the school who have any kind of special preparation bearing directly on health. In some cases, the principal of the small school assumes almost sole responsibility for organizing and conducting the health program especially in matters of health service and healthful school living. Also, some small schools are most fortunate in having the full or part-time services of a school nurse in conducting some health work.

There is a great need in the smaller schools for improved health work. The immediate efforts of those in the health field should be given to developing ways, means, and plans whereby the children in the smaller schools can be provided with better and more acceptable school health programs.

Fundamental Policies, Procedures, and Essentials in the Organization and Administration of the School Health Program.— If the school health program is to be organized and administered to the best advantage to the children, those responsible for the schools must have a clear concept of the relationship of health to the total educational program. Perhaps the first step in considering a school health program is to determine the aims and objectives and then proceed to the next step of setting up ways and means to accomplish them. In this the school administrators must accept the main responsibility in assuring that the aims and objectives are accomplished to the best ability of the school personnel. Connected with aims and objectives is the problem of determining the scope of the health program. Other fundamentals to be considered in the general organization of the school health program are:

1. The possible need of centralized control to assure the efficient functioning of the total program.
2. Adequate budget of finances to provide necessary salaries, supplies, and equipment.
3. Proper coordination of the various divisions, departments, and areas involved in the health program.
4. The selection of teachers and health specialists best qualified for the particular school and community.
5. The allotment of sufficient time in the school curriculum for the health program to function effectively.
6. Definite assignment of duties and responsibilities to teachers, health specialists, and administrative assistants.
7. The organization of a health teaching program on a school-wide basis.
8. Consideration of legal provisions and state and local laws and requirements pertaining to and affecting the school health program.
9. Provisions for assuring the maintenance of the school plant and facilities in a sanitary and hygienic manner.
10. Special measures necessary to recognize and provide for the individual physical differences of children.
11. Methods and plans for safeguarding the health of teachers as well as the children.
12. Evaluation of the total school health program.

Experience with health programs in the schools has shown very clearly that the success of a school health program is basically dependent upon the attitude of school administrators. When school administrators are in favor of and enthusiastic about the health program it is likely to be successful.

Questions for Discussion

1. What level of government is primarily responsible for policies and practices in the public schools?
2. What are the basic issues involved in the controversy about which should be responsible for and administer school health programs, the schools or the community health organization?
3. Why are school personnel members in a better position to deal with certain phases of the health education program than community health personnel?

4. What is the proper role of the medical expert in the preparation of elementary school textbooks and other teaching materials?
5. Regardless of the extent of community health participation in the school health program, upon whom rests the major responsibility for school health education?
6. Why is it essential that school personnel and community health personnel cooperate closely in the conduct of the school health programs?
7. What are the main considerations to be taken into account when organizing a school health program?
8. What is the role of the school administrator in organizing and conducting the school health program?

Suggested Class Activities

1. Study the relationship of the school and the community health organization in a community with which you are familiar. Report the organizational plan to the class and compare your findings with those of others in the class.
2. Have a round table discussion as to the relative merits of the plans most commonly found in the activity noted in item 1.
3. On the basis of personal study and observation, report to the class on cooperative activities engaged in by medical and educational personnel in the interests of various phases of the school health program.
4. Organize a committee to prepare some criteria for evaluating various plans of school health organization.

References

1. Brown, C. Adele, "Present Day Concept of the School Health Program", *Journal of the American Medical Women's Association,* Vol. 6, No. 3, March 1951.
2. Chenoweth, L. B. and T. K. Selkirk, *School Health Problems,* 4th edition, New York: 1953, Appleton-Century-Crofts, Inc.
3. Irwin, Leslie W., "Analysis and Consideration of the Controversy Regarding the Responsibility for School Health Education", *Education,* October 1949.
4. Joint Committee on Health Problems in Education of the National Education Association and the American Medical Association, *Health Education,* 4th edition, Washington, D. C.: 1948, National Education Association.
5. "Personnel and Relationships in School Health, Physical Education, and Recreation", Research Bulletin, Vol. XXVIII, No. 3, Research Division of The National Education Association, Washington, D.C., October 1950.
6. Turner, C. E., *School Health and Health Education,* 2nd edition, St. Louis: 1952, The C. V. Mosby Company.
7. "Working Together for School Health", Health Bulletin for Teachers, Metropolitan Life Insurance Company, Vol. XXI, No. 5, April 1950.

CHAPTER 3

TEACHER OBSERVATION OF THE HEALTH OF CHILDREN

The General Appearance of Health.—A seven-year-old boy was given several pictures showing some children in good health and some in various states of moderately ill health. Simply on the basis of their general appearance, he was asked to say which children he thought were healthy and which he thought were not feeling well. Without difficulty he distinguished the healthy children, stating happily, "He's healthy," or "She's healthy." Although feelings and health cannot be objectively appraised in this way it does indicate that, generally speaking, the healthy state is usually reflected through signs which are readily observable. These signs include the appearance of alertness and vigor, brightness of the eyes, and keen interest in life. When it is possible to observe the child, the signs of health also include the well-coordinated and confident manner in which he moves about, his enthusiasm for work and play, and his capacity to function reasonably effectively and happily as a group member.

The Daily Health Observation.—The teacher's daily observation of her class or classes for indications of departures from good health is a key factor in protecting the health of children. In the past, a daily health inspection was common practice at the elementary school level; however, in more recent years there has been a marked tendency to move away from this rather formal approach which relegated "health" to a specified few minutes each day. At the present time health observation is looked upon as being a continual process which takes place each day and throughout the school day. It is based upon the teacher's awareness of and sensitivity to matters of child health. The essential features of health observation are: (1) the teacher's constant alertness to matters of health, and (2) the teacher's awareness of the characteristics of normal health at the various age levels and the characteristics of common illnesses of children.

For the teacher to be continually alert to matters of health requires that she be health conscious. Also, the teacher should be safety conscious. In the present day it is taken for granted that in the matter of safety, it is necessary for teachers to be aware of what constitutes danger in the various aspects of the child's life. Thus, it is necessary to reckon with such things as traffic safety, home safety, playground safety and stairway safety. Similarly, in the matter of health, it is necessary for teachers to be aware of the typical signs of good health and of poor health.

Detecting Illnesses and Making Referrals.—The responsibility for continually observing children for evidences of departure from health and the making of suitable referrals does not carry with it the further responsibility of diagnosing specific illnesses. Diagnosis is a matter which rests with medical, psychological, speech and other specialists. However, the more detailed and accurate the teacher's noting of pertinent symptoms, the more valuable the information she can provide to those responsible for diagnosis. For example, a comment such as, "George does not seem to feel well today," gives the nurse or physician little specific aid; but a brief account of signs and symptoms exhibited by the child over a period of time that led her to believe that George was not feeling well is likely to be much more helpful.

A CHART OF SIGNS AND SYMPTOMS

POINT OF OBSERVATION	PHYSICAL SIGNS	BEHAVIOR	COMPLAINTS
General appearance and behavior	Excessive thinness; excessive overweight; very small or very large in body build for age; pallor; weary expression; poor posture; dark circles or puffiness under eyes.	Acts tired or apathetic; is easily irritated; makes frequent trips to toilet; has persistent nervous habits, such as muscular twitching or biting of nails or lips; is subject to spasms (fits), fainting spells, or frequent nosebleeds; gets short of breath after mild exertion and climbing stairs; lacks appetite; vomits frequently; has frequent accidents.	Feels tired; doesn't want to play; has aches or pains; feels sick to stomach; feels dizzy.

A CHART OF SIGNS AND SYMPTOMS—Continued

POINT OF OBSERVATION	PHYSICAL SIGNS	BEHAVIOR	COMPLAINTS
Hair and scalp	Stringy, lusterless hair; small bald spots; crusty sores on scalp; nits in hair.	Scratches head frequently.	Head itches.
Ears	Discharge from ears; cotton in ear; tired, strained expression long before day is over; watchful, sometimes bewildered expression.	Is persistently inattentive; asks to have questions repeated; habitually fails to respond when questioned; mispronounces common words; cocks one ear toward speaker.	Has earache; has buzzing or ringing in ears; ears feel stuffy; hears noises in head.
Eyes	Inflamed or watery eyes; frequent styes; crusted lids; cross eye.	Holds book too close to eyes; squints at book or blackboard; persistently rubs or blinks eyes; reads poorly.	Head aches; eyes ache or smart; cannot see well (blurred vision).
Mouth and teeth	Cavities in teeth; excessive tartar at necks of teeth; malocclusion (uneven bite); irregular teeth; bleeding or inflamed gums; swollen jaw; sores in mouth; cracking of lips and corners of mouth.	Acts depressed or resentful if many missing teeth or severe malocclusion subjects him to teasing or adverse comments from other children. This behavior is especially likely to occur in adolescence.	Has toothache; mouth or gums feel sore.
Nose and throat (upper respiratory tract)	Frequent or long-continued colds; persistent nasal discharge.	Is frequently absent from school because of a cold; constantly clears throat or has frequent coughing or sneezing spells; sniffling or blowing nose; breathes persistently through mouth.	Throat feels sore or scratchy; has difficulty in swallowing; nose feels stuffy or sore.
Skin	Rashes or inflamed skin areas; scales and crusts; persistent sores, pimples and blackheads on face; boils; hives; persistent warts; accidental injuries, such as cuts, scratches, bruises, burns.	Is always scratching himself; is subject to skin irritations (hives, eczema, puzzling rashes, etc.) which suggest sensitivity to one or more substances (allergic manifestations); is easily bruised.	Skin itches or burns; is concerned about pimples, blackheads, and other skin conditions which affect personal appearance.

*Courtesy of the Metropolitan Life Insurance Company.

Acute illnesses, such as the onset of measles and appendicitis usually attract attention quickly and offer relatively little difficulty in the way of diagnosis to qualified specialists. On the other hand, the less abrupt departures from health, such as growth failure due to certain diseases or malnutrition, and some behavior disorders due to problems in the emotional life of the child, tend to offer greater diagnostic difficulties.

Information that the teacher may provide may be of considerable value in identifying the nature of the child's problem. For example, the teacher may give details about a particular child's increased irritability, reduced vitality, or tendency to withdraw from activities which might not be apparent in an interview or medical examination but which might be important factors in general health appraisal.

The Bases of Good Health.—Although there are numerous factors in addition to freedom from disease which influence the quality of child health, for practical purposes it is desirable to pay particularly close attention to the following four considerations which are basic to good health throughout life: proper diet, judicious exercise, adequate rest and sleep, and a reasonable undisturbed emotional state.

It is important to stress that these bases of health are interdependent; for example, if a child does not get sufficient physical activity, he is not likely to eat well or to rest well and his emotional adjustments may be affected. If rest and sleep are inadequate his appetite is likely to be affected and his emotional reactions are almost certain to be negatively affected. If the child's diet does not include adequate amounts of the various essential foods, the effects will soon be apparent in terms of reduction in physical vigor, disturbed appetite, and altered emotional responses. And, finally, if severe emotional problems exist in the life of the child, his appetite, activity level, and sleeping habits are likely to be affected.

A defection in diet, physical activity, rest or emotional stability is probably the most frequent opening wedge that is driven into the health of children. On the other hand, close attention to these things is probably the best and most available assurance that we have that a healthy state will be maintained and that satisfactory recovery will be made in the event of accidents or invasion of the body by disease entities.

Health in Relation to Growth.—The teacher must be well-informed regarding certain principles of human growth in order to make intelligent observations of children's health. Although the growth of all normal children follows a general pattern, it is essential to realize that growth is a highly individual matter and that it does not progress at a constant rate. The old height-weight tables are no longer widely accepted as valid criteria of how much individuals of a certain height should weigh at a certain age because individual growth patterns simply do not conform to such standard specifications. The important thing is not that a child grow as others are growing, but that he grow properly in his own way and that he not stop growing. (A failure to increase in size for a three-month period should be taken as a sign of potential trouble needing medical investigation). What a child's own way of growth is depends upon such factors as his heredity and his particular body build or structure. Therefore, some children of a given age will be slender and some stocky. For them such a condition is healthy. Many parents and teachers have made the mistake of insisting upon "huskiness" as a criterion of health; and sometimes they have created difficult problems of an emotional kind by attempting to force heavy eating upon children who are naturally slight of build and light eaters.

In recent years means have been devised for taking into account the individual nature of growth. Various "grids" such as the Wetzel and Iowa grids are now available to many teachers which, simply on the basis of age, height and weight, reveal whether a child's growth is progressing properly in terms if his own body build and how his size compares with that of other children of his age.

The elementary school teacher is frequently responsible for weighing and measuring children. In some cases grids are provided for each child so that the process of growth may be recorded and observed in diagrammatic form. However, with or without a grid, this activity can serve as a means of determining whether growth is taking place in a satisfactory manner; and it can also be used as the basis of an exceedingly important educational experience for children. In relation to the weighing and measuring experience, children can be taught to keep a record of their own growth process and to realize that they are not growing in competition with other children; rather, they should learn that each must grow at his own particular rate and in his own particular way.

The teacher should have an intimate knowledge of the growth characteristics of the age level with which she works; however, the focus of the teacher's attention must remain upon the individual. Only in this way can she hope to note the various symptoms associated with abnormalities including growth failure.

Heredity and Health.—It should be recognized that "heredity" refers specifically to those characteristics that are transmitted from parents to children by the genes and chromosomes; heredity diseases should not be confused with those diseases or deformities caused during pregnancy or birth. One of the very significant developments in the field of modern health has been a greater understanding of the role of heredity in mental as well as in physical disorders. In past years, numerous diseases of both the mind and the body were generally accepted as being hereditary in origin. In fact, the label "hereditary" was likely to be placed on any physical disorder of unknown cause. Tuberculosis, syphilis, heart disease, cancer, "insanity," feeblemindedness and diabetes are examples of those diseases and disorders once thought to be hereditary. Some diseases, including tuberculosis and syphilis, have been eliminated from the hereditary list. More and more cases of diabetes, cancer, mental illness, and feeblemindedness are now recognized as being caused by things other than inheritance. It is now thought that inheritance is not a direct cause of most of the major mental or physical disease entities. However, in cases of some types of mental, emotional and physical disorders there seems to be a tendency to inherit some as yet unknown quantity that may render the individual more susceptible to certain specific disorders.

The Health Record Card.—Many school systems now provide health record cards for each child upon which teachers may note pertinent observations which lend insight into the status of health during the school years. Whether an official card or one devised by the teacher is used, care should be taken to include only that information which actually contributes to a knowledge of the child's history. For example, if indications of some visual difficulty are observed, this and the subsequent action taken should be noted. If appropriate treatment is given and improvement is noted, these facts too should be noted.

The health record card should also contain notes regarding behavior of an exceptional kind as well as evidences of good health to be used as a basis for future comparison. Experience has shown that a health record kept conscientiously over a period of years can be very useful in an analysis of present pupil health status.

Common Signs, Symptoms and Warning Signals.—The following outline of signs and symptoms is presented merely as a guide to common indications of trouble in regard to child health. In some instances, as in the case of vision and hearing, simple testing procedures are suggested which may be useful in very rough screening. When acute signs and symptoms are observed, arrangements should be made to get the child home, and the parents should be urged to consult a physician immediately. All schools should have established procedures to follow in the event of pupil illness or injury in the school.

1. FACIAL APPEARANCE.—The facial appearance of the child frequently gives an indication of present status.

The teacher should be alert to such symptoms as: unusual redness or pallor of the face, inflammation of the eyeballs, and a running nose. Such signs, individually or in combination, can be brought on by various diseases, but in any event they are common signs of trouble and should receive attention. Although these symptoms signal the onset of common respiratory illnesses, they are also symptoms of some of the most severe childhood diseases.

2. THE RESPIRATORY SYSTEM.—Respiratory diseases are the principal cause of absenteeism among school children and although they are not usually very severe, in some cases they are quite serious. Colds and other respiratory disturbances are thought to be most contagious in their early stages; that is, within the first two or three days. If children are kept at home when persistent coughing, sneezing and running noses are observed, infection of large numbers of other children and perhaps the teacher may be avoided. Since many more serious diseases, such as sinusitis, mumps, diphtheria, and poliomyelitis may resemble a simple cold in their early stages, the child should be watched closely for evidence of mounting fever, muscular pain, nausea, and other symptoms. Although there are not at present very effective means of curing colds, children should be taught the importance of wearing proper clothing, eating wisely and getting enough rest in order to keep the frequency and severity of colds to a minimum.

Teachers can easily check mouth breathers to determine whether they are unable to breathe through the nose freely. Inability to breathe easily through the nose is indicative of some form of nasal blockage which should receive medical consideration.

Special note should be made of those individuals who are subject to repeated colds and suitable referrals should be made. Frequent colds may be indicative of a dietary deficiency, some chronic infection, poor dressing habits, or other factors related to lowered resistance. They may also be related to a disturbed state in the emotional life of the child.

Cases of "strep" throat deserve immediate medical attention because they are associated with rheumatic fever, one of the most common of the very dangerous childhood diseases.

3. THE EYES.—Certain behavior patterns should give

rise to suspicion that the eyes are not functioning properly. For example, a child may hold reading material within a few inches of his face, he may squint and make faces as he strains to read what is on the blackboard, his eyes may be very sensitive to light, he may wipe or rub his eyes frequently or he may close one eye when trying to see. Upon being questioned he may complain of blurred vision, headache and dizziness when reading or doing close work, or of not being able to see the ball or other objects when playing games. In appearance, his eyes may be watery and inflamed and the lids swollen and encrusted.

Glasses do not always assure correction of visual defects. When children with glasses show signs of visual difficulty, it is well to bear in mind the possibilities that diagnosis may not have been correct and the glasses do not provide the necessary compensation, or that new difficulties have developed since the previous diagnosis.

Many schools now attempt to provide regular vision testing programs in which all children are screened for visual defects at regular intervals. However, in some cases it may be necessary for a teacher to administer a simple test such as the Snellen test to one or more pupils.

The teacher has an important role to play in encouraging children to wear their glasses, since it frequently happens that they refuse to wear them for fear of being teased or appearing "different." Skillful teaching can help to make glasses socially acceptable among children.

4. THE EARS.—Partial hearing loss can frequently be identified by certain typical behaviorisms of children. They may strain forward with an intent look when instructions are being given, turn one ear toward the speaker or cup a hand behind the ear. If a child cannot hear his own voice well, his speech may become flat and poorly modulated. It sometimes happens that children who appear dull or disinterested in class activities are merely unable to hear clearly what is taking place.

Screening tests should be conducted periodically in order to locate individuals with sub-normal hearing. Hearing testing programs are becoming standard practice throughout the country. In localities where programs of this kind are routine, large numbers of cases have been treated which had not previously been suspected. Even though screening is done, the teachers should remain alert to behavior which suggests the possibility of a hearing difficulty since infection, injury and wax accumulation can reduce acuity of hearing rapidly with the result that symptoms may appear suddenly.

There are simple tests which may be used by the teacher to check for gross hearing failure. For example, the watch test may be given. In this test, a watch, preferably with a loud tick, is held at various distances from the child's ear. The watch is shifted right and left and above the child's head; and in each position the pupil is asked to indicate whether he hears ticking. Eye blinders or other means should be used to prevent his seeing the position of the watch by peripheral vision. Occasionally the watch should be placed at a distance where it cannot possibly be heard in order to be sure that the pupil is not guessing. A stop watch may be used and snapped on and off occasionally to determine whether the pupil really hears. Of course badly blocked or damaged ears will not hear the tick even though the watch is very near.

5. THE NECK.—Lumps in the neck may be due to mumps which cause a swelling of the salivary glands or to swelling of the lymph nodes just below the ear and behind the jaw. Lumps of either kind should receive the attention of a physician. Swelling of the lymph nodes indicates the presence of infection, perhaps in the gland itself or in some other region of the head, the ear, scalp, or throat.

6. THE TEETH.—Dental screening in schools oftentimes reveals that approximately 80% or more of the pupils are in need of treatment. Although a satisfactory evaluation of dental health requires trained personnel, there are certain gross symptoms which the teacher should recognize. Some of these are: in very bad cases it is possible to see the dark yellow spots of decay at the base and sides of the front teeth; sometimes the foul smell of infection may be perceptible on the child's breath; the gums may be inflamed and sore, the upper and lower sets of teeth may not fit properly together when the mouth is closed; and the very obvious symptoms of toothache. Periodic dental screening should be done by qualified persons, but the teacher must remain alert to gross difficulties.

The teacher's role in dental health teaching is to cultivate the child's interest in his own total health, including his teeth, his realization of personal responsibility for his own health, and his knowledge of those practices which promote good health.

From a very early age pupils should be taught that certain foods such as fresh fruits, vegetables and milk are essential for the proper development of their teeth. They should also be made aware that certain other foods, principally sugars, may have the effect of damaging the teeth, especially if they are eaten in such quantity that they crowd essential foods from the diet. They should be taught how to clean the teeth properly and the wisdom of brushing the teeth or rinsing out the mouth after eating candy or other sweets.

The teacher can also play an important role in helping the child to form a desirable attitude toward having his teeth examined and toward making periodic visits to the dentist.

7. THE HAIR AND SCALP.—Ringworm is a condition of the scalp which may be recognized by the forming of nearly bald areas and crustiness of the scalp. It can spread rapidly from child to child.

Pediculi or lice usually appear in regions where living conditions are unhygienic but they may spread rapidly to anyone who is nearby. Recently developed insecticides simplify the handling of this problem; however, the teacher should be able to recognize the pests and become suspicious when the small eggs or nits are discovered clinging to the hair. Frequent itching of the scalp should be investigated for disease or infestation.

8. POSTURE.—Poor posture may take several forms such as the head carried too far forward, round shoulders, one shoulder held higher than the other, sway back or forward curvature of the spine, pronated ankles, and flat feet. The poor posture of some pupils is due to actual deformation of the skeleton and treatment is necessarily a medical matter. Most cases of poor posture are functional and due to difficulties other than skeletal abnormality.

It should be recognized that although poor posture may be due to bad habits of sitting, standing, and moving, or to the influence of unfortunate fads and styles, it is frequently a symptom of some underlying difficulty. Therefore, it is unwise to require pupils to begin taking exercises or other corrective measures until the cause is known. For example, it would plainly be unwise to initiate an exercise program for a round-shouldered boy if his stance is due to weakness from disease or malnutrition. Similarly, it would be unwise to suggest corrective activities to a pupil whose head-forward stance represents an attempted compensation for poor vision which actually can only be corrected by glasses. It is known, too, that prolonged emotional upset can be a cause of poor posture, and that improvement must begin with relieving the disturbing situation.

Once underlying causes for poor posture have been removed the task is to convince the pupil as to the advantages of good posture and to guide his self-analysis so that improvement can take place. Whatever its cause, poor posture may become a habit which is broken only with conscious effort. Therefore, it is plain that youngsters must want good posture if improvement is to take place. Posters which portray the ungainliness and inefficiency of poor posture and the attractiveness and gracefulness of good posture are satisfactory teaching aids if properly used.

Among very young children, improved use of the feet may result from teaching them to walk and run with the toes pointing forward. Older pupils can appreciate the principles of body mechanics involved. Of course, severe cases should be referred to physicians for evaluation and possible treatment.

The teacher's guidance can also be of great importance in the matter of selecting proper footwear. Pupils should be taught to have their feet properly measured and fitted; and they should be taught the hazard to their feet of wearing shoes that are in poor repair. For example, as a heel becomes worn on the inside, additional body weight is thrown upon the inside of the foot and there is an increased tendency towards pronation or forcing the ankle inward and downwards.

9. SPEECH DIFFICULTIES.—Speech defects should be mentioned because of their frequency, oftentimes in combination with hearing loss. The full implications of speech defects cannot be appreciated until they are considered in the light of: (1) their obvious interference with the most essential of our communication media, (2) the impact that they tend to have upon the emotions of the individual who possesses them, both because of the defective communication and because of the typical parental and other social reactions to them, and (3) the role that emotional upset commonly plays in the formation of speech defects.

Speech difficulties should be approached with caution because inept handling may complicate and aggravate rather than improve them. One well-known specialist on speech has pointed out that most speech problems have their start, not in the mouths of the children but in the mouths of their parents. This statement suggests that emotional problems are intimately involved in the speech situation, and it is likely that therapy in specific cases involves more than practicing saying words or being reminded not to stutter. As a matter of fact, the teacher who has not had specialized training in the area of speech correction should realize that this difficulty, like a physical or mental disorder, is best left to a specialist.

10. MENTAL AND EMOTIONAL HEALTH.—It is not possible to specify a list of behavior traits which always signal poor mental and emotional health because virtually all such traits are observed in the most normal of persons at one time or another. For example, daydreaming is commonly indicated as a symptom of "withdrawn" behavior; and yet we know that all normal children daydream, and we know that various factors such as boredom and emotional stress com-

monly lead to increased daydreaming. Consequently, when evaluating behavior for evidence of poor mental or emotional health, it is necessary to think in terms of *persisting* and *extreme* traits. Thus, habitual daydreaming may suggest a tendency to withdraw from reality. Similarly, habitual defiance of adult authority, cruelty, or extreme excitability would suggest a need for careful investigation by specialists so that the cause might be discovered. Although isolated episodes of these things might deserve noting, they would not in themselves necessarily be symptoms of behavior disorders.

The following list includes some behaviorisms which are sometimes associated with disturbance at the psychological level. *Individual cases must, of course, be reckoned with in terms of persistence and severity of the symptoms.*

> Withdrawnness, shyness, seclusiveness, timidity
> Daydreaming
> Fearfulness, strong anxiety
> Tenseness, excitability and lack of emotional control
> Extreme desire to please
> Lack of self-confidence, an "I can't" attitude
> Inability to assume responsibility for own errors
> Unhappiness, feelings of depression
> Suspiciousness
> Avoidance of need to adjust to others
> Inability to adjust to the group, especially at play
> Nail-biting, habit tics, finger or lip-sucking
> Failure to make progress which is in keeping with physical and mental capacity
> Hostile and aggressive behavior
> Destructiveness
> Cruelty
> Temper tantrums
> Irresponsibility
> Showing off and other attention-getting activities
> Lying, cheating, stealing
> Lack of self-control
> Preoccupation with sex

Because so many of the mental and emotional conditions among adults had their beginning in childhood, it is extremely important that teachers be ever alert to the mental and emotional deviations among children that may be the insidious beginning of mental or emotional ill health which reaches its climax in adult life.

Questions for Discussion

1. What, in general, are the characteristics of the healthy child?
2. What is the difference between "health inspection" and "health observation?"
3. To whom does the teacher commonly refer health problems that she observes?
4. Which are usually more easily noted, acute or chronic difficulties? Why?
5. What are some health problems that are commonly associated with the growth process?
6. How can the weighing and measuring program be used as an educational experience for children?
7. Other than freedom from disease, what are "the bases of good health?"
8. Of what value is the health record card and how should it be used?

Suggested Class Activities

1. Hold a round-table discussion in which participants describe health problems which they have observed in school children and tell how these problems were handled. Other discussants and class members make suggestions as to other ways in which the problems might have been handled.
2. Invite a school nurse in to discuss her role as the person to whom most child health problems are referred in schools. Ask her to propose ways in which the teacher may best utilize the nurse's services.
3. Invite a psychiatrist, clinical psychologist or other qualified mental health worker to discuss common mental health problems of school age children.
4. Compare procedures followed in schools known to the group when illness is observed in school. Take into account procedures such as notifying parents and getting medical attention.
5. If health record cards are provided in schools known to class members, invite a nurse, a school physician or a health coordinator to describe how the cards are supposed to be used by teachers. If such cards are not in use, form a committee to design one.

References

1. Breckenridge, M. E. and E. L. Vincent, *Child Development.* Philadelphia, 1949, W. B. Saunders Co.
2. Cromwell, G. E., *The Health of the School Child.* Philadelphia, 1947, W. B. Saunders Co.
3. Fraley, L. M., et al., *Physical Education and Healthful Living.* New York, 1954, Prentice-Hall, Inc.
4. Jacobs, L., "Mental Health in the School Health Program," *Journal of School Health,* March, 1953.
5. Langton, C. V. and C. L. Anderson, *Health Principles and Practices.* St. Louis, 1953, The C. V. Mosby Company.

6. Morehead, J., "The Teacher and Mental Health in the Classroom," *Journal of School Health,* October, 1951.
7. Moriarty, M. J. and L. W. Irwin, "A Study of the Relationship of Certain Physical and Emotional Factors to Habitual Poor Posture Among School Children," *Research Quarterly,* May, 1952.
8. Podolsky, E., "The Child as a Functional Unit," *Archives of Pediatrics,* August, 1954.
9. Podolsky, E., "The Mentally Ill Child," *Journal of School Health,* September, 1950.
10. Wheatley, G. M. and G. T. Hallock, *Health Observation of School Children.* New York, 1951, McGraw-Hill Book Co., Inc.
11. "What Teachers See," Metropolitan Life Insurance Co., One Madison Ave., New York City, Free.

CHAPTER 4

HEALTH GUIDANCE IN SCHOOLS

The Meaning of Health Guidance.—The modern concept of guidance in schools usually includes a broad program of organized activities, selected and designed to give assistance to students in solving present problems and in preparing them to make the best possible adjustment to life conditions which may face them now and in the future. The term "guidance," as used in the schools, was originally used primarily to refer to efforts made to help youth select professions and occupations compatible with their abilities and interests. In recent years the field of guidance has expanded to include other guidance services which should help the schools more fully achieve their total educational objectives. The fact that the place and importance of health is so well recognized as an educational objective should leave no doubt as to the justification of health guidance as one of primary concern in providing guidance service.

In that health guidance as such is a relatively new development in the area of guidance services in both elementary and secondary schools, it seems advisable to give more specific meaning to the term. In the early stages of any new educational development, it is likely that some misunderstanding is apt to occur. The misunderstanding of the term "Health Guidance" seems to be in its frequent confusion with the term "Health Teaching." Although considerable overlapping may frequently occur in dealing with the areas of health guidance and the teaching of health, nevertheless, it is necessary to distinguish between them in dealing with the many health problems of students. For example, it is suggested that a differentiation may be made on the basis of the immediacy of needs. In other words, it is felt that in health teaching "educators are capable of anticipating more or less distant needs of pupils and providing information whereby the problematical needs may be met."[6] Taking into consideration obvious and unavoidable overlapping, health guidance would then tend to be concerned with helping children and youth solve their immediate health problems. It becomes evident then that health guidance is frequently concerned with immediate and often urgent problems that are seldom present in organized health teaching. Moreover, health guidance may be needed in any and all stages of a student's growth and development.

Another approach to the meaning of health guidance and health teaching might be taken from the viewpoint that greater consideration should be given to their relationship rather than their differences. For example, health teaching is concerned with the provision of desirable learning experiences for the purpose of influencing knowledge, attitude and behavior relating to individual and group health. This being true, health guidance could then serve as an instrument for the implementation of health knowledge by encouraging pupils to improve their health behavior, and this can to some extent be accomplished through individual health counseling and group health guidance.

Need for Health Guidance in Schools.—When consideration is given to the present web of environmental forces in which the school child is placed, there is little doubt as to the importance of health guidance as a function of the schools. For example, such agencies as the home, school, church, clubs and recreational groups all have their effect upon the physical, mental, social and emotional well-being of the child. Moreover, such influences as radio, movies, and television may complicate the problem of environmental adjustment for the child. Certainly the child cannot be expected to face alone all of the complexities of contemporary society. In this respect it seems that the greatest penalty of the growing child and adolescent youth in the present day is that they must make the major decisions of their lives when they are least equipped by both knowledge and experience to make them. Indeed, children and youth need guidance in areas which affect their health, and the school appears to be one of the most logical and forceful means available in our society for providing this guidance.

Because the need for health guidance of children and youth may be reflected in the major health problems of modern day society, it might be well to examine some of these problems in terms of the role of the school in helping pupils adjust to the multiplicity of factors involved in developing and maintaining a happy and healthful life. For example, it has been estimated that more than one-half million people are suffering from mental illness to the extent that hospitalization is necessary. It has been further estimated that over one-half million more urgently need treatment. Also, in addition to those hospitalized and those urgently needing treatment, there are other millions having varying degrees of difficulties that have not been treated or for that matter even detected. If this is the case, and if it is true that a large majority of the psychogenic maladjustments of adults had their beginnings in childhood, then the school's responsibility in this area is readily apparent.

The fact that accidents take far too many school age lives in addition to the large number of injuries, and permanent disabling injuries, gives rise to the belief that more adult guidance is needed in the area of safety and accident prevention. In addition, problems concerning nutrition, dental caries, exercise, rest and sleep, family living, and communicable disease, along with others, point up the necessity for proper guidance in meeting the present and future needs of children and youth.

Another, one of the most important facts showing the need for health guidance, is concerned with biological factors with which children and youth are confronted in meeting the demands of life. These factors are concerned for the most part with the human development of the individual. Although a majority of children follow the normal course of human growth and development, a certain percentage of the school population can be expected to deviate from what is usually considered the normal. In this category are found children with a variety of physical, mental, social, or emotional anomalies. Health guidance can fill a gap in the lives of these exceptional children by helping them to a better understanding of themselves, including their physical and emotional problems, as well as the world around them.

Purpose of Health Guidance.—The broad function of the complete school guidance program is usually considered to be one avenue of approach in helping to achieve educational objectives. The total guidance program may be divided into various phases such as vocational guidance, educational guidance, health guidance and the like. It should be possible to identify the purposes of each of these phases in terms of what each contributes to the broad function of guidance.

While some overlapping is likely to occur, health guidance may serve certain unique purposes in the total guidance program. The following list shows the more or less general purposes of the school health guidance program for children and youth:

1. To help children and youth to better understand themselves in terms of factors which affect their physical, mental and emotional health and the health of others.
2. To help children and youth to identify problems which concern their health and the health of others.
3. To guide pupils in the solution of problems which concern their health and the health of others.
4. To help children and youth to gain a clearer understanding of the available health services in the school and community.
5. To guide students in planning physical activities commensurate with their physical capacities.
6. To reduce the number of remediable physical defects in the school population.

Problems in Which Children and Youth Need Health Guidance.—Problems of children and youth may be divided into a number of classifications. Among others, these classifications include school work and future education, vocational planning, social relations, leisure time activities, ethical concerns, home and family relations, finances, and physical, emotional and mental health. While there may be some overlapping among these areas, health guidance naturally will be most specifically concerned with problems of physical, mental and emotional health. The fact that this classification is extremely important was indicated in a recent study[11] which revealed that of 300 problems listed by the students of one large high school, almost one-third pertained to aspects of physical, mental or emotional health.

What, then, are some of the problems falling in this classification? In general, such problems pertain to nutrition and diet, exercise and rest, physical defects, chronic diseases and disorders, growth and development, and mental and emotional behavior. These sub-classifications can be further broken down into specific problems. For example, a recent survey[10] showed that pupils have problems in the following specific areas of health: Fifty-two per cent of the pupils in this nation-wide survey were interested in gaining or losing weight; 37% in how to improve posture or body build; 41% of girls and 7% of boys in how to improve their figures; 33% in how to get rid of pimples; and 24% in how to select foods that will do the most good.

In that it is a well-established and accepted fact that most young people have problems which concern their health, the school has a definite responsibility to discover those problems and help children and youth with the solution of them.

Bases for Determining Problems in Which Children and Youth Need Health Guidance.—It is now generally accepted by educators that the more that is known about a child the more it is possible to do for him. Consequently, adequate measures must be taken to discover problems which exist among the school age population. What, then, are some of the methods for determining these problems in order that sound health guidance may be given? The following list, although not all-inclusive, gives some ways in which health problems of children and youth can be discovered.

1. Health appraisal.
2. Teacher observations.
3. School records.
4. Devices for gathering information from pupils.
5. Surveys of pupil health needs.

HEALTH APPRAISAL.—Appraisal of the individual's health may serve as a point of departure in identifying immediate health needs for purposes of health guidance. This procedure may be considered as the sum total of all of the available means of arriving at a determination of the health status of the child. Health appraisal implies that such factors as medical examinations, teacher observations, use of screening devices, along with others, are used to arrive at a valid estimate of the child's total health status. The following list of aims and objectives serve as a guide to health appraisal of school children:

1. To find students in need of medical attention.
2. To find students in need of dental care.
3. To find students who have problems relating to diet and nutrition.
4. To find students who are maladjusted and in need of special care at school.
5. To find students who are maladjusted or who have problems serious enough to be referred to a psychiatrist or to a guidance clinic.
6. To measure the growth of children and youth in view of helping them to attain optimum growth and development.
7. To find children and youth with nonremediable defects who may require modified programs of education such as the crippled, partially-sighted, hard-of-hearing, and mentally retarded.
8. To find students who need a more thorough examination than is usually provided at school. The more thorough examination might require medical specialists, x-ray and extended laboratory examinations.

9. To find students who may be cared for best apart from the regular school situation.
10. To find students in need of special rehabilitation programs.

TEACHER OBSERVATIONS.—As mentioned previously, determining health problems through teacher observations may be considered as a part of the total health appraisal program. The fact that teachers are in a favorable position to discover health needs of children makes the technique of teacher observation a very desirable way to help identify problems in which children and youth need health guidance. This is particularly true at the elementary school level where a majority of the teachers spend most of the school day with pupils. Thus, elementary school teachers are in an excellent position to watch for day to day changes and to recognize deviations from the normal in which the child might need health guidance.

SCHOOL RECORDS.—Through a study of school records which reveal to some extent the backgrounds of students, it is possible to identify numerous health problems which may require guidance. Included here are the cumulative records, health and medical records and school absence reports. Such records should be studied and analyzed for health conditions that need attention and guidance.

DEVICES FOR GATHERING INFORMATION FROM PUPILS.—Included among the methods of determining problems are adjustment inventories, problem check lists, autobiographies and other free response techniques. Although these devices can serve as a desirable means of discovering health problems of pupils for guidance purposes, care should be taken in their administration. For example, it is highly important that pupils be informed, assured and convinced that these procedures are designed to help them. Furthermore, in order to get valid information, pupils should be assured and convinced that the results will be kept strictly confidential.

Teachers and others who use any of these methods for determining health problems should be fully aware of their limitations. For instance, students may be and commonly are incapable of diagnosing their own difficulties. Furthermore, there is the possibility that they may check problems on a check list which are not real problems to them. Moreover, reading ability may be such that some students may not have a clear understanding of what is meant.

When properly administered, and when teachers as well as students recognize that personal problems should perhaps be considered as *symptoms* of difficulties, devices such as adjustment inventories, problems check lists and the like become an invaluable means of determining problems for guidance purposes.

SURVEYS OF STUDENT HEALTH INTERESTS.—In a general way, health problems of group interest may be discovered by a study of the health interests of individuals. Recent studies of this nature have been useful in providing clues for health guidance purposes. For example, in a study[8] involving the health interest of 10,000 secondary school students, approximately 300 problems of interest were identified. In this study, greatest interest was shown in the following ten areas:

1. Sex instruction.
2. Cancer.
3. Juvenile delinquency.
4. Causes of suicide.
5. Tobacco and human health.
6. Problems of tooth decay.
7. Causes of mental illness.
8. Lifelong care of the eyes.
9. Safest age to have a baby.
10. How to use a gun properly.

In another study[4] several health problems of interest to college men were identified for use in the health guidance of men of college age. Health problems of greatest interest in this study were:

1. Sex education.
2. Communicable diseases.
3. Nutrition and foods.
4. Care of the sense organs.
5. Home hygiene.
6. Exercise, sleep and rest.
7. Heart disease.
8. Treatment of injuries.
9. Sanitation.
10. Mental hygiene.

Organization and Administration of the School Health Guidance Program.—It would perhaps be difficult at the present time to find a school where some form of health guidance is not in evidence. However, in most cases, health guidance is probably done on an incidental basis, as a majority of schools do not as yet have well-developed health guidance programs. Where health guidance does exist on an organized basis it has been found that best results accrue when the program is carried out cooperatively. For example, all departments and personnel of a school concerned with any phase or part of mental, emotional and physical health of students should cooperate and participate in the formulation of health guidance policies.

In that organized health guidance programs may be considered a relatively new development, it might be well to consider some of the fundamental factors which are basic to sound organization. In this respect, it seems essential that recognition be given to such factors as (1) desirable principles of operation, (2) media of health guidance, and (3) responsibilities of various school personnel.

DESIRABLE PRINCIPLES OF OPERATION.—As in other functions of the school, health guidance should be based on certain fundamental principles for effective operation. The following generalized list may serve as a guide for the establishment of such principles in local school situations:

1. The health guidance program should be such that it serves individual student needs.
2. The health guidance program should have the whole-hearted support of the school administrators.
3. Some means of in-service training in health guidance should be provided for teachers, administrators and other members of the school personnel.
4. There should be full cooperation and coordination of all of the school departments concerned with the health of students.
5. The purposes and scope of each school department concerned with student health should be clearly defined in order to assure the most efficient service to students.
6. Responsibility for leadership in the health guidance program should be centered in individuals who possess, in so far as possible, interest, ability and preparation for such service.
7. The responsibilities of all persons concerned with the program should be clearly designated.
8. The best possible procedures for effective school and community coordination in health guidance should be provided.
9. The health guidance program should be subjected to continuous evaluation so that constructive improvements may be effected.

MEDIA FOR HEALTH GUIDANCE.—All of the possible pathways for providing health guidance for students should be thoroughly explored. This has not always been done in the past, and as a result, many desirable media through which health guidance can take place may have been overlooked. While it is understood that conditions at the local school level are likely to govern the circumstances surrounding desirable health guidance media, in general, successful health guidance may be conducted through the following channels:

1. Guidance departments.
2. During medical examinations.
3. Homerooms.
4. Regular classrooms.
5. Special classes, such as rehabilitation and special education groups.
6. Physical education and home economics.
7. Extra-class activities, such as interscholastic and intramural athletics, and various types of clubs.

RESPONSIBILITIES OF VARIOUS SCHOOL PERSONNEL.—One of the principles previously mentioned suggested that the responsibilities of all persons concerned with the health of students should be clearly designated. This statement should perhaps be amplified to the extent that *EVERY* person in the school system should accept a certain responsibility for the health guidance of the school population. In other words, every person associated with the school should have the health of students at heart. While all school personnel should have an interest in the health guidance program, responsibilities naturally must be differentiated.

The following discussion indicates some of the more or less specific responsibilities of various members of the school personnel depending somewhat on the size and existing conditions within the individual school system.

1. *School Administrative Officers.*—The responsibilities of the superintendent and principals of the schools within the community center around the leadership necessary to carry out a successful health guidance program. It should be strongly emphasized that this should entail a cooperative kind of leadership in which the administrator plans with his staff on matters pertaining to the broad scope of the program. Administrators should also take the lead in coordinating school and community relationships and in providing adequate staff and facilities for carrying out a suitable program.

2. *Health Service Personnel.*—One of the main responsibilities of the school physician, nurse and others in health service is concerned with channeling information to the guidance department, teachers, and others in the school concerned with student problems and health. For example, certain pertinent information derived from examinations by the school physician can be relayed to teachers and guidance counselors through the proper channels. When the school nurse serves as a link between the home and school she is in a desirable position to refer to guidance counselors and teachers information which may reveal physical, mental and emotional health problems arising out of home situations.
3. *Health Coordinator.*—The person assuming the responsibilities as health coordinator should coordinate all activities concerning the health of students. In other words, the success or failure of a health guidance program may depend upon the extent in which proper use of information is made. For example, many schools have an excellent program of health appraisal, yet they do not have adequate organization, ways or means of following up the findings of the appraisals. The health coordinator should fill any gaps which may exist by coordinating all information which might be used to properly guide the student in matters which concern his health.
4. *Guidance Personnel.*—Guidance directors, counselors and other guidance personnel have the responsibility of following up information provided them by the health service. Those responsible for guidance and counseling in the present day school program should have sufficient background and understanding in health education to do a large share of all health guidance in that most of the problems found among children involve either directly or indirectly physical, mental and emotional health. They may also contribute to the health guidance program by offering in-service education to teachers and other school personnel with respect to best methods of counseling students with problems which involve physical, mental and emotional health.
5. *School Psychologist.*—In school systems where the services of a psychologist are available many contributions can be made to the health guidance program by the person serving in this capacity. At the present time, one of the major functions of the school psychologist is that of a psychometrist who administers group and individual psychological tests. In addition to this primary function, many school psychologists confer with parents and teachers about

individual students with problems that particularly concern emotional health. The school psychologist should be in close contact with such school personnel as the administrator, school physician, school nurse, teachers and others who may be in a position to act upon recommendations of the psychologist regarding students who are in need of adjustment to problems which concern their health.

6. *Elementary School Teachers.*—The classroom teacher is actually the hub in a successful health guidance program at the elementary school level. As mentioned previously, in a majority of cases, the elementary school classroom teacher is in a position to observe pupils day by day. It becomes her responsibility to detect anomalies and refer them to the nurses, physicians, administrators and others.

7. *Secondary School Teachers.*—Junior and senior high school teachers are not in as favorable a position as the elementary school teachers with respect to observing deviations from the normal. This is due to the fact that the secondary school teachers generally see the students for only a part of the school day. Because of this time limitation with their students, secondary school teachers have been more or less reluctant to accept any type of responsibility for the health of students. They usually feel that it is the responsibility of specialists entirely. Nevertheless, it is now generally recognized that secondary school teachers should have sufficient knowledge and background in health to accept their rightful obligation to detect and refer conditions which appear to be affecting the health of students.

8. *Special Teachers.*—Teachers dealing with special groups such as in rehabilitation, special education and the various "special" subjects such as physical education and home economics very definitely have considerable responsibility in all matters of student health, including health guidance. These teachers are in a very desirable position to assist students with problems which concern their health in that they ordinarily come in closer contact with situations which deal with health status. For instance, the physical education teacher has an opportunity to watch the organic development of pupils. Moreover, he meets the students on a more informal basis than most school personnel, and as a consequence, students may not be so reticent to discuss their health problems with him.

9. *Extra-Class Sponsors.*—Sponsors of such activities as interscholastic and intramural athletics, school clubs and the like can accept some of the responsibility for health guidance of students. This is substantiated by the fact that extra-

class sponsors are likely to come into closer contact with students, and at the same time they meet them on a more informal basis than the regular teacher. Furthermore, the low pupil-teacher ratio, ordinarily existing in these activities, gives the teacher-sponsor a greater opportunity to know and better understand each student as an individual.

Methods and Techniques of Health Guidance.—In general, methods of health guidance will fall into two broad categories of HEALTH COUNSELING and GROUP HEALTH GUIDANCE. However, a variety of techniques may be used in both of these processes.

HEALTH COUNSELING.—The health counseling procedures are concerned with health matters which pertain to the individual student. Health counseling may be considered a counterpart of health appraisal in that one of its major purposes is to follow up health appraisal with individual conferences with students and sometimes with parents. The following aims and objectives serve to show the extent of health counseling:

1. To convey a clear understanding of the beginning and growth of health problems.
2. To help students acquire a feeling of responsibility in meeting personal, family and group health problems.
3. To interpret to parents the importance of the results of health appraisals and to assist them in obtaining appropriate health and medical care for their children.
4. To contribute to the mental, emotional and physical health education of both students and parents by utilizing to the greatest possible extent health appraisal and counseling activities as a medium of education.
5. To guide students with nonremediable defects into school programs adapted to their interest, needs, capabilities and limitations.
6. To cooperate with and to secure the cooperation of both school and community groups and organizations in providing and making available facilities for the care and treatment of students.

Individual conferences may be carried on by guidance directors and counselors, health counselors, school psychologists, teachers, or various members of the health service personnel. It is extremely important that those persons who assume responsibility for health counseling be familiar with the most desirable counseling procedures. This is essential if the best possible results are to accrue. What, then, are some of the procedures which are commensurate with desirable health counseling?

One of the primary factors to consider is that most students are interested in developing a high degree of self-directiveness. In counseling students in matters which concern their health, every effort should be made to encourage this fundamental characteristic which is inherent in most individuals. Moreover, the health counselor should keep in mind that most students have the ability to adjust to their own problems, if placed in a position to do so. Consequently, it becomes the job of the counselor to draw upon those capacities that the student has for solving his own problems.

GROUP HEALTH GUIDANCE.—It was previously stated that health counseling is concerned with problems of the individual student. Group health guidance differs from counseling in that it pertains to health problems which are common to practically all students or to groups of students. In other words, any organized group approach that is made to help persons work out their common health problems, may be considered as group health guidance.

When it is possible to determine the common health problems of a group one wishes to serve, group health guidance becomes a very effective technique in the solution of these problems. For example, group health guidance may provide a background for counseling. In other words, when a student meets a counselor for a conference, his problem might have been discussed in a group, thus making him aware of the problem in his own life. As a result, the student should be in a better position to take the utmost advantage of individual health counseling.

Another important feature of group health guidance is that it helps students gain practice in the technique of problem solving. This is particularly true when the group case conference technique is employed in health guidance. For example, the skillful teacher or group sponsor may identify an attitude that has implication for health guidance. The teacher then frames a case paralleling an actual life situation within the experience of the group. A permissive atmosphere can be created and an attempt made to get the viewpoints of all students into the open for discussion. The understanding discussion leader neither shows approval nor disapproval. However, he may interject questions so that students may explore all consequences. This particular approach, when skillfully carried out gives students an opportunity to think and hence gain experience in solving or adjusting to a common health problem.

Evaluation and Appraisal of the Health Guidance Program.— In order to eliminate the undesirable practices and to perpetuate the best practices, it becomes necessary to evaluate and appraise the health guidance program. In the process of evaluation, reference should be made to the objectives of the program in attempting to determine if the objectives have been achieved. In that evaluation may be based on an examination of present practices and results achieved, criteria for evaluation should be devised with this in mind. Therefore, the following generalized list of criteria is submitted for use as a guide in appraising the school health guidance program:

1. Do all members of the school personnel have a full understanding of the need for and the purpose of health guidance?
2. Do all members of the school personnel recognize and accept the responsibility for health guidance of the school population?
3. Is the organization of the health guidance program such that the needs of all students are adequately met?
4. Is complete and extensive use made of all health guidance information?
5. Are individual students making more satisfactory adjustments in school situations which pertain to health?
6. Are there fewer absences from school due to health reasons since the health guidance program has been inaugurated?
7. Has the school program of activities been adapted to the health needs of all students in the school?

Questions for Discussion

1. How would you differentiate between health guidance and health teaching?
2. What are some of the factors in the child's environment that have created a need for health guidance in schools?
3. What are the major purposes of health guidance in schools?
4. What is the place of teacher observation in the school health guidance program?
5. Of the media for health guidance presented in this chapter, which do you think is the best? How do you support your answer?
6. What is the difference between health counseling and group health guidance?
7. What are some of the health problems of children and youth that may be approached through group health guidance?

Suggested Class Activities

1. Write a definition of health guidance and a definition of health teaching. Analyze the two definitions to find out where they are alike and where they are different.
2. Form a panel discussion group to consider the need for a health guidance program in a hypothetical school situation.
3. Prepare a list of problems in which children and youth need health guidance.
4. With other members of the class prepare a health problem check list which might be used as an instrument to collect information from pupils.
5. Take the part of a health counselor and counsel a member of the class concerning a hypothetical health problem. (The rest of the class members should act as an audience and give the counselor constructive suggestions when the interview is completed.)

References

1. American Association of School Administrators, *Health in Schools,* Twentieth Yearbook, Revised edition, American Association of School Administrators, The National Education Association, Washington, D.C., 1951.
2. Cowell, Charles C. "The Guidance Functions and Possibilities of Physical Education," *Journal of the American Association for Health, Physical Education and Recreation,* Vol. 20, No. 4, April, 1949.
3. Havel, Richard C., "The Role of the Coach in the Guidance Program," *Scholastic Coach,* May, 1950.
4. Humphrey, James H., "Health Problems of Interest to College Men," *The Research Quarterly of the American Association for Health, Physical Education and Recreation,* Vol. 23, No. 3, October, 1952.
5. Humphrey, James H., "The Homeroom As a Medium for Health Guidance," *The Journal of School Health,* Vol. XXII, No. 9, November, 1952.
6. Johnson, Warren R., "Health Guidance Through Athletics and Physical Education," *The Journal of School Health,* Vol. XXI, No. 2, February, 1951.
7. Joint Committee on Health Problems of the National Education Association and the American Medical Association, *School Health Services,* The National Educational Association, Washington, D.C., 1953.
8. Lantagne, Joseph E., "Health Interest of 10,000 Secondary School Students," *The Research Quarterly of the American Association for Health, Physical Education and Recreation,* Vol. 23, No. 3, October, 1952.
9. "Pupil Personnel Services in Elementary and Secondary Schools," Circular No. 325, Federal Security Agency, Office of Education, Washington, D.C., 1951.
10. Remmers, H. H., and L. M. Spencer, "All Young People Have Problems," NEA Journal, March, 1950.
11. Starr, Irving, "An Analysis of the Problems of Senior High School Youth, According to Age, Grade, Sex and Intelligence Quotient," Doctoral Dissertation, Boston University, School of Education, Boston, Massachusetts, 1953.

12. "What is New in '52 for Guidance and Health?" Coordinated Conferences on Guidance, Personnel Services, and Health Education, Sponsored by The University of Wisconsin, Wisconsin Association of Educational and Vocational Guidance, Industrial and Education Counselors Association, The State Department of Public Instruction, The State Board of Vocational and Adult Education and The State Board of Health, July, 1952.
13. Wheatley, George M., and Grace T. Hallock, *Health Observation of School Children,* New York, 1951, McGraw-Hill Book Company, Inc.

PART II
METHODS AND MATERIALS IN TEACHING HEALTH

CHAPTER 5

THE HEALTH TEACHING PROGRAM

The Need for Health Teaching In the Schools.—Many educators, medical specialists and laymen have questioned the need for health teaching in the schools at various times during the past few decades. The criticism of health teaching programs continues to some extent at present. Therefore, it is necessary for health educators and others interested in developing and maintaining acceptable and desirable health education programs in the schools to show clearly the need for extensive health teaching in all areas and levels of the school curriculum.

There are many things in the modern world that show very clearly the need for extensive knowledge of health and hygiene in maintaining individual and group health. A limited amount of thought, observation and reflection concerning the health habits, practices, mistakes and shortcomings of the adult population particularly, makes it luminously clear that there is an urgent need for better education and understanding of health and hygiene, if both individual and group health is to be improved and maintained on a basis commensurate with medical and scientific advancements in recent years.

The daily, monthly and yearly statistics on a national, state and community basis concerning illness and death bring prominently to our attention the need for greater effort on the part of the individual and the group in not only reducing unnecessary illness and death but in improving and maintaining a high level of positive health among all segments of our population.

The rapid advancements in science, medicine and public health make it necessary that the individual have sufficient knowledge to take advantage of and to understand and to make wise selections and decisions concerning the most recent developments.

The extensive and ever-growing amount of local, state, national and international legislation pertaining to public health and medical care involving millions of dollars of tax money makes it necessary that the individual voter be able to understand the issues involved in order to participate intelligently in the democratic process. In this respect the public is frequently called upon to support pending legislation sponsored by medical and public health experts. Some modern legislation of this nature may be so extensive that it may tax the ability of the community, state or nation to pay for it. Certainly, from the financial viewpoint of the taxpayer, the voting citizen must be well-informed regarding health and hygiene needs. Also, laws pertaining to such things as pasteurization of milk, enforcement of sanitary regulations, maintenance of community public health departments, qualifications of health and medical specialists and compulsory health insurance depends upon the knowledge and intelligence of millions of people comprising the voting group of communities and states throughout the country.

The gullibility of the public in spending millions of dollars each year on unnecessary and often harmful treatments, drugs, vitamins and patent medicines shows a need for better understanding of health and healthful living. Also, reports from national nutrition groups state that approximately one half billion dollars each year is spent by the American public on various kinds of food fads. In this case it is not only the waste of money involved, but many of the food fads and diets lead to malnutrition, ill health and suffering on the part of the gullible individual who follows advertising and incorrect advice suggesting the use of medication and faulty diets.

There is a need for greater health knowledge in preparing people to make the best and most intelligent use of available health services. Studies pertaining to the use of individual and group health services seem to show that there is a direct relationship between the level of knowledge and understanding of health and healthful living and the proper use of available health services.

The increasing number of both children and adults who are neurotic about their health points to another need for better health education.

It is frequently said that the number of people neurotic about their health increases almost in direct proportion to the amount and extent of *unorganized* and *haphazard* health instruction given to both children and adults.

The recent discoveries and developments in the area of the relationship of the emotions and physical health are extremely important in attaining and maintaining good health in the modern day. This rapid development in psychosomatic medicine brings to light one of the main reasons why it is so difficult for the individual to maintain optimum health under the stresses, strains and tensions of present-day life. It is now known that a host of physical disorders are psychogenic in origin. That is, they are basically caused and brought on by the emotions. Furthermore, most illnesses which are physical in origin become highly complicated by the emotions to the point where recovery is greatly handicapped.

Specialists skilled in the science of psychosomatic medicine state that the more knowledge and understanding the individual has about the close relationship of emotional and physical health the easier it is to maintain good health and the easier it is to help either the child or the adult to recover and regain good health following a physical disorder brought on by the emotions.

Another need for health education is shown by a study[1] of the extent and level of knowledge of a large number of typical fifth- and sixth-grade school children. This study was made in order to determine the prevalence of harmful health and safety misconceptions. In this case, misconceptions are considered erroneous ideas, notions or beliefs. The purpose of the study was: (1) to construct and evaluate an instrument for determining the prevalence of certain harmful health and safety misconceptions; and (2) to determine the prevalence of responses to this instrument which suggests the occurrence of certain harmful health and safety misconceptions and variations of this prevalence according to grade levels. Tables 1, 2, 3 and 4 show the percentage of fifth- and sixth-grade children who believe the misconceptions are true or sometimes true. It is readily evident that health and safety misconceptions are widespread among upper elementary school children.

A study of health and safety misconceptions of a group of tenth-grade girls was carried out similar to the study done with fifth- and sixth-grade children. Tables 5, 6, 7 and 8 show the percentage of the 216 misconceptions believed true by the 250 tenth-grade girls included in the study.

It is shown in tables 5, 6, 7 and 8 that there is strong evidence that even high school students lack proper education concerning health, hygiene and safety.

TABLE 1

VARIATIONS OF THE "TRUE" AND "SOMETIMES TRUE" RESPONSES OF FIFTH- AND SIXTH-GRADE CHILDREN TO CERTAIN EXTREMELY HARMFUL HEALTH AND SAFETY MISCONCEPTIONS

EXTREMELY HARMFUL HEALTH AND SAFETY MISCONCEPTIONS	Grade 5 T and ST	Grade 6 T and ST
1. The best doctors always promise to make people healthy.	73	67
2. The only good way to help a drowning person is to jump in the water to save him.	72	68
3. It is usually safe to go in swimming alone if you know how to swim.	60	45
4. Oil, grease, and gas fires should be put out with plenty of water.	57	48
5. A bullet cannot go off unless it is fired by a gun.	54	43
6. If your clothing catches fire, you should always run for water.	53	43
7. Bicycle riders should ride on the left hand side of the road to be safe.	50	52
8. Most mental sicknesses cannot be helped by any treatment.	47	51
9. It is a good idea to make an unconscious person drink something.	42	50
10. A person having a stomach ache should usually take a laxative.	41	42
11. It is best to go to doctors who advertise in newspapers.	40	31
12. It is impossible to cure any cancer.	40	36
13. It is all right to point a gun at someone if you are sure that it is not loaded.	39	29
14. A person always comes up to the top of the water three times before he drowns.	38	41
15. All mad dogs foam at the mouth.	37	37
16. Tuberculosis is a shameful disease to have.	35	30
17. A good way to treat a burn is to put iodine on it.	30	25
18. It is safe to cross the street without looking when the traffic light is yellow and red.	29	30

TABLE 1—CONTINUED

EXTREMELY HARMFUL HEALTH AND SAFETY MISCONCEPTIONS	Grade 5 T and ST	Grade 6 T and ST
19. Dynamite caps are always safe unless fastened to a fuse.	26	24
20. It is safe to cross the street without looking when the traffic light is red.	25	26
21. A person who has recovered after having tuberculosis cannot get it again.	25	20
22. Throwing oil or gasoline on a slow fire is a wise thing to do.	23	14
23. You should be ashamed if anyone in your family is mentally ill.	20	13
24. Bicycle riders do not have to obey traffic lights.	20	15
25. Unless someone in your family has tuberculosis there is no chance you will get it.	19	18
26. All laxatives are safe to use regularly.	19	22
27. Touching a light switch or light chain with wet hands is not dangerous.	18	14
28. When you are riding a bicycle you never have to use hand signals.	18	12
29. It is all right to use sleeping pills without a doctor's advice.	17	15
30. If you meet a dog that frightens you, it is always best to start running.	16	8
31. It is safe to cross the street without looking when the traffic light is green.	15	9
32. People have accidents only when their "number" is up.	13	8
33. Throwing a person into deep water is a good way to teach him to swim.	12	11
34. The eyes can be made stronger by looking at the sun.	12	9
35. When you are swimming it is a good joke to call for help when you don't need it.	9	3

Percentage Frequency of Responses

TABLE 2

Variations of "True" and "Sometimes True" Responses of Fifth- and Sixth-Grade Children to Certain Very Harmful Health and Safety Misconceptions

VERY HARMFUL HEALTH AND SAFETY MISCONCEPTIONS	Grade 5 T and ST	Grade 6 T and ST
1. The best way to get a tan is by sleeping in the sun.	80	66
2. There are some pills that people take which will cure the common cold.	79	78
3. It is always impossible for a person with cramps to swim.	75	76
4. There are certain cough medicines that will cure and prevent the common cold.	72	79
5. Spring water that is clear and cold is always safe for drinking.	72	67
6. Most fat people are very healthy.	68	69
7. If you have any disease or sickness you will always feel some pain.	67	65
8. All people with rosy complexions are very healthy.	66	68
9. Every disease needs a drug or medicine for its cure.	65	64
10. Any food that does not smell or taste spoiled is safe to eat.	60	66
11. Iodine is the best treatment for wounds caused by stepping on rusty nails.	59	67
12. All radio advertising about what is good or bad for your health is true.	59	61
13. People should walk on the right hand side of the road if there are no sidewalks.	57	55
14. It is always safe to drink water which has just been taken from a well or spring.	57	47
15. A good safety rule for bicycle riders is: "Ride on the sidewalk as much as possible."	55	34
16. All health advertisements in papers and magazines are true.	54	57
17. All advertising on television about what is good or bad for health is true.	52	56
18. Persons can clean their blood by eating certain foods.	49	50
19. A great deal of exercise can never hurt anyone.	48	55
20. Most accidents cannot be prevented.	48	42

TABLE 2—CONTINUED

VERY HARMFUL HEALTH AND SAFETY MISCONCEPTIONS	Percentage Frequency of Responses	
	Grade 5 T and ST	Grade 6 T and ST
21. Mental illness usually happens suddenly.	48	43
22. People who exercise a lot live longer than other people.	47	57
23. There are special laxatives that will help prevent or cure the common cold.	41	42
24. All children with heart murmurs will surely have heart trouble later on in life.	40	32
25. An exercise is not good unless it makes your muscles sore and stiff.	37	14
26. Blowing your nose as hard as you can is not harmful.	36	24
27. Most insane persons were born insane.	36	38
28. Most people who get tuberculosis will die in a short time.	34	43
29. Baby teeth need very little care because they will soon fall out.	32	28
30. Houseflies are harmless because they are unable to bite.	31	28
31. The first thing to do in treating a burn is to put cold water on it.	31	22
32. Eating meat more than once a day is harmful to most persons.	31	34
33. The best way to get water out of your ears after swimming is to hold your nose and mouth closed and blow hard.	30	22
34. Drinking raw milk fresh from the cow is a very healthy thing to do.	29	30
35. All persons should take laxatives whenever they are constipated.	25	30
36. A good way to take care of blisters is to pinch a hole in them.	25	25
37. If you feel all right, you can be sure that you do not have tuberculosis.	25	18
38. You should never eat when you are sick because you feed the disease.	24	21
39. Everyone should take a laxative once a week.	23	27
40. Fresh raw milk is a better food for your health than pasteurized milk.	23	25
41. Measles is never harmful.	22	26
42. Sickness is usually punishment for being bad.	22	19

TABLE 2—CONTINUED

VERY HARMFUL HEALTH AND SAFETY MISCONCEPTIONS	Percentage Frequency of Responses	
	Grade 5 T and ST	Grade 6 T and ST
43. It is possible to tell what is going to happen to people from their dreams.	20	36
44. You don't need to worry about having tuberculosis unless you are coughing a lot.	19	18
45. Some people should drink very little water because it turns to fat in their bodies.	19	14
46. It is safe to use toothpicks or matchsticks for removing wax from ears.	18	14
47. When tuberculosis is getting started a person always has a pain in the chest.	17	22
48. Squeezing the pus out of boils and pimples with your fingers is good for your health.	17	16
49. Whooping cough is never harmful.	17	18
50. Smart children usually die at an early age.	17	12
51. Teeth need care only when they ache.	15	9
52. The best way to remove pus from boils and pimples is with your fingers.	15	14
53. Looking into the sun can never hurt your eyes.	14	12
54. A good way to treat frostbite is to rub the frostbitten part with snow.	14	14
55. Most illnesses are caused by constipation.	14	18
56. All persons would be healthier if they ate only raw food.	14	21
57. Fat people can feel quite sure that they will never get tuberculosis.	12	11
58. Eating little or no breakfast is a good health habit for all people.	10	9
59. The best place for shelter, during a thunderstorm, is under a tree.	7	6

78 *Methods and Materials in Teaching Health*

TABLE 3

VARIATIONS OF THE "TRUE" AND "SOMETIMES TRUE" RESPONSES OF FIFTH- AND SIXTH-GRADE CHILDREN TO CERTAIN MODERATELY HARMFUL HEALTH AND SAFETY MISCONCEPTIONS

MODERATELY HARMFUL HEALTH AND SAFETY MISCONCEPTIONS	Grade 5 T and ST	Grade 6 T and ST
1. Brushing your teeth every day is a sure way of stopping decay.	95	97
2. Most fat people are happy and jolly.	84	80
3. Nose drops will cure a cold which is causing a stuffy nose.	81	81
4. Any person who feels all right is sure to be in good health.	78	68
5. Taking vitamin pills will guarantee you good health.	72	76
6. Wearing bathing hats or ear plugs while swimming will give a person complete protection for his ears.	71	74
7. All persons should use nose drops and mouth washes daily when they have a cold.	69	65
8. There are some pills that people can take which will prevent the common cold.	68	75
9. Wearing sunglasses will give your eyes complete protection from the sun.	68	71
10. Most persons who look thin are certain to be underweight and in poor health.	68	68
11. Taking vitamin pills is the best way to get your necessary vitamins.	67	64
12. The use of skin lotions is a healthful way to make any skin beautiful.	67	65
13. It is necessary to go to a doctor only when you feel sick.	67	52
14. Wearing eyeglasses will always make a person's eyes stronger.	65	68
15. Everyone who has weak feet should wear arch supports to strengthen them.	64	70
16. If your eyes do not hurt, you can be sure they are healthy.	64	57
17. You can be sure anything a scientist says about health is true.	63	60
18. Bad breath can be stopped for good by using special mouth washes.	62	63
19. Most colds can be cured by taking vitamin pills.	62	57

Percentage Frequency of Responses

TABLE 3—CONTINUED

MODERATELY HARMFUL HEALTH AND SAFETY MISCONCEPTIONS	Grade 5 T and ST	Grade 6 T and ST
20. Pain near the heart is generally a sign of heart disease.	60	62
21. Any food that smells and tastes good is safe to eat.	60	51
22. Sugar diabetes is caused by eating too much sugar.	59	64
23. A daily bowel movement is always necessary so a person can stay healthy.	59	68
24. The use of tooth powders and pastes is sure to make a person's gums firm.	59	69
25. The use of skin creams and lotions will make any skin clear and healthy.	59	58
26. The only good way to lose weight is by exercising.	58	61
27. Cotton should be the first thing put on a cut to stop the bleeding.	57	45
28. Mouth washes are sure to prevent or cure diseases of the mouth and throat.	56	59
29. The only good treatment for weak arches is to have arch supports placed in the shoes.	55	65
30. Expensive food is always the best food to eat.	54	52
31. Eating between meals causes most children to have poor health.	53	56
32. The vitamins in certain pills are better than the vitamins in natural foods.	53	57
33. Unlucky people are sure to fail at the new things that they try to do.	53	40
34. Any exercise is bad for persons who have heart trouble.	52	61
35. You can always tell if a dog is friendly by his looks.	52	40
36. The best medicines are the medicines that taste the worst.	50	56
37. A fortune teller can tell your future by looking at the lines in the palm of your hand.	48	40
38. Skipping one or two meals a day is a healthy way to get thin.	44	24
39. Some persons have the ability to tell your fortune.	44	40

TABLE 3—CONTINUED

MODERATELY HARMFUL HEALTH AND SAFETY MISCONCEPTIONS	Grade 5 T and ST	Grade 6 T and ST
40. A good way to help a person get rid of the hiccoughs is to frighten him.	44	53
41. Most persons need big muscles in order to be healthy.	44	38
42. Good doctors usually advertise.	43	41
43. Smoking is not harmful because many doctors and athletes smoke.	43	40
44. Most colds cannot be prevented.	41	42
45. An all vegetable diet is the natural and best diet.	41	37
46. Persons who have pimples or boils usually have bad blood.	40	46
47. Sunburns are harmless even when they are painful.	39	33
48. Most cases of baldness can be cured if treated early.	38	40
49. Good health does not depend on what you eat.	38	41
50. Food that tastes good is usually bad for your health.	38	42
51. Nighttime is the only time that one ever needs sleep or rest.	37	32
52. It is always good for your health to eat overripe fruits.	37	31
53. Exercising regularly is a sure way to prevent disease.	36	38
54. Cancer is catching.	35	34
55. If a person wants to be strong and healthy, he should eat plenty of raw meat.	34	24
56. The best way to treat a black eye is to put a piece of raw meat on it.	33	40
57. Drinking water with your meals is always bad for your health.	33	31
58. Bananas should be kept out of a good diet because they are hard to digest.	32	33
59. The best way to brush your teeth is sideways.	32	23
60. Only bad smelling odors can be harmful to your health.	31	26
61. All cosmetics are healthful to use.	30	30
62. All sick people should drink bottled mineral water to bring back their health.	29	26

Health Teaching Program 81

TABLE 3—CONTINUED

MODERATELY HARMFUL HEALTH AND SAFETY MISCONCEPTIONS	Grade 5 T and ST	Grade 6 T and ST
63. Missing a bowel movement for one day is always a sign of constipation.	28	33
64. Most people who have tuberculosis were born with it.	28	29
65. People should use headache pills every time they have a cold.	28	29
66. Cheese is bad food to eat because it is hard to digest.	27	28
67. The first and best thing to do in caring for a cold is to take a laxative.	27	27
68. People can never change their food likes and dislikes.	26	28
69. Wanting to eat candy and sweets is always a sign that your body needs sugar.	26	24
70. A person's health depends mostly on his luck.	26	10
71. Cheese should be kept out of a good diet because it is constipating.	25	18
72. Eating fruits and vegetables at the same meal is a bad health practice.	25	24
73. All vegetables and fruits should be eaten raw.	25	22
74. It is very hard for thin persons to keep from getting tuberculosis.	24	29
75. If you are hungry most of the time, you can be sure you have a tapeworm.	24	16
76. A cold can usually be cured by eating raw onions.	24	25
77. All medicines that have alcohol in them are harmful.	23	22
78. Adding certain bath powders to the bath is a healthful way to lose weight.	22	17
79. All children with heart murmurs are sickly.	21	22
80. It is generally a good idea to have a radio in your bathroom.	21	28
81. A good health rule for all people to follow is: "Eat only the foods you like best."	20	14
82. Wearing eyeglasses will always make a person's eyes weaker.	20	19
83. A good health rule to follow is: "Feed a cold and starve a fever."	19	21

Column header note: Percentage Frequency of Responses

82   *Methods and Materials in Teaching Health*

TABLE 3—CONTINUED

MODERATELY HARMFUL HEALTH AND SAFETY MISCONCEPTIONS	Grade 5 T and ST	Grade 6 T and ST
84. If you break a mirror you will have seven years of bad luck.	18	15
85. When you walk or run it is best to point your toes out toward the side.	15	11
86. A good way to treat a black eye is to press the eye with a knife handle.	12	11
87. A good way to help digest your food is to smoke a cigarette after you eat.	12	10
88. A person's future is determined by the star under which he is born.	12	10

TABLE 4

VARIATIONS OF THE "TRUE" AND "SOMETIMES TRUE" RESPONSES OF FIFTH- AND SIXTH-GRADE CHILDREN TO CERTAIN SLIGHTLY HARMFUL HEALTH AND SAFETY MISCONCEPTIONS

SLIGHTLY HARMFUL HEALTH AND SAFETY MISCONCEPTIONS	Grade 5 T and ST	Grade 6 T and ST
1. To go on a diet always means to eat less food.	80	76
2. Everyone who is on a diet is trying to lose weight.	80	74
3. Any person who sees clearly can be sure he doesn't need glasses.	80	76
4. The use of tooth powders or pastes will always cure a person's bad breath.	74	79
5. Some people are born lucky.	71	64
6. Most colds can be prevented by taking vitamin pills.	69	69
7. Men with large muscles are always healthier than men with small muscles.	68	69
8. Using a toothpick is the best way to get things from between your teeth.	67	63
9. A mouth wash is healthful because it helps kill germs in the mouth and throat.	65	73
10. There are no living germs in pasteurized milk.	58	57
11. Anyone who keeps his skin clean will never have pimples.	58	56

Health Teaching Program

TABLE 4—CONTINUED

SLIGHTLY HARMFUL HEALTH AND SAFETY MISCONCEPTIONS	Grade 5 T and ST	Grade 6 T and ST
12. People are born with their food likes and dislikes.	50	51
13. Persons should eat only when they feel hungry.	50	42
14. A pain in your right side usually means that you have appendicitis.	49	49
15. People should protect themselves from catching cold by gargling with a mouth wash.	42	46
16. Fish is a food that is very good for the brain.	42	44
17. Cutting or shaving a person's hair makes it grow faster and thicker.	41	51
18. Honey is a good food for sweetening a sour stomach.	41	37
19. Most dogs do not remember the people who were mean to them.	41	34
20. It is a bad health habit to drink water while you exercise.	38	49
21. Bananas should be kept out of a good diet because they make people fat.	38	39
22. White bread that is enriched with vitamins is a better food than whole wheat bread.	38	36
23. Milk is pasteurized to make it easy to digest.	36	29
24. Friday the Thirteenth is an unlucky day for most people.	34	43
25. Eating two or more different kinds of fruit during the same meal is a bad health practice.	32	29
26. Swallowing the seeds of fruits generally causes appendicitis.	32	34
27. Persons who open umbrellas indoors will bring themselves bad luck.	32	28
28. You will have bad luck if a black cat crosses the path in front of you.	32	26
29. Drinking milk while you are eating fish is a bad health practice.	27	23
30. A good health rule to follow is: "Do not eat fruits that have been mixed with milk."	25	22
31. Persons can always prevent pimples by eating more raw foods.	25	18
32. Sleeping on your left side is bad for your heart.	23	19
33. Baldness is usually caused by wearing hats.	18	21
34. Some houses are visited by ghosts.	7	5

Table 5

PREVALANCE OF CERTAIN EXTREMELY HARMFUL HEALTH AND SAFETY MISCONCEPTIONS AMONG A GROUP OF TENTH-GRADE GIRLS

EXTREMELY HARMFUL HEALTH AND SAFETY MISCONCEPTIONS	Per Cent T and ST
1. A person having a stomach-ache should usually take a laxative	62
2. A person always comes up to the top of the water three times before he drowns	54
3. The only good way to help a drowning person is to jump into the water to save him	54
4. The best doctors always promise to make people healthy	54
5. A bullet cannot go off unless it is fired by a gun	50
6. All mad dogs foam at the mouth	46
7. Bicycle riders should ride on the left side of the road to be safe	46
8. It is usually safe to go swimming alone if you know how to swim	46
9. It is a good idea to make an unconscious person drink something	36
10. Most mental sicknesses cannot be helped by any treatment	36
11. It is impossible to cure any cancer	30
12. Oil, grease, and gas fires should be put out with plenty of water	28
13. It is best to go to doctors who advertise in the newspapers	26
14. It is all right to point a gun at someone if you are sure it is not loaded	26

Table 6

PREVALENCE OF CERTAIN VERY HARMFUL HEALTH AND SAFETY MISCONCEPTIONS AMONG A GROUP OF TENTH-GRADE GIRLS

VERY HARMFUL HEALTH AND SAFETY MISCONCEPTIONS	Per Cent T and ST
1. There are certain cough medicines that will cure or prevent the common cold	86
2. People who exercise a lot live longer than other people	76
3. There are some pills that people can take which will cure the common cold	72
4. It is always impossible for a person with cramps to swim	70
5. Any food that does not smell or taste spoiled is safe to eat	68

TABLE 6—CONTINUED

VERY HARMFUL HEALTH AND SAFETY MISCONCEPTIONS	T and ST
6. Iodine is the best treatment for wounds caused by stepping on rusty nails	62
7. Spring water that is clear and cold is always safe for drinking	60
8. People should walk on the right hand side of the road if there are no sidewalks	60
9. If you have any disease or sickness you will always feel some pain	58
10. All people with rosy complexions are very healthy	58
11. Every disease needs a drug or medicine for its cure	56
12. A great deal of exercise can never hurt anyone	56
13. Persons can clean their blood by eating certain foods	54
14. All radio advertising about what is good or bad for your health is true	48
15. All persons should take laxatives whenever they are constipated	46
16. Most people who get tuberculosis will die in a short time	46
17. The best way to get a tan is by sleeping in the sun	42
18. Measles is never harmful	40
19. Mental illness usually happens suddenly	38
20. There are special laxatives that will help prevent or cure the common cold	36
21. All advertising on television about what is good or bad for health is true	36
22. Most fat people are very healthy	36
23. Most illnesses are caused by constipation	34
24. Fresh raw milk is better food for your health than pasteurized milk	32
25. Most accidents cannot be prevented	32
26. All health advertisements in papers and magazines are true	26
27. All children with heart murmurs will surely have heart trouble later on in life	26
28. A good way to treat frostbite is to rub the frostbitten part with snow	26
29. Everyone should take a laxative once a week	26
30. A good safety rule for bicycle riders is: "Ride on the sidewalk as much as possible"	26

TABLE 7

PREVALENCE OF CERTAIN MODERATELY HARMFUL HEALTH AND SAFETY MISCONCEPTIONS AMONG A GROUP OF TENTH-GRADE GIRLS

MODERATELY HARMFUL HEALTH AND SAFETY MISCONCEPTIONS	Per Cent T and ST
1. Brushing your teeth every day is a sure way of stopping decay	92
2. Everyone who has weak feet should wear arch supports to strengthen them	90
3. A daily bowel movement is always necessary so a person can stay healthy	86
4. Nose drops will cure a cold which is causing a stuffy nose	82
5. The only good treatment for weak arches is to have arch supports placed in the shoes	80
6. Wearing bathing hats or ear plugs while swimming will give a person complete protection for his ears	74
7. Sugar diabetes is caused by eating too much sugar	72
8. Persons who have pimples or boils usually have bad blood	68
9. All persons should use nose drops and mouth washes daily when they have a cold	64
10. Wearing eyeglasses will always make a person's eyes stronger	64
11. Most fat people are happy and jolly	64
12. The best way to treat a black eye is to put a piece of raw meat on it	62
13. The use of tooth powders and pastes is sure to make a person's gums firm	62
14. There are some pills that people can take which will prevent the common cold	60
15. Eating between meals causes most children to have bad health	60
16. You can be sure anything a scientist says about health is true	58
17. Wearing sunglasses will give your eyes complete protection from the sun	56
18. The use of skin creams and lotions will make any skin clear and healthy	56
19. Taking vitamin pills will guarantee you good health	54
20. Bad breath can be stopped for good by using special mouth washes	54
21. The use of skin lotion is a healthful way to make any skin beautiful	54
22. Most cases of baldness can be cured if treated early	50
23. The vitamins in certain pills are better than the vitamins in natural foods	50

TABLE 7—CONTINUED

MODERATELY HARMFUL HEALTH AND SAFETY MISCONCEPTIONS	Per Cent
24. Most persons who look thin are certain to be underweight and in poor health	50
25. Any exercise is bad for persons who have heart trouble	46
26. Pain near the heart is generally a sign of heart disease	40
27. Exercising regularly is a sure way to prevent disease	40
28. Taking vitamin pills is the best way to get your necessary vitamins	40
29. The only way to lose weight is by exercising	40
30. Missing a bowel movement for one day is always a sign of constipation	38
31. Good doctors usually advertise	38
32. Mouth washes are sure to prevent or cure diseases of the mouth and throat	38
33. Any person who feels all right is sure to be in good health	38
34. Expensive food is always the best food to eat	38
35. If your eyes do not hurt, you can be sure they are healthy	38
36. Good health does not depend on what you eat	36
37. Food that tastes good is usually bad for your health	34
38. The first and best thing to do in caring for a cold is to take a laxative	32
39. People can never change their food likes and dislikes	32
40. A cold can usually be cured by eating raw onions	30
41. Most colds can be cured by taking vitamin pills	30
42. Wanting to eat candy and sweets is always a sign that your body needs sugar	30
43. It is very hard for thin persons to keep from getting tuberculosis	28
44. Bananas should be kept out of a good diet because they are hard to digest	28
45. An all vegetable diet is the natural and best diet	26
46. You can always tell if a dog is friendly by his looks	26

TABLE 8

PREVALENCE OF CERTAIN SLIGHTLY HARMFUL HEALTH AND SAFETY MISCONCEPTIONS AMONG A GROUP OF TENTH-GRADE GIRLS

SLIGHTLY HARMFUL HEALTH AND SAFETY MISCONCEPTIONS	Per Cent T and ST
1. A mouth wash is healthful because it helps kill germs in the mouth and throat	80
2. Cutting or shaving a person's hair makes it grow faster and thicker	76
3. The use of tooth powders or pastes will always cure a person's bad breath	70
4. Most colds can be prevented by taking vitamin pills	56
5. Any person who sees clearly can be sure he doesn't need glasses	56
6. A pain in your right side usually means that you have appendicitis	54
7. It is a bad health habit to drink water while you exercise	48
8. Men with large muscles are always healthier than men with small muscles	48
9. Anyone who keeps his skin clean will never have pimples	48
10. Some people are born lucky	46
11. Persons can always prevent pimples by eating more raw foods	46
12. Everyone who is on a diet is trying to lose weight	44
13. There are no living germs in pasteurized milk	40
14. To go on a diet always means to eat less food	40
15. Fish is a food that is very good for the brain	38
16. People should protect themselves from catching cold by gargling with a mouth wash	38
17. People should eat only when they feel hungry	36
18. Friday the Thirteenth is an unlucky day for most people	36
19. People are born with their food likes and dislikes	32
20. Most dogs do not remember the people who are mean to them	30
21. Using a toothpick is the best way to get things from between your teeth	28

The Place of Health Education in the Schools.—In order to properly understand the place of health education in the schools it may be helpful to briefly consider what we have been doing in the past and what we are now doing. For many years some educators have considered health education an important part of the school program. During the past two or three decades in particular, health education has been offered in many elementary and secondary schools under varying circumstances. Unfortunately, in a majority of the schools where health education was a part of the program, conditions under which health teaching was conducted were not particularly conducive to good results.

The trial and error methods of teaching health in the past have revealed the difficulty in getting the proper attitudes and practices established. Consequently, there have been many criticisms by educators of the ways, methods and means in which health has been taught. Frequently, one may hear a few educators say that health education cannot be justified if the pupils fail to form proper attitudes and proper health habits immediately following teaching. It should be clearly understood that a main purpose of health teaching is to impart knowledge regardless of whether proper attitudes and habits are immediately formed. It is granted at once, of course, that it is highly important to develop proper habits and attitudes and strong emphasis should be placed on this phase of the program. There is no justification however, for withholding knowledge concerning health and healthful living from children even though the most desirable attitudes and practices are not immediately established following health teaching. There is no certain way of knowing just when students begin to practice desirable health habits following teaching. For example, pupils in a fifth grade may be taught to brush their teeth regularly. Perhaps a number of the pupils soon establish the habit. They all may know the reason why they should brush their teeth, yet it may be one, two, three, or more years before some of them establish regular habits. Nevertheless, the chances are great that if children never receive information regarding the brushing of teeth, they are not likely ever to give sufficient attention to it. The native in the primitive state does not brush his teeth in the modern way. He never heard of such a thing. It is evident at once then, that the native will never brush his teeth in the modern way, unless he is first taught how and is given an understanding of what civilization considers a hygienic practice. It should be kept in mind by teachers then that following teaching some children may start at once to put into practice the most desirable health teachings in all situations. In other cases some children may practice proper habits a part of the time, particularly when circumstances are favorable, and in still other cases some of the children may not form the most desirable health habits and practices for some time following teaching. In some cases perhaps some of the children will never form the proper habits regardless of the knowledge they may gain through teaching.

Another example of attempting to get the proper health habits established is that in which a group of elementary school children is taught about nutrition in an effort to get them to form the proper habit of selecting and eating proper foods. Following teaching it is likely that at least a few of the children will soon establish a habit of giving attention to and selecting the right food, at least part of the time. All of the children may understand the reasons why they should select and eat the right food. Yet, it may take as long as three or four years for some of the children to establish the proper habits of eating which will be evident a large percentage of the time. A main point to be drawn from the examples cited concerning the establishment of proper health attitudes and habits is that if children never receive instruction in health and healthful living the chances are great that they are not likely to ever give attention to and establish proper habits. It follows then that knowledge is primary and basic. The children must be taught about health and healthful living, otherwise there is little hope that they will ever develop the proper habits, attitudes, practices and appreciations.

It should be kept in mind that health knowledge and information is only one part of the process of helping children to establish proper habits, attitudes, practices and appreciations. However, it is extremely difficult to form habits and attitudes without the proper knowledge and understanding. The statement of an able psychologist concerning learning applies in this case. He said, "By learning we may live better or worse but we are sure to live according to what we learn." Even though sound knowledge of health and healthful living does not assure the formation of habits and attitudes, without such knowledge there is little or no hope for improvement in habit formation and practices.

The question often is raised as to why it is so extremely difficult to get a large majority of children and youth to form the proper and correct health habits. On first consideration it would seem that with proper emphasis and motivation during teaching a majority of the children might form the correct practices almost at once. One main reason why it is so difficult for the teacher to get immediate results is that a large part of her teaching is dissipated when the children mingle in adult society. The children come in contact with adults who fail to observe even the most fundamental health practices. The example set by adults tends to minimize the importance and the need for proper health habits in the minds of children and youth. Too, the home conditions of some children are such that it is next to impossible to follow the teachings of healthful living.

Another point that should be kept in mind in attempting to get the proper health attitudes and habits established is that the laws and rules of health and hygiene can be too rigid. There come times in the lives of all of us when it is necessary to momentarily forego what we know is the best health practice. This holds true not only for adults but for children as well. For example, if because of some emergency situation such as illness in the family a person fails to get sufficient sleep, it would perhaps be best for his health if he could take time from his daily duties to get sufficient sleep. However, in many situations it would be impossible for him to take time from his daily work to practice what he knows would be the best for his health. It is evident then, that there are times in the lives of all people when it is a question of selecting and doing the best under the circumstances even though it is not the best for the health of the individual.

The Value of Health Teaching.—Because of the adverse influence of adult society on certain phases of the school health program, the value of health education should be considered perhaps from the viewpoint of the length of time necessary to raise the level and standards of the population as a whole. That is, the ultimate value of the school health teaching program cannot be wholly determined on a daily, weekly, monthly or even a yearly basis, but more likely on the basis of a generation. The health teaching carried on with the present generation of the school population should raise the standards of adult society to a certain extent during the next generation. Then, as each succeeding generation of youth grows to maturity, the level of health standards and practices should be higher than the preceding one. In this way the school health education program should become increasingly effective as generations pass. The level of health standards and practices in future generations of adult members of society depends to a great extent upon the effectiveness of the present as well as future school health education programs. It should be clearly recognized though, that the most desirable health attitudes and practices are not likely to be established throughout society as a whole in one or even two generations, regardless of the amount of time and attention given to education for both children and adults.

A widespread program of adult education in health and healthful living would help greatly in making the school program more effective. Although even a minimum amount of adult health education is helpful, the chances of widespread health teaching for adults on an *organized* basis comparable to that of the schools are somewhat remote. There is no way of reaching a high percentage of the adult population in an *organized* health teaching program comparable to that found in the schools. Under certain conditions it is possible to get a very small percentage of the adult population in organized health work of various kinds, but this is more often the exception rather than the rule.

The adult health education programs carried on through such mediums as television, radio and the press, although more or less haphazard when compared to the organized methods of conducting educational programs in the schools and colleges, are somewhat helpful in raising the standards of the present adult population. These mediums cannot be viewed as a means of marked advancement of a kind comparable to the possibilities of the school health education programs. As a matter of fact, surveys of the results of adult health education by the methods ordinarily used indicate that many misconceptions may be conveyed to the public. There is a need at the present time for very careful study and consideration of the ways, means and methods of attempting adult health education in the United States.

The fact that it is practically impossible to reach even a small percentage of the adult population in organized instruction of any type indicates the great importance of making certain that extensive and effective health education programs be conducted in the schools where it is possible to reach a large percentage of the future adult population. One main reason why health teaching on a widespread basis depends so much upon the schools is the fact that the school is the only agency in society today whereby it is possible to even closely approximate reaching the entire future adult population in a carefully controlled and highly organized teaching program. Consequently, schools must be depended upon to reach the adult population even though it takes one, two, three or more generations.

The Scope of the School Health Teaching Program.—In order to determine properly the scope of health teaching in the school program it is necessary to consider the needs of children and youth at all age levels from the kindergarten throughout the elementary, junior and senior high school.

Organized health instruction should be provided for at all grade levels throughout the elementary and secondary schools. There are a number of important reasons why it should be offered at all levels. First, the body of knowledge concerning health and healthful living in the modern world is so extensive that it is necessary to offer it over a period of years in order to properly impart the knowledge needed. Second, there is a need for a certain amount of health knowledge at all ages even including the kindergarten children. The degree of maturity of children in the elementary grades is such that they cannot be given the extensive knowledge needed for adult life. Yet, it is highly important that instruction be given and that the various phases of health and healthful living be introduced to the children as rapidly as their maturity and level of intelligence will permit.

From the viewpoint of psychology it is much easier to establish proper habits of health and healthful living early in the life of the child. Also, the child needs to practice good health and safety habits just as much at an early age as later. Therefore, it seems psychologically sound to teach as much as possible about health just as early as possible, considering the stages of maturity of the children. An example of this is in the area of nutrition which is a phase of the health education program at practically all grade levels. The subject of nutrition should be introduced and developed as far as the ability of the children at any particular age level permits, for nutrition is a functional part of the life of the child of primary age just as much as in later years. If, by educating the child in nutrition to the extent of his capacity to be educated at the primary level we can better assure his optimum nutrition, then it is obvious that the subject should be introduced just as early in school as possible. Another example is in the area of safety. Even though children of primary age are not mature enough to be given all of the safety information they need for life, nevertheless, it is highly important that they know as much about safety as possible in order to safeguard their lives while growing up. As an example, the failure to teach the elementary school child certain facts about traffic safety could result in his death or permanent disability.

Plans for Health Teaching.—For health teaching to be most effective it must be organized and conducted on a basis comparable to other school subjects and activities. Sufficient time must be allotted in the program, the same as for other activities, otherwise there is little chance for it to be successful. Also, the teacher must place as much emphasis on teaching health as she does on other subjects. The proper preparation and presentation of health education materials are highly essential to teaching health successfully. Two main reasons why health teaching is often considered unsuccessful in many schools is that sufficient time is not given to it and that teachers frequently fail to prepare to teach it as they do other subjects. A third reason is that sufficient time is not set aside for health teaching in the curriculum. Far too often teachers have attempted to teach health entirely by incidental methods, correlation and integration. Although these methods are important and helpful if they are properly employed, they should be considered only as supplementary means of imparting health knowledge and establishing the proper habits, attitudes and practices. It has been learned through experience that there must be planning such as the construction of units and the preparation of lessons and presentations if the health teaching program is to be most successful. Actually, it is highly questionable whether teachers should attempt any type of health teaching if it is not given full status in the program on a basis comparable to other activities and subjects. Certainly the attempts to teach health only by integration, correlation and by incidental means have not been very successful in most schools. The results of experience have shown conclusively that full dependence upon methods of this type often has an adverse effect upon the child. An example of the adverse effects certain kinds of health teaching may have upon the child, particularly in the elementary school, is that in which a teacher attempts to teach health incidentally or as the occasion may arise. The latter is sometimes referred to as the opportunistic plan. This may also involve the integration and correlation methods. Because there is a lack of definite time for orderly presentation and preparation, the process is likely to resolve itself largely into preachment and nagging on the part of the teacher. The preachment and nagging process may be continued at home by the parents and even relatives. It may become so bad that almost everywhere the child turns he is warned, preached to and nagged about his failure to eat the right foods, wear his rubbers or cap, read with sufficient light and a host of other practices the average child is prone to follow, especially if he has not had the benefit of instruction and guidance under the proper and most desirable conditions. In some cases the adverse effects upon children of this nagging and preachment process of "education" by teachers, parents and others is such that by the time children reach the upper grades in elementary school they are conditioned against any type of health teaching to the point where they often prefer to do just the opposite from what is taught. They frequently resent the mention of "health." This adverse reaction of children frequently causes them to resent any attempts to teach health. An example of this is that in which a fifth-grade teacher attempted to conduct an organized health teaching course for the children. Prior to the time the teacher planned the direct teaching course, health had been taught entirely by incidental, integrated, and correlated methods which resulted, as so often happens, in a nagging and preachment process. The arrangement for the direct health course was that the teacher set aside a daily thirty-minute period for the fifth-grade health class which was to be conducted in the elementary school science laboratory. On the first day that the children reported for the health course they were looking forward with interest and enthusiasm to the class they were to have in the science laboratory. They had not been previously informed as to the nature of the course. Almost immediately upon entering the laboratory the children plied the teacher with questions in a very enthusiastic manner concerning the nature of the class. When it was announced to the children that it was to be a class in health education they were immediately crestfallen and showed their dissatisfaction and disappointment in no uncertain terms. Nevertheless, the teacher continued with the class. Her analysis of the reaction of the children as time passed showed that the first attitude had developed largely as a result of the nagging and preachment type of health education they had been subjected to in the earlier elementary grades. It was learned that the teaching in health had been unorganized and haphazard and that as a result the children did not have even a bare fundamental understanding of the reasons for practicing health habits. Consequently, the teacher placed strong emphasis upon developing unit materials in the proper sequence to present to the children as a basis for understanding health and healthful living other than just merely following the laws laid down for healthy living. The results of this course convinced the teacher as well as others who were interested in the project that when materials in health education are presented on a basis comparable to other school subjects, children develop a keen interest in and appreciate the health teaching.

In health courses in junior and senior high schools it has not been an unusual practice for teachers with little or no preparation to be assigned to the teaching of health. As a matter of fact, many times teachers are expected to teach health education courses in junior and senior high schools without study materials of any sort. Although in other areas such as science, where school administrators and teachers would not think of attempting to teach the course without proper demonstration materials, laboratory facilities, textbooks and reference materials, it is not uncommon at all to ask the health teacher to proceed to teach a course lacking in all of the essential teaching materials that would make the course successful. Attempting to teach a class in health education without the proper teaching materials practically assures in the beginning that the course cannot be successful. Results of experiences with junior and senior high school health courses taught under the proper conditions and by properly prepared teachers shows beyond question of doubt that they can be successful and that the students have taken a keen interest in health education courses and materials.

In past years some educators have often criticized health education on the basis that health education courses were tried in the school but that they did not prove successful. However, in practically all cases an investigation of the conditions surrounding the way the health courses were organized and conducted showed that they did not have much chance to be successful due to the failure to provide the necessary materials, methods and properly trained teachers.

One of the best arguments in favor of direct or concentrated health courses in the secondary schools is the fact that many schools throughout the United States are conducting very successful health education courses. If in any one particular school, health courses have not been successful or they are not considered successful at the present time, it is very likely that the things necessary to make them successful have not been provided and are not present. Therefore, under such circumstances school administrators and other school personnel are advised to give attention to conditions under which the courses are being taught if they wish to find the reasons why they are not successful.

Health Teaching in the Elementary School.—The classroom teacher plan of organization in the elementary school somewhat simplifies the problem of organizing the framework for a health teaching program. The usual recommendations are that classroom teachers assume the responsibility for teaching health to the children in their rooms. Even though there are health specialists available who might take the responsibility for teaching health in the various grades, it is usually not recommended that they do so unless the specialist has had specific training and experience in elementary school teaching methods. Ordinarily, the classroom teacher can have better success in the teaching of health to her pupils than the health specialist. This does not mean to imply that the health specialist lacks sufficient specialized knowledge for teaching health, but rather that the classroom teacher may be more successful in teaching health if she has the proper background and training in health education, because she has had also the background and training for teaching elementary school children which the health specialist is likely to lack. In past years it has sometimes been recommended that health specialists attempt to teach health in the schools. However, experience has shown that in most cases this plan has not been successful particularly at the elementary school level. It does not seem to make any difference how much knowledge a person may have concerning a subject if that person lacks preparation in teaching methods and does not have the background considered necessary to teach elementary school children, the extensive knowledge is not necessarily helpful in teaching and imparting knowledge to children. There is no more reason why we should recommend that a health specialist teach health in the elementary school than we should recommend that a person with a doctorate degree in mathematics teach mathematics in the elementary school. The point is that the extent of knowledge to be imparted to the children is not so great or extensive that it requires such a highly specialized person to do the teaching.

If it is possible then for the classroom teacher to be more successful in teaching health to elementary school children than the health specialist, the problem of establishing and improving health teaching in the schools is one of proper preparation and education on the part of classroom teachers rather than employment of health specialists to do the actual teaching. The health specialist, however, can be of much assistance to the classroom teacher in the way of acting as consultant and helping in various ways to coordinate the entire school health program.

The attitude and support of the elementary school principal is highly important to the success of the health education program. In a majority of schools throughout the country the leadership, supervision and coordination of the elementary school health education program rests largely with the principal because health specialists are not likely to be available to take the responsibility.

It is extremely important that the elementary school health education program be well-coordinated to prevent overlapping from one grade to another. One reason why many children are conditioned against health teaching is because of the overlapping in teaching from grade to grade. This overlapping usually results from a failure to place health materials on a graded and progressive basis.

It has been mentioned previously that many of the same health topics should be presented for successively advanced exploration and study at practically every grade level in the elementary school. If the total school program from grade to grade is not well-coordinated the teacher in one grade may repeat much that has been presented in the previous grade. For example, a fifth-grade teacher may devote a part of the health teaching time to a unit dealing with nutrition. When the fifth-grade children progress to the sixth-grade, the sixth-grade teacher may give some time to the study of nutrition supposedly at a level in advance of any previous study of the subject. If the sixth-grade teacher is not fully aware of the extent of the teaching and study carried on in the fifth-grade, she may repeat much of the material the fifth-grade teacher presented the year before. It should be kept in mind in regard to the teaching of advanced units in the same subject in the same area that there is no objection to a review of the health materials presented in the previous grade. When reviews of previously studied materials are presented, however, it should be made clear to the children that they are merely reviews and not something being presented for the first time.

Some schools attempt to prevent overlapping of teaching by arranging health subjects and units on an alternating yearly basis which is often called the cycle plan. The cycle plan for health materials is sometimes evident beginning with the first grade and continuing throughout the elementary, junior and senior high school. Schools using the yearly basis for presenting the same health topics and those using the cycle plan in which various units have been alternated on a yearly basis or on a two- or three-year basis have reported excellent results. In other words it is possible to use either plan successfully in presenting health materials particularly throughout the elementary school.

Health Teaching in the Junior High School Grades.—The various plans of organization for education must be taken into account in the process of establishing the best possible health education programs in the junior high school grades. The traditional plan of organization in which the seventh and eighth grades are a part of the elementary school is still used in this country. The more modern junior high school plan which employs special teachers and which is organized along the lines similar to the high school is another established type of organization for students in the seventh, eighth and ninth grades. Between the traditional organization in which the seventh and eighth grades are organized as a part of the elementary school and the more modern junior high school plan, there exist numerous ways of organizing education for students at this level. In some cases, a modified junior high school plan is used in which the seventh and eighth grades only are organized on a junior high school basis. The specialized subject fields are then handled accordingly with specialized teachers in charge of the work. In some other schools the traditional classroom teacher organization continues but with certain areas and fields of education taught and handled on a specialized basis.

A more recent development in educational organization which affects the junior high school grades is the six-four-four plan. In this type of organization the first six grades of the elementary school form one unit, the seventh, eighth, ninth and tenth grades form a second unit and the eleventh, twelfth, thirteenth and fourteenth grades form the third unit. The thirteenth and fourteenth grades correspond to the junior college level.

The plan of education in operation at the junior high school level in any community affects to some extent the organization and conduct of the health education program. In the more modern plan of junior high school education in which the teachers are specialized more along the lines of the high school teacher, it is possible to employ teachers who have had some specialized training in health education. It may be possible, particularly in some of the larger junior high schools, to have the services of health educators. In most schools though, the responsibility for teaching health in direct teaching courses is more likely to be taken by science teachers, home economics teachers, physical education teachers or others who have had some basic preparation which tends to qualify them for the work. It should be mentioned at this point, though, that neither science teachers, physical education teachers nor home economics teachers are qualified to teach the health education courses in the junior high school unless they have had specific preparation in health education.

In a majority of those schools in which the seventh and eighth grades remain a part of the elementary school the classroom teacher will have to be responsible for teaching health the same as in other grades of the elementary school.

In the six-four-four plan of education the second unit is usually recognized as the high school level. In a majority of those communities where this plan of organization is in operation usually there are sufficient resources to employ health specialists to assume responsibility for the health teaching program. There should be health educators on the faculties of these schools, if at all possible, to coordinate the health work and to teach the health education courses.

Most of the health teaching carried on at the junior high school level should be done through direct teaching courses. The health courses should be given sufficient time in the curriculum and they should be conducted on the same basis as other school subjects if they are to be most successful. In addition to the health courses offered on a semester or yearly basis there should be correlation and integration of health through other school subjects such as science, social studies, home economics and physical education. One of the most successful ways of correlating and integrating health education through other school subjects is by the use of definitely planned units whereby the health factors are clearly evident.

In planning health education at the junior high school level the previous education and background of the students should be taken into account. If the students have had the advantage of a broad program of health education in the elementary school grades, health education materials in the junior high school should be of an advanced nature. Overlapping of health content should be as carefully controlled in a junior high school as in the elementary school. If overlapping occurs in a form that is more than a brief review of the previously presented material the students are likely to become bored and lose interest in health, which creates an unsatisfactory learning situation.

It is recommended for the junior high school level that the cycle plan be used to prevent overlapping of health materials from one grade to another rather than attempting to teach all areas and units every year.

It is usually thought best, if at all possible, that a health education course be given at each grade at the junior high school level.

In ordinary circumstances the content of the health courses in the junior high school should be advanced study and exploration of many of the units offered in the upper grades of the elementary school. Usually, there should be a more intensive study of the fundamentals of hygiene and physiology in the junior high school grades in order that the students will have sufficient background to understand and appreciate somewhat more advanced health and hygiene materials. Also, there should be some time given to an introduction and study of community health and hygiene, particularly in the upper grades of the junior high school.

Health Teaching in the High School.—It is extremely important to have a well-organized health teaching program at the high school level because the majority of the students will not have an opportunity for organized instruction of any kind after graduation from high school. It is the duty of those directly in charge of the high schools to be certain that the health education of the students is as complete as possible by the time they graduate from high school. The plans and methods used in attempting to complete the health knowledge of students in preparing them for adult life depends materially upon the extent and background of health knowledge of the students when they enter the high school. Experience shows that students enter high school with widely varying backgrounds of knowledge in health and hygiene. If complete and comprehensive health instruction is given in elementary and junior high schools the task of completing the education of the students in health in high school would be materially simplified. However, at the present time a high percentage of students reach high school lacking the health knowledge and information they should have acquired in the elementary and junior high schools.

The health courses in the high school should be organized on a semester or a yearly basis. It is usually recommended that at least one course be given at the ninth or tenth grade level and a more advanced course be given in the eleventh or twelfth grade. In some cases, health specialists have recommended that a health education course on a yearly or semester basis be given at each grade at the high school level. This, perhaps, would be an ideal situation but in most schools throughout the country time has not been made available for so much health teaching. Although a few schools have offered health courses at all grade levels in the high school it is the exception rather than the rule. As a matter of fact, if a direct teaching course in health education is offered at the lower grades of the high school and another at the upper grades, there is no great need for health courses at all grade levels providing the students have had a satisfactory background in health in elementary and junior high school.

In the past, one common way in which health education was organized in the high schools was to allot a certain number of regular school periods each week to health and physical education. Then a part of the time was devoted to physical activities and a part to health teaching. An example of this was in those schools where five class periods each week were given to health and physical education and in which two or three periods were devoted to health teaching and two or three to physical activities. In cases where health and physical education were organized as a unit, it was usually the duty of the teacher of physical education to do the health teaching. This arrangement was sometimes satisfactory so far as the health teaching was concerned, provided the physical education teacher had sufficient background, preparation, experience and interest in health education. In many cases physical education teachers lack sufficient preparation in teaching methods of the kind necessary to conduct health classes satisfactorily and on a basis comparable to other academic courses.

The plan in which health and physical education is combined is not recommended because in the present day it seems best to completely separate physical education from health education as far as teaching is concerned and organize the health courses similarly to the way other academic courses are organized. Furthermore, because physical education teachers very often are not qualified to teach health education and because frequently they are not interested, the health education courses are far more likely to be successful if a teacher specifically prepared in health education is assigned to teach the courses.

There has been a misunderstanding concerning the qualifications of physical education teachers to teach health in past years. It should be kept in mind that, of the more than five hundred schools in the United States educating and preparing physical education teachers, perhaps not more than seventy-five of these schools properly prepare teachers to teach both physical education and health education. It is estimated that approximately seventy-five per cent of the physical education teachers in the United States have neither the background of training nor the experience to teach health education courses successfully. Some physical education teachers can teach health successfully and they are now doing so but these teachers are usually from the schools where they have received a background of education and training which has prepared them more adequately to teach health. However, because in a large majority of the schools throughout the United States the physical education teacher must teach the health courses if they are taught at all, teacher-education institutions for many years to come should try to properly prepare physical education teachers to teach health courses.

Perhaps the most satisfactory arrangement in the health teaching program in the high school is to have the courses taught by a health educator. In the absence of a health educator other health specialists such as physicians, nurses, science teachers and home economics teachers may be assigned the duty of teaching health and hygiene. However, this arrangement is not wholly satisfactory because physicians and nurses, the same as many physical education teachers, lack education, training and teaching methods of the kind so necessary for conducting health classes on a basis similar to other school subjects.

Perhaps the best solution to the problem of personnel to successfully teach health and hygiene courses in the high schools is to prepare sufficient health educators to accept the responsibility. A few health educators are now being prepared at the undergraduate level in some colleges in the United States. However, it will be many years before they are available in sufficient numbers to take the responsibility for a major part of the health teaching in the secondary schools.

A word of caution should perhaps be given here concerning the minimum amount of time that should be allotted to the health education courses. A common practice in the past has been to devote one class period weekly to health teaching. Experience with this over a period of many years has shown that it is not successful in a large majority of the schools where it has been tried. Unsuccessful attempts to teach health on a one-day a week basis is one reason why many school administrators have been dissatisfied with the health courses. One of the main difficulties in the one meeting period per week for the health courses is that periods are so far apart that all continuity of instruction is likely to be lost from one class meeting to another. Under such circumstances it is extremely difficult for a teacher to organize and present materials on a basis comparable to other school subjects. So, very often the one-period-per-week health course turns out to be a period in which it is necessary for the teacher to try to do something to entertain the students in one way or another because it is practically impossible to do the proper kind of teaching.

The phases of health to be included and stressed at the high school level should be in advance of the program given in the junior high school. Some more intensive study of basic physiology and hygiene in relation to healthful living as well as community hygiene is recommended for high school students. In connection with the teaching of physiology it should be remembered that the pure physiology courses at the high school level were common at the turn of the century. Largely because of the teaching methods used and the uninteresting features of the subject, physiology courses as such gradually passed out of the curriculum. The physiology included in modern health education courses should be more or less limited and largely for the purpose of preparing the students to understand health and hygiene.

At the high school level the same as at other levels precautions should be taken to prevent overlapping of health content. Again at the high school level the plan of arranging materials on a cycle basis is sometimes used. Ordinarily, however, it does not make too much difference at the high school level whether health materials are on a cycle basis or otherwise for usually the study is far in advance of the health content presented in the junior high school.

There are certain things connected with the teaching of health courses that should be avoided. In past years as well as at present it has been a practice in some schools to have extremely large health classes. This situation has ordinarily come about because the health teaching program has been closely connected with physical education. For example, in many schools throughout the country, students from all grades in the high school may be found in one physical education class. Furthermore, the classes in physical education sometimes range as high as 150 or more students. It is evident at once then that a classroom instruction course cannot be conducted successfully on such a basis. If the health teacher is expected to take the total physical education class with the mixture of students from the various grade levels on alternating days with physical education, it is readily evident that successful health teaching cannot be done under the circumstances.

Another condition that has been responsible for poor health teaching is that in which a physical education teacher attempts to teach health to a class only on days when the weather is too inclement to be outdoors for physical education. It is evident at once that the teacher cannot plan the proper kind of a health teaching program and conduct it successfully any more in health education than could be done in other academic subjects where such a situation would not be tolerated.

In the absence of direct health teaching courses some health education has been done on a limited basis in areas such as social studies, general science, home economics, biology and other related courses. In some cases, special health units have been included in other courses. The health units in related courses can be successful. However, it should be realized that there is not much chance of covering the field of health education as it should be by placing isolated units in other subject matter fields. Experience with this plan throughout the country has shown that it is practically impossible to include sufficient health materials in science instruction or other related courses to prepare the students properly for adult life. It has been shown that if a science teacher attempts to present the amount of health materials the students should have, he has practically no time left for teaching science.

The Use of Courses of Study and Curriculum Guides.—The question is often raised concerning the use of courses of study or curriculum guides. Frequently, the question arises as to whether or not the individual school should develop a curriculum guide or a course of study aside from those that are usually available from state departments of education. The question as to whether the individual school should develop its own curriculum guide depends materially upon conditions within that state and community. If there are health curriculum guides or courses of study available from the state department of education there may not be so great a need for a course of study to be developed in the particular community. However, many schools prefer to develop their own courses of study and curriculum guides because it is felt that each community has different problems to face and that by so developing the course of study that peculiar and individual community's problems can be met better than by considering a state-wide project. Whether or not the individual community develops its own curriculum guide or course of study, it is recommended that a committee or health council give consideration to the gradation and progression of health materials from primary grades throughout the junior and senior high school. In this way, the overlapping of health materials can be avoided.

Teaching Health Through Correlation.—Almost from the beginning of health teaching in the schools, there have been attempts to teach sufficient health materials entirely by correlation methods. Experience with attempting to teach health through correlation has shown that it can be only partially successful in imparting the broad and extensive knowledge needed by students for adult life. Teaching health through correlation implies the use of other subject matter areas within the curriculum as means by which health information is imparted. For example, there is no question but that a certain amount of personal and community hygiene can be taught in courses such as the biological sciences, general science, social science, home economics and other related areas. In other words, the feeling of some educators was that sufficient health information is evident in these related areas to complete the necessary knowledge on the part of the students. Also there has been another approach to correlation in recent years. That is, in direct health teaching courses found in the curriculum, there have been attempts to correlate other materials such as science, home economics and other related areas in health education courses. There is no question that correlation should continue in the school program and that health education should be correlated with other subjects and that it should be a reciprocal procedure. In certain of the areas, such as the biological sciences, a certain amount of correlation is evident regardless of whether it has been planned for. It remains for the teacher to place enough emphasis on the natural relationships between other subject matter and health education to make it effective. It has been learned through experience, though, that the broad area of health knowledge cannot be imparted entirely by correlation means. If this is attempted then there is not sufficient time left in the other subject matter areas to impart sufficient information in those areas. In other words, with all the correlation that can possibly be done with the related courses in the school curriculum, there remains a need for direct health teaching courses in order to properly educate youth in health for adult life.

Teaching Health Through Integration.—One difference between integration and correlation is that the integration of learning experiences centers around a core or group objective. However, it should be recognized at once that the term integration has been used in a number of ways in its application to the school curriculum. It has sometimes been used to refer to the procedure of integrating materials within a subject matter field. It has also been used to indicate the integration of the student as a whole. Then, the broader application and use of the term integration has had to do with the integration of the total school curriculum. In this sense, integration sometimes means the tendency toward the elimination of subject matter areas, as such, into a broader whole and on a problem basis. It is in this sense that teaching health through integration has been used most frequently; that is, the attempt to integrate health throughout all school areas, whether or not there are subject matter lines and division. There is a need for the integration of health materials in all school experiences. It should be planned for, the same as in other areas. However, again experience has shown that attempts to teach health only by integration have not been sufficient to impart the broad area of information the student should have for adult life. Furthermore, the teaching of health by integration through such procedures as the core curriculum shows that much of the teaching is left to chance and might be termed "accidental," depending upon whether or not, in the process of studying the greater areas, problems of health will arise in sufficient numbers to give the proper amount of education and background. When plans for integrating the entire school curriculum are developed to the point where they are considered successful enough to eliminate the subject matter areas, then perhaps health education will have developed within the framework sufficiently that the health knowledge of the students can be completed entirely on an integration basis.

Questions for Discussion

1. What evidence is there for maintaining that there is a need for health teaching in schools?
2. Briefly, what would you say the findings of the health and safety misconceptions study suggest?
3. At the present time, why must we be content to impart sound *knowledge* and *understanding* of health rather than insist upon immediate improvement in health attitudes and practices in all cases?
4. What factors account for the belief that the objectives of health education will not be realized on a general basis for three or more generations?
5. To what extent are the so-called mass-media (e.g., newspapers, radio and television) effective in educating the general public in relation to health?
6. What are the major plans for teaching health?
7. What are the major arguments in support of providing direct health courses?
8. What are some factors which have caused many children to react adversely to health instruction in schools?
9. What can be done about the factors mentioned in item 8, above?
10. Why is it usually assumed that the classroom teacher is in the best position to teach health at the elementary school level?
11. Why is it essential that there be careful curriculum planning which takes into account what is taught at all grades of the elementary school?
12. What is the cycle plan for teaching health and why is it used?

13. In what ways should the health teaching content at the junior high school level differ from that of the elementary school level? How should the junior high level content differ from the senior high?
14. What difficulties commonly arise when health courses are combined with physical education at the high school level? With science?
15. Who should be primarily responsible for the teaching of health at the high school level?
16. What are the rules of integration and correlation in a good health teaching program?

Suggested Class Activities

1. Analyze your own school situation or one that is well known to you and prepare a list of factors which indicate a need for health teaching.
2. Administer the "Extremely Harmful" and "Very Harmful" health and safety misconceptions tests to a group of school age children with whom you have contact. What appear to be the major misconceptions? What conclusions can you draw from your findings?
3. Discuss the "Extremely Harmful Health and Safety Misconceptions." Indicate why each item is a misconception.
4. Discuss the relationship of health education for adults and health education for children.
5. Hold a round-table discussion on the problem of adult education in health and ways in which some of these problems might be handled.
6. Discuss the uses of incidental methods, correlation and integration in health teaching.
7. Select a school that is well known to you. List the factors in that school that are conducive to good health teaching and those that are not. What general evaluation would you give to the conditions for health teaching?
8. Outline the role of each of the following in the teaching of health at the secondary school level: the health educator, physical education teacher, home economics teacher, science teacher.

References

1. Dzenowagis, Joseph G. and Leslie W. Irwin, "Prevalence of Certain Harmful Health and Safety Misconceptions Among Fifth and Sixth-Grade Children," *Research Quarterly of the American Association for Health, Physical Education and Recreation,* Vol. 25, No. 2, May 1954.
2. Dzenowagis, Joseph G., Patricia V. McPherson and Leslie W. Irwin, "Harmful Health and Safety Misconceptions of a Group of Tenth-Grade Girls," *Journal of School Health,* Vol. XXIV, No. 9, November 1954.
3. Hicks, Dora A., "Scope of Health Instruction, Grades 1 to 12," *Journal of School Health,* Vol. XXIII, No. 6, June 1953.
4. Hill, Patricia J., "Unmet Needs in Teacher Education for Health," *Journal of*

the *American Association for Health, Physical Education and Recreation,* Vol. 25, No. 1, January 1954.
5. Moss, Bernice, "Health Teaching—A Physical Educator's Responsibility," *Journal of Health, Physical Education and Recreation,* Vol. 25, No. 9, November 1954.
6. Rash, J. K., "Scheduling and Sequence of Health Instruction, Grades 1 to 12," *Journal of School Health,* Vol. XXIV, No. 5, May 1954.
7. Starr, Helen M., "Today's Pupil—Health-Informed or Health-Educated," *Journal of Health, Physical Education and Recreation,* Vol. 25, No. 7, September 1954.
8. Streit, W. K., "Health Education from Kindergarten Through High School," *Journal of School Health,* Vol. XXIV, No. 9, November 1954.

CHAPTER 6

THE RELATIONSHIP OF HEALTH AND SAFETY IN THE SCHOOL PROGRAM

It is extremely important for school administrators and teachers to have a clear understanding of the relationship of health and safety education in the modern school program. Rapid advances and marked growth and development of school health and safety education programs during the past two or three decades has shifted responsibilities and changed relationships very greatly in these areas. Teachers, parents, and others interested in and responsible for the optimum growth and development of the school child should be cognizant not only of the problems in health education, but in safety and accident prevention as well. For many years the schools have accepted responsibility in health education in attempting to help each child develop to his greatest possible capacity not only academically but emotionally and physically as well. In accepting this responsibility in the area of health education, naturally, teachers and others have attempted to do everything possible to educate the children concerning health as well as to try to help them maintain good health and to protect them from ill health and disabling diseases and disorders. In recent years it has been recognized that safety ranks in the same category in the attempt to assure the optimum growth and development of children. If teachers think in terms of protection and providing for the optimum health and growth of children, then they cannot fail to assume responsibility in the area of safety education, the same as in health education. One of the main reasons for this is the fact that more children are killed each year in accidents than by any single disease. As a matter of fact, more children are killed in accidents each year than by approximately the total nine leading childhood diseases.

Deaths and Injuries from Accidents.—Although the problem of accidental deaths and injuries has assumed major proportions in the United States, most people are not as yet thoroughly conscious of the modern problem of safety and accident prevention. Do you know how many people are hurt and killed in accidents each year? Have you ever been in a city with a population of 100,000? Each year in the United States approximately 100,000 people are killed in accidents. You may not hear or read about many of these accidents for they are scattered throughout the entire country. Yet, if all of the yearly accidental deaths happened in one place, a city of 100,000 people would be completely wiped out at the end of each year. Think of all these accidental deaths which happen over a period of ten years. The following ten cities have a population of approximately 100,000: Little Rock, Arkansas; Sacramento, California; Peoria, Illinois; Lansing, Michigan; Altoona, Pennsylvania; Waterbury, Connecticut; Charlotte, North Carolina; and El Paso, Texas. If all of the accidental deaths during the past ten years had happened in these cities instead of being scattered throughout the country, practically all of these ten cities would have been wiped out. Or, if the approximately 1,000,000 accidental deaths during the past ten years had all happened in one city such as St. Louis, Missouri, which has a population of approximately 1,000,000, there would be very few persons alive in that city today.

Besides the large number of people killed in accidents each year, about 330,000 sustain injuries from which they never fully recover. Louisville, Kentucky is a city of approximately 330,000 people. If all of the injuries from which people do not completely recover happened in Louisville in any one year, then practically everyone there including men, women, and children, would be crippled in some way. Think what it would be like. Everyone in Louisville, crippled in such a way that he could not work or play as usual and many could not work or play at all. A large number of them would be crippled so badly they would have to be cared for by others the rest of their lives. Now consider the crippling injuries which happen over a period of ten years. With approximately 330,000 occurring each year, then about 3,300,000 have occurred during the past ten years. A number almost as large as the population of a city the size of Chicago, Illinois. If all of the permanently disabling injuries during the past ten years had happened in Chicago, then nearly every person living there would be crippled in some way.

In addition to the many people killed and permanently disabled each year, about 10,000,000 people sustain injuries which disable them for a time. You can better understand this large number when you remember that there are approximately 160,000,000 people in the United States. In the last ten years the number of people hurt equals many more than one-half of the number of people in the United States. Think of the large amount of time lost from both school, work and play as well as the suffering and pain from these injuries. Also, a large percentage of persons injured each year are men and women who earn the living for their families. When an injury happens to a worker the children and others who depend upon him for a living may suffer from a lack of proper food and other things necessary for life.

Safety Prior to Modern Times.—The human race has always been exposed to hazards and dangers of many kinds. The history of the development of man reveals many and varied hazards. The instinct of self-preservation and the urgent desire for freedom from bodily harm have remained dominant forces in the quest for security. The history of safety and freedom from bodily harm parallels the development of man. The quest for safety began when prehistoric man first realized the necessity of defending himself against the elements in his physical surroundings which might cause injury or destroy life. Such dangers as cold, hunger, wild beasts and his fellow man were the hazards confronting man in ancient times. As time passed, man, at first leading a solitary existence or organized only in a family group, formed tribes which eventually united into states and nations. A fundamental basis for the banding together of men and tribes was the need for protection against the common enemies of the people. As civilization advanced, communities were organized for the protection of all. Governments gradually assumed greater responsibility for the welfare of all the people. The right and duty of a government to insure a reasonable degree of protection for its citizens is of ancient origin and has become firmly established in the customs of the present day. Community police and fire protection plus regulations protecting health and safety are examples of broader protection which people have come to expect of the community.

Safety in the World Today.—Many of the hazards which formerly existed for man are gone, but in their place have come others far more numerous and serious. Modern machines have become an element of major importance in the life of everyone. Motor vehicles, locomotives, airplanes, steamships, electrical appliances, chemicals, poisons and explosives as well as the recently developed atomic energy are examples of modern developments which have introduced, created and multiplied hazards in the modern world. The hazards have become so numerous, the methods of meeting them so varied and complicated and the intellectual and emotional preparation needed to live safely among the hazards is so extensive, that safety has emerged as a major problem of civilization.

A fundamental obligation of our democratic society however, is to assure and provide safe living conditions for its members. The problem of safety in the world today has grown to assume such proportions and magnitude as to challenge society in its ability to assure and provide safe living conditions for all. The yearly fatal accident rate has increased in many areas since the year 1913. At the present time there is very little evidence to indicate that any major reduction in the yearly number of accidents may occur.

Classification of Accidents.—The yearly statistics dealing with accidental deaths and injuries in the United States indicate an appalling situation. The use of these statistics in attempting to reduce the accidental death and injury rate have been questioned at times as somewhat inadequate. Nevertheless, statistics showing how and where people are killed and injured continue to be the basis upon which organized efforts are founded in educational and prevention programs.

To gain a proper perspective of the total accident situation it is necessary to know as accurately as possible the number of people involved in accidents resulting in death, permanent disability and disabling injuries. In order to deal intelligently with the accident problem it is important to show also the many accidents occurring within the activities in which human beings participate from day to day. For example, if teachers in the schools are to help reduce the number of deaths and injuries to school children, it is very important that they know just where and how accidents occur not only in and about the school building and grounds but on the way to and from school and in the home as well.

The National Safety Council classifies accidents into four main divisions. These four main divisions have been found to be very useful in studying and clarifying accident statistics for use by teachers and other groups interested in and working in the area of safety education. The four main or general classifications are: motor vehicle accidents; home accidents; occupational accidents; and public accidents (exclusive of motor vehicle accidents.) Of course, it is necessary to make many classifications within the four divisions if we are to know exactly where and how accidents happen. It is one of the duties of teachers and others in safety education to reclassify accidents in such a way that they will be helpful in teaching safety and accident prevention.

Risk and Exposure to Accidents.—The attitude of many people regarding risk and exposure to accidental injury and death is that nobody is involved or concerned but the individual involved. It is evident at once that this attitude is fallacious for, in practically all cases of accidental death or injury of any seriousness, others besides the injured person are involved. The family of the injured person, the employer, or society as a whole may be affected. It is true that unless there are large numbers of fatalities and injuries, the load placed on society is not particularly great. Yet, even at the present time there is no question but that the social order is bearing a financial burden greater than it should because of the many accidents resulting in death and injury.

There are certain activities necessary for the function and maintenance of society in which risks must be assumed. In such cases and in such occupations the ideal is to provide the safest possible conditions in relation to the necessary risk involved. There are activities also which are not necessary to the function and maintenance of society in which seemingly great hazards are evident. The question then is, should activities of a more hazardous nature which are not necessary for the maintenance of society be continued? This immediately brings up a question of the consideration of various activities from the point of view of safety and risk so far as their value to society is concerned. An example of this is football in the high schools. It is readily granted and statistics bear out that football is more hazardous than many other sports. Because football is not necessary to the function and maintenance of society it is the contention of some people that football should be abandoned and a less hazardous game be established to take its place. On the other hand, those opposed to this opinion argue that there are developmental features in the game of football that warrant the risk being taken and the hazards involved. The decision regarding an activity such as high school football cannot be made with a clear-cut and definite conclusion. There always will be those who feel that the high school boy would be better off without the game of football and those who feel that the hazards involved are not too great for the values received. It is quite possible that the determination of risk in such instances should be left to those controlling a particular situation. There are cases in schools where football with all its hazards would be highly desirable because of the particular type of boy involved. There might be need in a particular situation to develop more rugged individuals which could be brought about in no other way than through exposure to hazards of more rugged activities.

Perhaps in all cases where risk is involved two phases should be given careful consideration, that is, the effect the risk or possible injury might have on a particular individual and his immediate family and associates, and the effect that possible injury might have on society as a whole.

Mental, Emotional and Physical Factors Involved in Safety and Accident Prevention.—There are numerous indications throughout the field of safety and accident prevention that those working toward the reduction of accidents and the removal of both mental, emotional and physical hazards are faced, at least in part, with a very definite psychological problem. Perhaps one of the most convincing indications that safety is a psychological problem may be gained from the fact that safety engineers and experts estimate that a high majority of accidents resulting in death and injury can be prevented. Of course in order to prevent many accidents, it would require the elimination of many hazards, but in the main it is largely a problem of individual and group attitudes and reactions. An example of this is that statistics show that only a small percentage of the motor vehicles involved in accidents have faulty mechanisms. This seems to indicate that the trouble lies largely with the driver and not necessarily with the machine.

In industry and occupations the large reduction in the number of accidents during the past four or five decades indicates that the problem is largely one of attitudes and practices. Although employers have gone to great expense and trouble to be sure that all machines and working conditions are safe, many accidents occur each year because of the human element involved.

It is apparent then that, even though all conceivable types of safety devices may be provided for society in building and constructing safe living and working conditions, a large percentage of accidents cannot be eliminated merely with safe machines nor with foolproof safety devices. In late years, engineers in all fields of human endeavor have been striving to make safer conditions for the individual and for society. Unless the individual and the group cooperate and know how to make intelligent use of safety devices provided for them there is not likely to be any material reduction in the present accident rate regardless of the emphasis placed on removing hazards.

The attitudes of individuals are especially important in the present accident situation. This is particularly true in the field of motor vehicle safety. Everyone is more or less familiar with the different attitudes that may be found among motor vehicle drivers. Reckless drivers who do not give consideration either to themselves or to others are seen in far too great numbers. State laws have been enacted whereby youths below certain ages cannot drive cars. A factor in the development of state laws regarding age limits for drivers is the emotional nature of the adolescent. What is not given consideration is that many adults never seem to progress beyond the emotional level of the adolescent.

Emotional stability is certainly one of the most important factors in the accident situation. More and more time and attention are being given to the study of the emotions in an effort to lower the accident rate. There are admittedly many physical attributes related to the problem of the psychology of safety. Such physical attributes as age, race, sex, native coordination, skill, reaction time, vision, stimulation, fatigue, physical condition and many others are directly related to the safety of both the individual and the group. Practically all of the physical attributes are, however, so closely related to emotional and psychological aspects that it is usually impossible to separate them as causative factors in the accident situation.

It is usually next to impossible to determine the particular mental or emotional attribute responsible in case of accidents where it is clearly evident that a mental or emotional factor is at fault. More often it is likely to be a combination of a number of mental and emotional attributes involved in the particular accident situation. Some of the mental and emotional attributes important in safety are native intelligence, knowledge in relation to safety, judgment in relation to safety, experience, attention, memory, absent-mindedness, imagination, concentration, boredom, decisiveness, worry and mental balance. Closely correlated with the numerous mental and physical attributes affecting safe conduct is emotional stability. Both the mental and physical attributes of the individual can be highly conducive to safety, but, if the emotions are not reasonably stabilized, the mental and physical qualities may be rendered ineffective, particularly in situations where emotional control may be easily lost. More time and attention are being given to the study of emotions in relation to the accident situation.

Some Basic Causes of Child Accidents.—The accidental death and injury of children of school age is due in part to school and community failure to eliminate hazards, provide adequate control, set up safety standards for activities, furnish capable and qualified supervision and to provide education in safety and accident prevention for children.

Although the causes of child accidents are numerous and varied, the following list of common accidents and contributing factors shows where some immediate attention is needed.

A. Street and Highway Accidents
   Unsafe play areas
   Walking or playing in streets and on highways
   Crossing streets between intersections
   "Jaywalking" in streets
   Increased congestion of highways
   Disregard of drivers for regulations and safe practices
   Lack of safe practices in pupil transportation
   Improper use of bicycles, scooters, and motorcycles
   Failure to provide safe places for skating and coasting

B. Accidents on School Premises
   Faulty conditions or unsafe practices in school buildings
   Unsafe practices in school shops and laboratories
   Inadequate control of, and preparation for, competitive sports

C. Home Accidents
   Carelessness leading to fires and burns
   Unsafe storage of firearms and fireworks
   Disorderliness and poor housekeeping leading to falls and other accidents
   Careless use of external and internal poisons
   Unsafe practices with gas

D. Accidents in Recreational Activities
   Swimming and ice-skating in unsupervised places
   Lack of swimming and lifesaving skills
   Improper use of boats and canoes
   Unsupervised playground activities
   Inadequate supervision during fishing, hiking or camping trips
   Unsafe practices with firearms and fireworks
   Unsafe practices in non-school play areas

Habit Formation in Safety.—Although the formation of habits is closely related to practically all mental and physical factors, there is one phase of habit formation that should be given close study in the safety education of both youths and adults. The teaching of safety is extremely important in attempting to reduce accidents. Yet, until and unless the proper habits and attitudes can be established there is not likely to be any material reduction in the present accident rate. Therefore, teachers should do their utmost when teaching safety to get the proper habits and attitudes established, otherwise the children are not likely to act on the knowledge they may gain concerning safety and accident prevention for the welfare of themselves as well as of society.

The Probable Value of Safety Education.—The value of safety education in the school program is more or less problematical depending upon a number of factors. It is the opinion of some groups that safety education alone is ineffectual if extra means are not taken to establish desirable attitudes, habits and practices. Although great emphasis should be placed on the development of attitudes and habits, education is the first and primary step in bringing about a greater degree of safety within society. If safety is not taught, it is impossible to establish proper attitudes and habits. Neither the child nor the adult can form the right habits and attitudes without first knowing the factors involved. Consequently, *education* is the first and foremost step in safety.

The probable value of safety education for the various grade levels or for the total school program has not been clearly determined. The safety education in the school at the present time gives evidence of good results so far as large numbers of school children are concerned. In some programs immediate results in the way of proper habits and attitudes have not been forthcoming. It must be kept in mind though that the schools can educate children in safety and they perhaps could get immediate desirable results in the proper practices. However, when the child mingles in society with adults who do not place importance on safety practices and who fail to set good examples, a large part of the teaching in the schools may be dissipated.

The process of safety education must be thought of in terms of gradually raising the level of the population in safety knowledge, habits, attitudes and practices over a period of two or three generations. This process seems necessary largely because of the adverse effects of adult society on education of any type directed toward establishing definite habits and attitudes.

Organization and Supervision of School Safety Programs.— The program of safety within the schools should be directed and controlled by the school authorities. The School Committee or Board of Education should at all times have ultimate authority in all phases of the safety welfare of the school child. Organizations outside of the school may be permitted to render services in the school safety program. Yet, they should never be permitted to have final control and responsibility for any phase of the safety program. Next to the school committee or the board of education, the superintendent of schools should be responsible for safety education in the schools. Then, so far as the total safety education program of pupils is concerned, everyone connected with the school organization owes a duty to the school child in helping to create and maintain a safe school environment. The organization and supervision of a safety education program will vary, naturally, with the size of the school system and the nature of the program. No single organizational pattern can be prepared to fit all school situations. In the matter of supervision of safety, many cities have appointed a supervisor of safety education who has direct responsibility for coordinating the safety program. In smaller communities the supervisor may also be in charge of health, physical education and recreation, or he may be a teacher on the staff particularly interested in and having a knowledge of safety and accident prevention. The supervisor should work with school principals, department heads and teachers in planning, reviewing and carrying out the program. In some cities the supervisor of safety education works with directors and supervisors of special subjects, such as industrial arts, vocational education, household arts and health and physical education, and with other staff members who can aid in the development of a safety program.

Non-teaching staff members including the school custodian have supporting supervisory functions in the safety and accident prevention program. School committees or boards of education should prepare and issue regulations through the school administrators having to do with the responsibilities for the protection of school children and school property. These regulations should normally cover such subjects as responsibilities of principals, teachers and custodians, inspection of school buildings and grounds, fire and civil defense drills, accident reporting, first-aid procedures, pupil transportation, and safety procedures in school shops, gymnasiums, laboratories and on the playgrounds. Many cities have city-wide safety councils or committees in which the superintendent or an assistant, or the supervisor of safety education is an active participant. These committees ordinarily include representation from various city departments such as police, fire, health, welfare and recreation. Private agencies are also usually represented, for example, automobile clubs, scouting organizations, chambers of commerce, parent-teacher associations and various other community voluntary organizations.

Home Accidents.—Most people think of home as being a place of safety and security. Yet, thousands of men, women and children are killed and about 5,000,000 injured each year in home accidents. Many of the 5,000,000 injured receive some type of permanent disabling injury.

The deaths and injuries which happen in the home are largely caused by two things. First, there are many things in the home which are dangerous if they are not handled properly. Second, many people are careless. A great many of the injuries and deaths in the home are due to falls and burns. Falls rank first as a cause of accidental death among people sixty-five years of age and over. Burns and poisons rank first among children four years of age and under and firearms rank high as a cause of accidental death among people between the ages of twenty-five and forty years of age.

Mechanical factors frequently are contributing causes of home accidents. Many people seem prone to use equipment improperly or to try to use something unsuited for the task or to use equipment that is rickety or broken.

Although mechanical factors often contribute to home accidents, the human element is involved more often. Poor judgment, haste, intoxication, ignorance regarding safety practices, fatigue and physical defects are personal elements responsible for a large number of home accidents. Appliances in the modern home such as irons, toasters, gas stoves, washing machines, refrigerators, sewing machines, knives, cooking and eating utensils, are a few of the things which, if not used properly, may lead to death or injury.

The kitchen is a place where injuries frequently occur. Many wounds are caused by the careless use of knives, forks, ice picks, and can openers. Water and grease on the kitchen floor are the cause of many falls resulting in injury. Hot grease and cooking utensils on the stove cause many burns. Many children are burned when pans of hot water or hot food are knocked off the stove. If gas is used for cooking there is always danger of gas poisoning. Sometimes the flame goes out and lets the gas escape into the room or the handle of the gas jet may be accidentally opened without the person knowing it.

Many injuries from burns and falls happen in the living room. Falls from slipping on waxed floors happen frequently. Waxed floors should be rubbed down well after the wax is applied to keep them from being too slick. Sometimes small rugs on a floor slip when stepped on and cause someone to fall. Running on slick floors is a frequent cause of injury by falls among children. Sparks from the fireplace often cause fires. A fire screen should be placed snugly before a fireplace to prevent sparks from starting fires. Electric lamps and cords in a living room should be handled with care. Lamps and cords should be placed so that children will not trip over them. Children often leave toys on the floor. Many serious injuries happen every year when people trip and fall over toys. Parents should teach children to form the habit of putting toys in their proper places when they are through playing with them.

Although the bedroom in the home is looked upon by most people as a safe place, nevertheless, many serious injuries from falls happen in bedrooms each year. Many falls happen when people get out of bed in the dark and stumble over furniture. Lights should be placed so that they can be turned on before getting out of bed. Many babies and small children are seriously hurt when they roll out of bed while they are asleep. Accidents of this kind are caused by carelessness on the part of those caring for children. There should always be a railing on a small child's bed to keep him from rolling out.

The bathroom in the home is a place where serious accidents can happen. Many of these occur in the bathroom as a result of falls, electric shock and poisoning. Touching electric switches or electric equipment when the body is wet results fatally in many cases. This is especially true if there happens to be a short circuit or broken installation. Electric switches and equipment should be placed so that they cannot be reached when one is in the bathtub. Many deaths occur when radios fall from a chair or shelf into the water when someone is taking a bath. Serious falls frequently happen in the bathroom. Falls may happen when getting into or out of the bathtub or getting into or out of a shower. Rubber mats or safety mats placed in the bathtub and shower help to prevent falls. There should be a sturdy handgrip fastened to the walls to grasp for support while getting into or out of a bathtub. Water on the floor in the bathroom causes many falls. Also, soap dropped on the floor may cause falls when it is stepped on. The family medicine cabinet is usually kept in the bathroom. Many poisons, drugs and medicines may be kept in the medicine cabinet. Care must be taken by both children and adults in using a medicine cabinet to prevent accidental posioning.

Injuries occur in the halls and on stairways in the home. Going up or down stairs in the dark or in a dim light may lead to falls. Carpets which are not fastened securely on steps may cause falls. Toys and pieces of furniture left on a stairway or in a hallway cause falls. Both children and adults should keep one hand on the rail when going up or down stairways.

There are many ways to be injured in the basement of the home. Many falls happen on the stairway leading to the basement. The steps of the stairway leading to the basement should be strong and kept in good repair. They should be kept free from objects which may trip or cause a person to fall. The stairway should have a good light and the switches should be placed so that the light can be turned on either at the top or at the bottom of the stairway. The last step of the stairway leading to the basement should be painted white so that you will know when you reach the bottom. The basement should be kept free from waste or rubbish. Fires start easily in piles of dry rubbish and waste.

Many serious injuries from electrical equipment happen in the basement. You should always use great care in handling electric wires and switches in the basement. Usually the floors are wet or damp. Even a light electric shock may prove very serious if you are standing on a damp floor.

Electric cords used on washing machines in the basement should be covered with heavy rubber insulation. An asbestos cord which is ordinarily used on a heating appliance like an electric iron is not satisfactory where there is water. Asbestos covering of cords soon becomes soaked with water on a wet floor. When it becomes soaked with water, the wire is no longer properly insulated. The water makes electric shock stronger. Heavy rubber insulation on electric wire does not become water soaked. Many people have been killed by electric shocks when using an electric cord covered only with cloth or asbestos in a damp basement.

One of the greatest obstacles to home accident prevention is the fact that the head of each household must be his own safety engineer and most householders are not aware that there are so many serious hazards in and around the home. At the present time there are approximately 45,000,000 families in the United States. About 32,000,000 live in single family dwellings, 5,000,000 in two story residences and 8,000,000 in buildings which house more than two families. It is conceivable that managers of large apartment buildings could contribute substantially to the home safety of their tenants, but their efforts would touch only one household in ten. Nearly 6,000,000 families live on farms and about 9,000,000 others live in rural non-farm areas including towns with less than 2,500 population. The remaining 30,000,000 families live in urban areas. That is, they live in towns and cities with more than 2,500 population or in the urbanized fringes. Thus, two-thirds of the homes are fairly closely grouped and one-third are scattered over a wide area. Nearly 9,000,000 people live in houses or apartments which were built since 1944. Three million live in places built from 1940-1944 and 6,000,000 live in places built since 1930. Thus, four families in ten have fairly modern homes. Another 9,000,000 families are in houses or apartments built in the ten-year period from 1920-1929, while the remaining 19,000,000 families are in places dating from before 1920. It should be remembered, however, that there is not necessarily a relationship between age of dwellings and the existence of hazardous conditions. In cities and older suburbs, the old mansion has been cut up into efficiency flats, while on the metropolitan fringes, new community developments spring into being almost daily. To make each of these independent dwelling units as accident-free as possible is a task of home safety.

Motor Vehicle Accidents.—Accidents involving both motor vehicles and pedestrians are responsible for a large number of deaths and injuries each year. The number of persons killed in motor vehicle accidents each year ordinarily exceeds 35,000, although this figure will vary some from year to year. In late years it has more frequently exceeded 35,000. In addition to the more than 35,000 killed in motor vehicle accidents each year, approximately 1,000,000 people are injured. Because of the nature of motor vehicle accidents, in which such heavy equipment is involved, the injuries are usually severe. Quite a large number of those injured each year are permanently disabled in some way. It is extremely difficult to determine the cause of many motor vehicle accidents because in most cases there are a combination of causes and because few accidents are investigated carefully enough to find out the exact factors involved.

Excessive speed for existing conditions is perhaps one of the greatest single contributing factors to motor vehicle accidents. This does not mean necessarily high speeds, but rather too great a speed for the condition of the roadway. For example, a speed of 60 miles an hour on an open highway where there is little or no traffic and the pavement is dry in clear weather would probably be a safer speed than that of 25 miles an hour in a congested area on icy streets. Other things which contribute to the accident situation are improper and reckless driving, violating the right-of-way, improper passing, and driving on the wrong side of the road.

Unsafe acts by pedestrians bring death and permanent injury to many persons each year. It should be pointed out at this point that quite a large number of the deaths and injuries among pedestrians are children of school age. Approximately two out of every three pedestrians killed by motor vehicles either violated traffic laws or acted in an obviously unsafe manner. The violation which most frequently results in death or injury to pedestrians is crossing streets between intersections. This is quite true also of children of school age.

Reports of the National Safety Council indicate that at least one of every five fatal accidents involves either a driver or a pedestrian who has been drinking. The problem of alcoholic drinks in relation to accident frequency continues to grow in importance, not only so far as motor vehicle accidents are concerned but in practically all phases of human endeavor.

Fatigue on the part of drivers is a common cause of accidents. Drivers and pedestrians with physical defects such as bad vision and hearing are responsible for many accidents. It is estimated that approximately one-tenth of all fatal accidents involve either a driver or a pedestrian who has some type of physical defect.

Defective motor vehicles are reported as a cause of a few accidents. Although unsafe machines may be a contributing factor in some cases, the cause of accidents usually can be traced to the driver or to a pedestrian rather than to a defective machine.

Darkness is a major contributing factor to motor vehicle accidents in that the fatal accident rate per mile of travel is much greater during the hours of darkness. More than half of the fatal motor vehicle accidents occur at night.

Although road and weather conditions have considerable bearing on motor vehicle accidents, the yearly statistics show that more accidents occur during clear weather than during times when it is raining or snowing or when the weather is cloudy or foggy. Apparently, drivers are more careful when road and weather conditions are unfavorable.

Occupational Accidents.—From 15,000 to 16,000 people are killed and approximately 2,000,000 are injured each year in work and occupational accidents. When consideration is given to the fact that modern industry is so highly mechanized it would seem that with all the people engaged in work, the number of accidental fatalities in the occupational area would exceed those resulting from either motor vehicles or home accidents.

One of the reasons why the occupational accident rate is lower in comparison with the motor vehicles and the home rate is that there has been an organized and controlled effort to reduce accidents in industries and occupations which has proved highly successful. While in a modern industrial plant it is possible to eliminate hazards on an organized basis and to some extent to control safety practices, it has been next to impossible to control the safety practices of individuals in the home or the acts of the individual driver of the motor vehicle. In order to overcome the tendency of people to become careless and to become unduly exposed to hazards within a given industry, employers have established rules and regulations in regard to safety which the employees are expected to follow. Because an employer must pay the costs involved in accidental death or injury it is to his advantage to prevent accidents. Often the penalty for not observing the safety rules and regulations is that the worker who fails to obey is discharged. Even though the death and injury rate in the field of occupations is lower than home accidents or motor vehicle accidents, nevertheless, the time lost from work and the costs are staggering as a result of those accidents that do happen. The approximate number of man hours lost from work as a result of accidents in occupations in any one year is approximately 250,000,000. In addition to the time lost from work by those injured, there is also a loss by others. Time lost by workers other than those injured arises when they stop work to help the injured person and also, to discuss the accident. Also, suspension of work caused by damaged equipment and the time required to replace or repair damaged machinery often results in much loss of time and production.

Public Non-Motor Vehicle Accidents.—From 15,000 to 16,000 people are killed in public non-transportation accidents each year and approximately 2,000,000 are injured. Drownings rank high as a cause of accidental deaths in public accidents. Approximately 5,000 to 6,000 people drown each year. A high percentage of the number of fatal drowning accidents each year are children and youths under 24 years of age. Railroad and airline accidents as well as falls in public places rank very high.

School Accidents.—Every year thousands of accidents happen to school children resulting in injury and death. Many of the injuries which happen in school are minor but some are very serious. In any one year, approximately six thousand children between the ages of five and fourteen are killed in accidents.

Among children aged five to fourteen years, accidental deaths decreased from a high of nearly 10,000 per year in the mid 1920's to about 6,000 in recent times. The substantial decrease has been accomplished despite the increase in number of children age five to fourteen years with the result that the death rate dropped from approximately 40 per 100,000 children to just a little over 20 per 100,000. For young persons age fifteen to nineteen years, the yearly total accidental death rate is somewhat less than for the five to fourteen year age group, but this is due to the smaller number of persons in the older group. Actually the death rate is about twice as high, 52 per 100,000 in the fifteen to nineteen year age group compared with 23 per 100,000 for the five to fourteen year age group. Also, it might be pointed out here that in the older age group from fifteen to nineteen years, the death rate has not changed very much since the mid 1920's.

One of the main reasons why the death rate among children five to fourteen years of age decreased is that in elementary schools throughout the country teachers and others have placed greater emphasis on safety education and protection for the elementary school children.

It might be well at this point to compare more fully the accidental death rate among children and the various diseases that take the lives of children. In recent years, accidents have come to be the leading killer of children. The following list shows the number of deaths due to accidents and diseases among children one to fourteen years of age during a recent year. The number of deaths due to each cause listed below varies little from year to year.

Accidents 10,950
Cancer 3,270
Pneumonia 3,027
Congenital malformations 2,177
Tuberculosis 1,075
Gastritis, enteritis and colitis 874
Poliomyelitis 769
Nephritis 765
Rheumatic Fever 553
Meningitis (nonmeningococcal) 540

The school building should be a safe place for children to live and work in. Schools having well-organized and planned safety programs have a minimum of serious accidents. The following are some accident prevention measures that may be taken in the school.

1. Periodic inspection of buildings to locate hazards and deficiencies and guide remedial efforts.
2. Designated areas for parking and for loading and unloading school buses.
3. Separate well-protected delivery entrances to fuel storage areas, cafeteria and shops.
4. Adequate, protected and supervised play areas for pupils.
5. Proper selection, training and supervision of school custodians.
6. Adequate illumination, as recommended by the American Standards Association, and fire protective devices approved by the National Board of Fire Underwriters.
7. Specific regulations published by the School Committee or Board of Education having to do with fire drills, duties of custodians, responsibilities of principals and teachers, school bus regulations, school shop regulations and first aid plans and procedures.

In the matter of the construction of new buildings or the rehabilitation and redesigning of old buildings, the following things should be kept in mind:

1. In the design of new buildings, the safety program should be planned for rather than included as an afterthought.
2. Principals and supervisors should have the opportunity to confer with architects regarding design and construction.
3. Buildings should be located as far as possible from heavily traveled highways and with adequate space for playgrounds and athletic fields.

4. All buildings should be of fire-safe construction.
5. Shop, laboratory and gymnasium equipment should be selected by those who are going to supervise its use.
6. Play ground apparatus should be carefully selected and playground surfacing should meet safety standards.

Liability and Responsibility for School Accidents.—Although teachers have always been concerned about accidents involving school children, a study of the accident situation in the schools shows that in the past there has been a lack of the proper understanding on the part of some teachers as to the full responsibility of school people in accidents involving school children.

The changing attitude of the public regarding the accident situation in the United States has caused greater emphasis than ever before to be placed on the responsibility of the schools for the safety of the school child. Also, the accident situation in schools is a greater problem than in earlier years because of the extended school program and wider variety of activities offered. Formerly, and before the widespread use of mechanized equipment, the school program was limited to a narrow curriculum which did not include some of the more hazardous activities offered today. Programs of physical education, athletics and recreation, industrial arts, home economics, science laboratories, bus transportation of pupils, safety patrols and driver training work, are some of the additions within the modern school program which increase hazards for school children.

The question is frequently asked, "Why is there a greater tendency in modern times to attempt to hold the teacher financially liable for injuries to pupils?" The answer to this question is in part that in modern times the general public has come to expect that accidents be paid for. When an accident occurs resulting in injury to an individual usually the first question asked is, "Who is to pay for the accident?" The development of the Workmen's Compensation Laws in industry which place the burden of cost of accidents on the employer, the growth of liability insurance, and the trend in the present day for society as a whole rather than the individual to bear the costs of accidents have helped to develop the attitude that accidents should be paid for. It is only natural, then, that some parents may expect to be paid in case of a school accident resulting in injury to a pupil.

The common law in the United States, in the absence of specific state legislation, does not grant that boards of education or school committees can be held financially liable for accidents to school children. In other words the school funds, raised by taxation in most cases, cannot be used for any purpose other than education. This leaves the teacher practically the only source through which remuneration may be gained.

It is now fairly commonly understood that a teacher, in case of negligence, can be held financially liable for accidental injury to a pupil. Increasing numbers of court procedures throughout the country involving teachers and damage suits for injuries through accidents to school children are being recorded.

The law of negligence is partly based on the theory that everyone has the right to live safely and must be protected from the negligence of others in this right. In the school situation the teacher owes a duty to the school child. In many cases the failure to act to prevent an accident to a school child would be considered negligence on the part of the teacher.

The law of negligence implies, so far as the duty of the teacher to the pupil is concerned, that there must be forseeability. The teacher acting as a reasonably careful and prudent person should anticipate danger or an accident. The failure to anticipate an accident may be considered negligence by a lay jury. The question, then, is not "did she forsee an accident," but "should she have foreseen an accident."

Judging by the modern trend in making society as a whole rather than the individual pay the cost of injuries through accidents it seems right that the cost of injuries to school children be paid by the group rather than by the parents of the injured child. With the immunity of boards of education and school committees, particularly in those states which have not passed direct legislation to the contrary, according to the common law there is no way the group as a whole can bear the cost of injuries to pupils. In the absence of state legislation, boards of education or school committees are not even permitted to spend tax-raised funds to purchase liability insurance.

In addition to the possibility of the teacher being held financially liable for the injury of a child especially in a case of negligence, there is another factor that should be taken into consideration. In many cases, the teacher may not be vulnerable from the viewpoint of financial liability. However, she may be quite vulnerable from the viewpoint of failing to take the proper responsibility in case of an accident to a child. That is, although the teacher could not be held financially liable for the accident, nevertheless, the superintendent of schools or the school committee could hold her negligent and perhaps censor or even discharge the teacher for failing to use reasonable care in providing safe conditions for the child.

Responsibility for Safety Education in the School Program.—Because safety education is a comparatively new area in the school program and because it has not as yet become well-established in schools throughout the country, there is widespread misunderstanding concerning the responsibility for safety education in the schools. For example, most teachers feel that safety education is the responsibility of safety specialists or specialists in certain related fields such as physical education or health education. However, it should be kept in mind that all teachers including elementary, junior and senior high school teaching personnel have certain responsibilities for the safety education and safety welfare of the school child.

In elementary schools the classroom teachers form the nucleus for the teaching of safety. In a large majority of the elementary schools throughout the country the classroom teachers are the only teachers available for the teaching of safety. Even in the large city school systems where specialized safety directors or supervisors are employed the classroom teachers are the ultimate source of safety teaching for the children. However, in the schools where a safety director or supervisor is employed, the problems of a classroom teacher are materially simplified in that assistance is readily available in planning safety projects, determining teaching content, and selecting methods of teaching.

In the elementary schools in small and medium-sized communities, where it is not possible to have a director or supervisor of safety education, it is usually thought desirable to have a safety coordinator. The safety coordinator should be some member of the faculty who has an interest in and some training in the field of safety education. If there are no teachers on the elementary school faculty qualified to assume the duties of safety coordinator, the principal of the school will likely have to take the responsibility for coordinating safety education. If a school employs a health education supervisor or even a physical education supervisor, it may be desirable for them to take some responsibility for coordinating the safety education program providing they have had a background of training and experience in safety education. If a school does not have the services of a health supervisor or others to coordinate the safety education program in the elementary school, it remains the duty of the classroom teachers under the direction of the principal to do the best possible under the circumstances in providing an organized program of safety education for the children.

Without question, the safety education program throughout all grades in the elementary school will not be as effective without proper coordination, yet, it is possible for the teachers to do a certain amount of coordination through the exchange of ideas. Also, if the elementary school principal assumes some responsibility for the safety education program in the school, considerable coordination can be done through discussions at teachers' meetings as well as through written directions and outlines prepared by the principal or by a committee of teachers.

At the junior high school level there is a need for a safety director or supervisor the same as in the elementary school. In that the traditional junior high school is usually located in communities where resources are available for very desirable programs of education, there is more likely to be a specialized safety education teacher on the junior high school faculty. One of the main reasons why a director or supervisor of safety is needed in junior high school is that safety units are frequently included in various specialized courses in the junior high school curriculum. Obviously, then, teachers of a number of academic courses in the junior high school must take some responsibility in the actual safety education of the students. In many of the more modern junior high schools health courses as such are offered.

In recent years, part of the time given to health teaching is devoted to safety instruction and the two are coordinated in a direct teaching course. This is an excellent arrangement in most cases because the person teaching health education usually has some background in safety education as well. Also, in some schools, a safety education course as such is offered. This is to be recommended, of course, if there is time available and qualified teachers to handle the course. When direct safety education courses are offered they are usually on a semester or yearly basis at some one of the grade levels in the junior high school.

The organization for safety in the high school is quite similar to that of the junior high school. If the school does not have the services of a director or supervisor of safety or if there are no teachers with safety training available, the responsibility for coordinating safety may be assumed by a special teacher in a related field such as health education, industrial arts, or physical education, providing those specialized teachers have some background of training and experience in safety. In the small high schools where it is impossible to find anyone on the faculty who can act as safety coordinator it is the responsibility of the high school principal to see that at least a minimum amount of safety is taught. In the small schools it is likely that safety knowledge will have to be imparted through units in other high school subjects and through various types of safety projects. If there are no teachers in the high school who have had sufficient training in safety to act as coordinator the school administrator should look forward either to employing a teacher with training in safety or to designating some member of the faculty, preferably one with an interest in safety, to acquire the training.

Safety Teaching at the Elementary School Level.—Safety education should have a place at each grade level throughout the elementary school.

Although the methods of teaching safety and the various phases presented may vary somewhat from one school to another the important safety elements at each grade level should be taught to the children. The importance of certain phases of safety naturally will vary among communities depending upon the particular school situation and the location of the school. It is obvious that an elementary school located in a metropolitan area should emphasize certain elements and fundamentals of safety at given grade levels much differently from an elementary school in a rural area.

Although there are numerous aspects of safety that should receive varying degrees of emphasis in schools of different localities, there are some more or less established phases of safety that should be taught in all schools. Also, the methods of teaching established phases of safety are likely to be very largely the same regardless of the location of the school.

Safety materials included in the program of study should be selected on the basis of the amount of time devoted to safety and the way it is to be taught, that is, whether safety is taught through integration or correlation with other school subjects, through various projects, by direct teaching units or merely through incidental teaching. The organization for teaching makes considerable difference in the number of safety topics included and the extent in which the topics can be explored. If a limited amount of time is given to safety education through correlation or integration, for example, the time spent should not all be devoted to one topic or phase for at any grade level there are a number of important topics that should be presented.

The arrangement of safety topics may be on a daily, weekly, monthly, seasonal, or yearly basis. Here, again, the way safety is taught and the amount of time devoted to it should be considered in the final arrangement of safety materials. Frequently, safety materials and topics are arranged in units if sufficient time is allotted for the teaching of units. If only a small amount of time is allotted to safety education it is usually considered best to arrange the materials in topic form.

Experience with various methods of teaching safety in the elementary school has shown that it is desirable to arrange safety topics into definite and direct teaching units when there is enough time and assistance available. Usually, the direct teaching units should be included either at the primary level or upper elementary level or both.

When direct teaching units are included, there is usually a definite daily period of time for safety throughout a semester or a school year. Sometimes the safety units may be included as a part of other courses. Units in safety are frequently included in science, social studies, and health education.

The construction of direct teaching units is similar whether they are used in strictly safety education courses or included as units in other fields of study. However, the content of the units is somewhat different depending upon whether they are for use with units in other fields or for safety courses.

Each direct teaching unit in safety constructed for use in a safety education course usually covers some one phase of safety. The units in safety to be included in other subjects may cover more than one phase of safety. They are frequently presented in a general way with the purpose of giving a background or basis for understanding safety.

One of the main purposes in including a special course composed of direct teaching units in safety at any level in the elementary school is to impart safety knowledge in a more organized and comprehensive way. When time is given for a course in safety, the topics within the units can be taught more intensively and there is less chance that important parts will be excluded or overlooked.

The formation of desirable and proper safety habits and attitudes should be given careful consideration in the selection of activities to be included in the safety units. In the process of imparting knowledge concerning safety, the teachers should continuously strive to establish proper habits and attitudes. Education, habits and attitudes form the basis for safe conduct on the part of the pupils.

Although the safety education content may vary from one community to another and from one section of the country to another depending upon the needs, the various safety topics taught and emphasized are usually identical.

The following suggested topics arranged on a seasonal basis may be presented in the primary grades and may be arranged on a weekly, monthly, or unit plan. They may be added to or omitted, according to the needs of a particular group, school and community.

SOME SAFETY TOPICS SUGGESTED FOR THE PRIMARY GRADES

AUTUMN

Traffic Safety

1. Pedestrian safety
    a. Traffic signs
    b. Traffic lights
    c. Safety habits in crossing streets
    d. Traffic officers
    e. Traffic patrol boys and girls
    f. Proper use of sidewalks
    g. Safest way home
    h. Dangers in riding on bicycle handlebars
    i. Dangers of playing in streets
    j. Dangers in hitching play equipment to moving vehicles

2. Passenger safety
    a. Safety on the school bus
    b. Safety in waiting for a bus
    c. Safety as a passenger in an automobile

Fire Safety

1. Reporting fires
    a. Notify adults
    b. Report by telephone
    c. Give accurate directions to fire officials

2. Rescue procedures
    a. Roll victim with clothing afire in a blanket or a rug
    b. Crawl on floor in a smoke-filled room

3. Accident prevention at fires
    a. Keep away from fire apparatus

Relationship of Health and Safety 135

    b. Keep away from equipment used by firemen
    c. Keep away from burning buildings
4. School fire drills
    a. Purpose
    b. Behavior
    c. Emergency conduct

SAFETY AT SCHOOL

1. Playground and gymnasium
    a. Safe use of equipment and apparatus
    b. Play fairly
    c. Wear shoes with rubber soles in the gymnasium
    d. Play safe games
    e. Refrain from interfering with others when using equipment or apparatus
2. School building
    a. Keep equipment in the proper place
    b. Use things such as pencils and scissors carefully
    c. Use care in opening and closing doors
    d. Walk in the halls
    e. Refrain from running and pushing when going up and down stairs
    f. Keep to the right in halls and on stairs

WINTER

HOME SAFETY

1. Accident prevention in the home
    a. Toys kept in place when not in use
    b. Proper use of electrical equipment in the bathroom or where there is water
    c. Dangers of playing on stairs and bannisters
    d. Dangers of standing or climbing on chairs or pieces of furniture
    e. Care, use and danger of matches
    f. Dangers of playing too near bonfires and fireplaces
    g. Care in handling hot pots, pans, kettles and other cooking utensils
    h. Safety at Christmas time
    i. Care in use of knives
    j. Proper disposal of broken glass

SAFETY IN WINTER SPORTS

1. Sleds and skates
    a. Safe places to coast and skate
    b. Dangers of interfering with others using sleds and skates

    c. Dangers of hitching sleds to motor vehicles
    d. Use of sleds and skates on slides
 2. Snowballs
    a. Safe ways of snowballing
    b. Use of targets in snowballing

First-Aid

 1. First Aid for minor injuries
    a. Care of small cuts and scratches
    b. Use of antiseptics
    c. Need of bandages
    d. Importance of cleanliness
    e. Objects in the eye
 2. Poisoning
    a. Care and the use of medicine cabinets
    b. Dangers of drinking unknown liquids
    c. Dangers of eating spoiled or partly decayed food
    d. What to do in case of poisoning

SPRING

Outdoor Play and Sports

 1. Wagons, skooters and tricycles
    a. Dangers when used in streets
    b. Dangers of hitching to moving vehicles
    c. Need for keeping in good repair
 2. Roller skates
    a. Dangers of skating in street
    b. Safety at street intersection
    c. Dangers of speed skating in congested areas
 3. Unsupervised play periods
    a. Danger of running into streets for ball or other play equipment
    b. Hazards of unduly rough play
    c. Dangers of throwing stones and sharp pointed sticks
    d. Safe use of playground apparatus
    e. Waiting turns on equipment
    f. Keeping away from swings and other moving equipment when being used by others

Vacation Safety

 1. Water Safety
    a. Possible dangers of swimming in deep water
    b. Dangers of diving in shallow water
    c. Selecting safe places to swim

d. Dangers of swimming alone
   e. Obeying lifeguards
   f. Refraining from rough play in or near the water
   g. Dangers of staying in the water too long
2. Hikes and picnics
   a. Care of food
   b. Safe drinking water
   c. Proper way to walk on a country highway
   d. Proper clothing
   e. Selecting safe places
   f. Learning to recognize and keep away from poison ivy
   g. How to give first aid for poison ivy
3. Sunburn
   a. Dangers of severe sunburn
   b. How to keep from getting severe sunburn
   c. First aid for sunburn
4. Safety on the farm
   a. Care and use of farm tools
   b. Safety around farm animals
   c. Dangers of climbing on buildings, heavy machinery and trees
5. Fourth of July Safety
   a. Dangers in the use of fireworks
   b. Safe activities as a substitute for fireworks

Many of the topics included for study in the primary grades should be reviewed, extended and expanded in grades 4, 5, and 6. The extent of exploration of each topic depends materially on the needs and the amount of time available for safety education. Also, additional topics may be added to the instruction program at the intermediate grade levels. The following topics are suggested for use in the intermediate grades in the elementary school.

SOME SAFETY TOPICS SUGGESTED FOR GRADES FOUR, FIVE, AND SIX

AUTUMN

Community Organization for Traffic Safety

1. Traffic
   a. Need of traffic regulations
   b. Functions of traffic officers
   c. Duties of community officers in relation to safety
   d. Traffic regulations within the community

        e. Specific regulations involving motor vehicles, pedestrians and bicycles
        f. Regulations concerning the movement of fire apparatus
        g. Safety of passengers in public conveyances
    2. Bicycle safety
        a. Rules concerning safety in riding a bicycle
        b. Motor vehicle traffic regulations in relation to bicycle safety
        c. Dangers of carrying passengers on a bicycle
        d. Safe places to ride a bicycle
        e. Needed safety devices for a bicycle
        f. Need of keeping a bicycle in good repair

Fire Protection

1. Fire protection within the community
    a. General community organizations for fire protection
    b. Community fire department
    c. Inspectional duties of a fire department
    d. Need of fire escapes and exits in buildings
    e. Knowledge concerning fire alarms
    f. Ways to prevent fires
2. Forest fires
    a. Ways of preventing forest fires
    b. Importance of preventing forest fires

WINTER

Safety in the Home

1. Safety hazards frequently found in the home
    a. Location of hazards
    b. Types of hazards
2. Safety in relation to heating and lighting
    a. Knowledge of heating equipment
    b. Knowledge about lighting equipment
    c. Elimination of hazards in the operation of heating equipment
    d. Safety in the use of heating and lighting equipment
    e. Care in the use of electrical apparatus
3. General safety practices in the home
    a. Safety in using kitchen equipment
    b. Safety in using the bathroom
    c. Common hazards and safety practices in the basement
4. Hygienic practices in relation to safety
    a. Care of food
    b. Safe water supplies
    c. Personal hygiene practices

5. Indoor and outdoor play at home
   a. Safe and unsafe things for play
   b. Dangers from fire in certain kinds of play
   c. Dangers of falls while playing in hazardous places

School Organization for Safety

1. Location
   a. Consideration of the location with respect to safety
   b. Traffic hazards
   c. Natural hazards
   d. Building and construction hazards
2. General school organization for safety
   a. Safety council
   b. Classroom management
   c. Safety patrol organizations
3. School building and construction in relation to safety
   a. Exits and fire escapes
   b. Lighting
   c. Hygiene of the school plant
4. Safety in the Gymnasium
   a. Apparatus and equipment inspection
   b. Use of apparatus and equipment
   c. Regulations concerning the safe use of the gymnasium
5. Playground safety
   a. Regulations concerning the safe use of the playground
   b. Apparatus and equipment inspection
   c. Supervised and unsupervised play
   d. Protecting young children on the playground
   e. Dangers of playing hard baseball on the school playground
6. Transportation safety
   a. The school bus
   b. Safety in riding street cars
   c. Bicycle safety in going to and from schools
   d. Roller skating safety to and from school
   e. Safety in walking to and from school

First Aid

1. Introduction to Important Topics in First Aid
   a. The needs and uses of first aid
   b. Simple dressings and bandages
   c. Information about shock
   d. Care of minor wounds of various types
   e. Artificial respiration
   f. Information about poisoning
   g. Everyday problems in first aid
   h. First aid materials

SPRING

Recreation Safety

1. Playgrounds
    a. Advanced knowledge concerning playground safety
2. Recreation programs
    a. Community organizations conducting safe programs
3. Swimming pool safety
    a. Conduct in swimming pools
    b. Safety rules and regulations
    c. Safe water games
    d. Cooperation for safety in the swimming pool
    e. Safety in diving
    f. Safety through the development of skill and ability in the water
4. Hiking
    a. Value of planning
    b. Selection of safe routes
    c. Need of a first-aid kit
    d. Proper clothing
    e. Dangers of hitch-hiking rides
5. Safety in the use of boats
    a. Ordinarily not safe for children when alone
    b. Safety in using a row boat
    c. Weather in relation to safe boating
6. Camp safety
    a. Safe camp sites
    b. Safe water supplies and sources
    c. Dangers from campfires
7. Safety on the farm
    a. Safe use of farm equipment
    b. Safety in managing farm animals

Safety Education in the Junior High School Grades.—The safety topics and units in the junior high school grades include many introduced in the upper elementary school grades. The number of safety topics offered at the junior high school level that are first introduced at the fourth, fifth and sixth grade levels is governed largely by the extent of exploration of the topics in the intermediate grades. A topic having to do with some phase of traffic safety, for example, may be introduced as low in the elementary school as the primary grades. Additional teaching of the topic may be done at each grade level in the intermediate grades. If the topic is only briefly stressed at these grade levels due to a lack of time or for other reasons, it will be necessary to explore the topic further in the junior high school. If sufficient time is given to the teaching of safety in the primary and upper elementary grades the safety education in the junior high school may be established on a much more advanced level. These considerations underscore the need for curriculum planning which takes into account both the elementary and secondary school.

It is highly desirable that sufficient time be devoted to the teaching of safety at the primary and upper elementary grades in order that the safety work in the junior high school can be of an advanced nature. Then, the units in safety can be arranged in such a way as to bring out the relationship of safety to society as a whole. That is, instead of placing the greater emphasis on a type of safety education directed largely toward the knowledge of specific safety situations and the formations of proper habits and desirable attitudes in those situations, the emphasis can be placed more on the appreciation of safety in relation to life in general and the entire social order.

The following safety topics are suggestive of those which may be used in the junior high school grades.

SAFETY TOPICS FOR THE JUNIOR HIGH SCHOOL OR ADVANCED ELEMENTARY GRADES

AUTUMN

SAFETY IN SCHOOL LIFE

1. Review of safety taught in the intermediate grades
    a. Pass to the right in halls and on stairs
    b. Avoid pushing, shoving and running in the school building
    c. Know the location of exits and fire escapes
    d. Go through doors carefully
2. Gymnasium safety
    a. Equipment in good condition
    b. Skill in the intelligent use of equipment
    c. Play under the direction of trained supervisors
    d. Safe shower room conduct
    e. Proper dress for activities
3. Vocational shops
    a. Care in the use of machines and tools
    b. Proper and safe storage of tools
    c. Working under supervision
4. Home economics
    a. Development of skill and care in handling of equipment
    b. Safety in the use of flammable materials and substances

5. Laboratories
   a. Care in the use of equipment and chemicals
6. Safety on the athletic field
   a. Safety skills in organized athletic activities
   b. Intelligent and safe use of equipment
   c. Knowledge of the importance of medical examinations
   d. Knowledge of the rules of the game for safety
7. Activities on the playground
   a. The practice of safety in free play
   b. The importance of immediately reporting injuries
8. Safety en route to school
   a. Safety as a passenger in a car, bus or street car
   b. Safety as a pedestrian
   c. Safe and unsafe habits on the part of both children and adults
   d. Knowledge and practice regarding systems of traffic control
   e. Community traffic enforcement
   f. Statistics concerning accidents to school children en route to and from school

Fire Prevention

1. Fire
   a. Nature of fire
   b. Causes of fire—careless use of such things as cigarettes, matches, kerosene, gasoline; careless use of equipment and apparatus such as chimneys, stoves, furnaces, and electrical appliances; spontaneous combustion; incorrect disposal of ashes; and the accumulation of rubbish and litter.
   c. Fire escapes—purposes and correct use
2. Effects of fires
   a. Statistics on injuries and loss of lives
   b. Statistics on the economic loss through fires
   c. Hospitalization due to burns
   d. How the cost of fires is carried
   e. First aid for burns
3. Controlling the fire menace
   a. Safety inspection of homes and public buildings
   b. Individual responsibility in the fire problem such as carefulness, knowledge of first aid, use of fire extinguishers, fire drills and emergency exits.
4. Forest conservation in relation to fire
   a. Knowledge of the work of forest rangers
   b. Economic loss through forest fires
   c. Individual responsibility for fire safety on the part of campers, hikers, fishermen and lumbermen.

Relationship of Health and Safety 143

TRANSPORTATION SAFETY

1. Traffic laws
   a. Why they are needed
   b. Who makes traffic laws
   c. Community regulations
2. Regulations and requirements for drivers
   a. Regulations pertaining to a driver's license
   b. Different types of driver's licenses
3. Enforcement of traffic regulations
   a. Direction of traffic, inspection of vehicles, examination of individuals for drivers' licenses, traffic courts, and the effects of public attitudes
4. Organization for traffic safety and regulations
   a. Knowledge concerning the work of local, state and national organizations.
5. Safety in using public conveyances
   a. How to ride public conveyances safely
   b. Safety with respect to all phases of the school bus
6. Safety in railroad transportation
   a. Statistics regarding railroad accidents
   b. Railroad safety regulations
   c. Grade crossings
   d. Dangers of trespassing on railroad property
   e. Organized efforts of national and private agencies for railroad safety
7. Water transportation safety
   a. Extent of water transportation
   b. Statistics of water transportation accidents
   c. Safety methods and regulations pertaining to water transportation
   d. The work of the United States Government in water transportation safety such as weather bureaus, warnings, inspections, licenses, lighthouse service and the Coast Guard
8. Air transportation safety
   a. Kinds of air service
   b. Statistics on aviation accidents
   c. Causes of aviation accidents
   d. Prevention of aviation accidents

WINTER

SAFETY IN ACTIVITIES

1. Skating and coasting
   a. Recognition of dangers related to skating and coasting
   b. Precautions to take in assuring safety in skating and coasting

2. Snowballing
    a. Recognition of dangers involved
    b. Rights of pedestrians
3. Holiday safety
    a. Christmas—safe and unsafe gifts, dangers of firearms

Safety in the Home

1. The existing home accident situation
    a. Statistics on the various types of home accidents
2. Causes of home accidents
    a. Personal factors such as skill, judgment, fatigue, hurry, worry, age characteristics and physical handicaps
    b. Mechanical factors such as arrangement within the home, equipment in the home and safety habits of the occupants
    c. Places in the home where accidents occur, such as stairs, kitchen, bedroom, basement, porch, yard, bathroom, dining room and living room
3. Types of home accidents
    a. Burns, conflagrations and explosions
    b. Falls of all types
    c. Poisoning, including gas poisoning
    d. Firearms and fireworks
    e. Mechanical suffocation

Safety in Occupations

1. Welfare of the individual pupil in the particular community
    a. Survey of community occupations and the health and safety hazards inherent in them
    b. Consideration of physical and mental capacities of pupils in relation to hazards of occupation
2. Effects of industrial accidents on the family
    a. Economic, social and psychological
3. Preventive measures employed in occupations and industry
    a. Education, machine protection, regulations, inspection, protective personal equipment, medical service, supervision for safety, publicity and rewards
4. The results of safety work in the industrial field
    a. History, statistics and methods of safety

SPRING

First Aid

1. Advanced knowledge concerning supplies needed for first aid kits
    a. Various articles to be included

2. Basic principles of first aid
3. Symptoms and care of specific injuries
   a. More extensive knowledge and practice of the first aid taught in the intermediate grades plus an addition of other usual injuries that occur
   b. More specific knowledge and practice of artificial respiration

How Safety Protects the Individual and the Group

1. Bicycle safety
   a. Statistics pertaining to the bicycle accident situation
   b. Extended knowledge of bicycle safety such as care of the safety devices on the bicycles, skill in riding, safety habits on the streets, employing proper signals and obeying all rules and regulations
2. Swimming and boating
   a. Causes of drowning
   b. How to prevent accidental drowning—water skill and safety, knowledge and practice of safety habits in the water, safe use of boats and weather conditions
3. Hiking
   a. Extended knowledge of hazards involved in hiking
   b. Knowledge concerning the prevention of hiking accidents
4. Camping
   a. Observance of safety in swimming, boating and hiking
   b. Knowledge of safety concerning safe camp sites, fire prevention and weather conditions
5. Firearms and fireworks
   a. Statistics regarding firearm accidents
   b. Safe storage of firearms
   c. Recognition of dangers of fireworks

Safety Education in the High School.—Safety education in the high school depends greatly upon the program offered in the elementary and junior high school. If sufficient time and attention are devoted to the teaching of safety in the grades below high school the problem of safety education is materially simplified. Therefore, the determination of the safety program in the high school must be on the basis of the previous education of the students. The construction of a safety program in any high school usually must be done on an individual school basis because of the varying amounts of safety training offered in the elementary and junior high schools.

It is conceivable that the program of safety in the high schools should be largely the fundamentals of safety practices. This would be true in cases where little or no safety instruction was given in the grades below the high school. On the other hand the student may arrive in a high school with enough knowledge and training in safety so that a minimum of time need be devoted to safety instruction in specific situations. In such instances the time allotted can be given to an appreciation of safety in society as a whole. Although it is entirely possible that sufficient time and attention might be devoted to safety at the elementary and junior high school levels to eliminate the need for a highly organized program of safety in the high school, there would remain the need for emphasizing certain types of safety that are beyond the capacity of pupils of elementary and junior high school age. Furthermore, the ideal situation wherein pupils below the high school level are brought to a high degree of development in safety and accident prevention seldom exists. Therefore, in a large majority of the high schools of the country there is a definite and distinct need for a well-organized program of safety.

The problem of organizing and conducting an effective safety education program in the secondary school is quite different from that of the elementary school. In the elementary school the traditional classroom teacher organization lends itself readily to the efficient conduct of an effective safety program. In the high school, teachers are largely specialized in definite fields or subjects without the more or less total responsibility for a given group of students. While the homeroom organization in the secondary school does provide to some extent for a teacher to assume some responsibility for a particular group, under ordinary circumstances the amount of time given to homeroom activities is insignificant in comparison to the time available in the elementary school classroom teacher organization.

Another factor that makes the secondary school problem of safety education more difficult than the elementary school problem is explained by the psychological nature of high school students. Characteristics of students of secondary school age include their desire for adventure which at times may border on recklessness particularly from the viewpoint of safety. Also there is a tendency for students of high school age to ridicule restraint which is seemingly negative. Often the teaching of safety may appear to the students to be negative and inhibitive and in direct contrast to the spirit of youth in that it appears to place restraint on their natural ways of reacting to life.

For many years high schools lagged behind elementary schools in providing a well-balanced program of safety education. However, the high schools have stressed and taught safety in certain specific fields and areas. In vocational and industrial arts, the teachers have stressed safety in their courses largely because of the more hazardous nature of the work. Also, for obvious reasons, safety has been stressed in science laboratories, home economic rooms, gymnasiums, swimming pools and on the athletic field.

With the development of the field of safety education high school educators came to realize the need for a broader and more comprehensive program of safety throughout the high school. Experience with various methods of organizing, teaching and presenting broader programs of safety has led to the following ways of offering curriculum material.

1. Organizing safety as a separate subject
2. Teaching safety as units included in other subjects
3. Teaching safety through the homeroom organization
4. Arranging a safety education program around pupil organizations and special projects
5. Correlating and integrating safety with many other subjects and activities
6. Combining safety teaching with health teaching

Perhaps the greatest need for organizing general safety as a separate subject is found in those schools in which the students have not had the benefit of a broad safety program in the elementary school. When a separate course in safety is offered in the high school, it should be organized on a unit basis with due consideration for past education and experience of the students enrolled in the course. The content of the units should embody advanced safety materials. Considerable stress should be placed on activities of a practical nature. Activities in which students participate in the high schools should be analyzed and the safety elements incorporated in the units. Also, the relationship of safety to community and adult life should have a prominent place in the safety course.

The inclusion of units in safety education in other school subjects can be an effective way to offer safety education in the high school when it is necessary. In the absence of a separate course in safety there is a distinct need for the inclusion of safety units in other fields. When safety units are included in other subjects they should be arranged to embody material not usually given as an integral part of courses such as industrial arts, home economics, health education and physical education. Some of the subjects in which distinct safety units may be readily included are, health education, social studies, science, English, and home economics.

In the absence of a separate course in safety or units included in other school subjects, it is possible to impart a reasonable amount of safety education through the homeroom organization provided the material is well-organized and arranged and the teaching closely supervised by someone competent in the field of safety education. At best, however, the homeroom plan of safety education is inferior to the separate course or units in other subjects.

The arranging of safety education through pupil organizations and through special projects is considered largely a supplementary way of teaching safety. With any type of organization for safety it is deemed desirable to capitalize on student organizations and special projects to broaden the scope of safety education but these methods are insufficient in themselves. However, in the absence of other means of imparting safety knowledge, they are at least helpful. Some of the student organizations and special projects, through which safety can be taught, are assemblies, the school newspaper, posters, school safety patrols, school clubs, driver education and training and field trips.

When safety education is properly correlated and integrated with other school subjects and activities, there is an advantage in presenting it in connection with situations as they arise. This precludes the necessity of adding and introducing a subject into the curriculum. On the other hand, there is a disadvantage in diffusing the safety responsibilities so that there is a possibility of the complete neglect of vital safety material on the part of some teachers lacking proper safety consciousness. When a total safety education program is conducted through correlation and integration, definite responsibilities in the teaching of safety should be assigned. That is, teachers of specific subjects within fields should be held responsible for the safety knowledge that should be imparted in relation to their subjects and the accompanying activities. For example, teachers in physical education should teach safety having to do with participation in physical education, athletics and games and sports. Teachers in science should teach safety in relation to the usual activities surrounding the science laboratory. Shop teachers should teach shop safety and home economic teachers should stress safety in relation to the performance of activities in home economics.

Although the correlation and integration of safety education with other subjects and activities are desirable and helpful regardless of other ways of imparting safety knowledge, they are not entirely satisfactory in giving a complete and comprehensive education in safety. Therefore, they must be considered largely as supplementary means of imparting safety knowledge.

Some of the areas and topics that should be taught and explored at the high school level are: street and highway accidents; water safety; railroad safety; water transportation; home accidents; electricity and electrical appliances; gas and gas appliances; burns; falls; use of flammable materials; school accidents; fire prevention; safe use of laboratories; safety in aviation; safety in industry; forest conservation; first aid; the psychological aspects of safety and accident prevention; safe use of firearms; safety practices in farming; dangers of contaminated food; poisons; injurious plants and animals; alcohol and narcotics; and driver education and training.

Community Cooperation for Child Safety.—It is a fundamental obligation of every community to provide as safe a living condition as possible for every child. In providing and assuring the safest environment for the child, there is a need for community organization. Every community should recognize and plan for child safety in such ways as protection against physical dangers and disease and in the provision of safe and wholesome places for play and recreation. To furnish maximum protection for the child, cooperation between school and community agencies will prove advantageous since the greatest percentage of accidents to children occur in places other than school. Some of the community organizations and agencies that should be expected to cooperate with the schools are: police departments, fire departments, recreation departments and health departments.

Police departments can provide protection at school crossings by regulating vehicular and pedestrian traffic, by helping to train and supervise school safety patrols and auxiliary guards, by restricting traffic in designated coasting areas and by blocking off certain streets and congested areas as play streets. Fire departments can inspect schools and buildings and recommend changes to assure safety, plan with schools for fire and civil defense drills, demonstrate care and proper use of fire extinguishers, help promote special fire prevention and protection activities and assist in home inspection campaigns. Community recreation departments can maintain safe play and recreation areas, furnish skilled supervision for all recreational activities, train and furnish lifeguards for pools and swimming areas, make first aid supplies and services available when necessary and furnish instruction in the safe use of recreational equipment, apparatus and play areas. Community health departments can provide health services such as, examination and treatment of injuries in emergency cases, maintaining sanitary conditions in swimming areas, and posting and enforcing sanitary regulations.

It should be recognized that the school is only one of many agencies in the community interested in the common problems of safety. The safety of school children moreover, is a single but inseparable phase of this common problem. As a community is rendered safer for all, so will it be safer for school children. For this reason as well as for the broader reason that education is maintained by society to serve society, the school administrator should view himself as a community leader in safety and accept the responsibility for assisting in any appropriate projects of other community agencies. In this respect he may be guided by considerations such as the following:

1. All cooperative activities planned for the school should be sound from an educational point of view.
2. Activities which provide for pupil participation should be welcomed in community projects.
3. There are good public relations values in having school staff representation at safety council meetings, parent-teacher meetings on community safety and other programs of a public nature in this field.
4. The utilization of school children to make parents aware of home and traffic hazards and the need for correction and control of these hazards.
5. The use of such mediums as the newspapers, radio and television as well as special meetings for adults can be very helpful in both adult and child safety and accident programs on a community-wide basis.

Questions for Discussion
1. How do the yearly number of deaths caused by accidents compare with those caused by diseases each year in the United States?
2. What are some important factors in the historical evolution of safety education?
3. Why is safety education so closely allied with health education?
4. How is it justifiable to provide potentially dangerous activities such as sports in schools?
5. What are some implications of mental and emotional factors for safety and safety education?

Relationship of Health and Safety

6. What is meant by the statement that proper safety habits and desirable safety attitudes are based upon safety education?
7. What are some major causes of children's accidents?
8. Who should be responsible for the school safety education program?
9. What are the major functions of the school safety program?
10. To what extent is the home a factor in the total accident problem?
11. What are the major causes of traffic accidents?
12. What are some important steps which may be taken to reduce the frequency of accidents in schools?
13. Under what conditions is the teacher liable in the event of a serious accident involving a school child?
14. Who is responsible for teaching safety at the different school levels?
15. Why is it important that planning for safety teaching take into account all grades of the school?
16. What is the role of the health coordinator in the safety education program at the elementary school level?
17. What groups are ordinarily involved in city safety councils or committees?
18. In what specific ways will the pupils' past experiences with safety education influence the present teaching of safety?
19. What are some special problems related to teaching safety at the high school level?
20. What are the advantages of viewing school safety as a phase of total community safety?

Suggested Class Activities

1. Obtain figures showing the numbers of accidents caused by various factors: (a) in the home, and (b) in the community.
2. Form a committee to prepare a sample check list of possible home hazards, room by room, which may be used by children in evaluating the safety status of their own homes.
3. Form a committee to prepare a sample check list to guide the inspection of the school plant and grounds for safety hazards.
4. Prepare a list of safety measures employed in a school that is well known to you. Evaluate this list and indicate how it might be made more adequate.
5. Form committees to outline teaching units on home, traffic, and other community safety subjects which might be used at the various school levels with which class members are most concerned.
6. Prepare a list of major sources of safety materials suitable for use in (a) the elementary grades, and (b) the secondary grades.
7. Form a panel to discuss and evaluate the various plans for teaching safety, i.e., as a separate subject, by integration, by utilizing opportunities ("teachable moments") as they arise.
8. Prepare a plan for teaching safety in a school that is well known to you. Take into account the special circumstances of that school which are likely to influence the type of safety education program that would be most feasible at least in the first stages of its development.

References

1. Accidents in the School Ages, Health Bulletin for Teachers, Volume XXIV, February 1953, Metropolitan Life Insurance Company.
2. Dzenowagis, Joseph G., and Leslie W. Irwin, "Prevalence of Certain Harmful Health and Safety Misconceptions Among Fifth and Sixth Grade Children," *The Research Quarterly of the American Association for Health, Physical Education and Recreation,* Volume 25, May 1954.
3. Irwin, Leslie W., *The Curriculum in Health and Physical Education,* 2nd edition, St. Louis, 1951, The C. V. Mosby Company, Chapter XV.
4. Irwin, Leslie W. and James H. Humphrey, *Principles and Techniques of Supervision in Physical Education,* St. Louis, 1954, the C. V. Mosby Company, Chapter XVII.
5. National Safety Council, "Accident Facts," Published annually.
6. Stack, Herbert J., Elmer B. Siebrecht and J. Duke Elkow, *Education for Safe Living,* 2nd edition, New York, 1949, Prentice-Hall, Inc.

CHAPTER 7
CONCEPTS OF METHODOLOGY IN HEALTH EDUCATION

The Meaning of Method.—It has been expressed previously that health education is concerned with the provision of learning experiences for the purpose of influencing knowledge, attitudes and behavior relating to individual and group health. If the best results are to accrue the most desirable teaching and learning situations should be provided. If one accepts the thesis that learning results in modification of behavior and that teaching is the guidance and direction of behavior which results in learning, it becomes essential that there be a full understanding of the meaning of method when applied to health education.

The term "method" can be arbitrarily defined as an organized, orderly and systematic way of achieving a given purpose or objective. Reduced to plain and practical terms, method is concerned with "how to do" something in order to achieve desired results. Applied to health education, method is concerned with how best to provide learning experiences so that the individual's behavior will be modified in the best interest of his own health and the health of others. More specifically, the teacher must be concerned with how a teaching-learning cycle can be evolved so that optimum learning and achievement can take place.

Importance of Methods of Teaching.—For the most part, methods of teaching have held an important place in the American education system for many decades. The significance of method in education is clearly shown by the fact that philosophers of education in the United States have been recognized and followed largely on the basis of their contribution to methods.

Oftentimes certain types of educational methods are subjected to extensive criticism. However, this provides for a desirable situation as long as criticism is of a constructive nature and results in improved methodology. Indeed, methods in any educational endeavor are of extreme importance, and any desirable improvements which can be made should always be welcomed by those engaged in the direction and guidance of learning.

The importance of sound methods in health education should not be minimized, and the exploration of new and better methods in this area should always be under consideration. This is particularly true because the provision of learning experiences so often has a direct influence upon the health of the individual as well as the health of the group. Because mental, physical, and emotional health and well-being are involved, methodology in health education can be considered more important than in many of the other subject matter areas.

Early Methods of Health Education.—Educational history reveals scant mention of the study of health as an important part of the education of the child. Locke, the Seventeenth Century English philosopher, recommended it in writing about a "sound mind in a sound body." Later, Horace Mann, the prominent mid-nineteenth Century American educator, gave strong emphasis to the need for the subject of health as a part of the curriculum. He was of the opinion that there should be a study of "the rules and observances by which health can be preserved and promoted." Possibly, as a result of the declaration by Mann, some schools offered courses in physiology and hygiene before 1880. For example, a law passed in California in 1866 indicated that "instruction shall be given in all grades of schools, and in all classes, during the entire school course, in manners and morals, and the laws of health."[7]

Beginning during the period between 1880 and 1890 some states passed laws which required instruction regarding the effect of alcohol and narcotics. In that many of the state laws indicated that instruction concerning alcohol and narcotics should be part of the teaching of physiology and hygiene, this period can be considered the beginning of health and hygiene teaching in the schools. With the spread and development of health and hygiene teaching in the schools there has been an ever-increasing need for better ways, means and methods of teaching in this comparatively new area.

Two prevailing concepts of the time served as a basis for the methods used in imparting health knowledge to pupils. First, there was the idea that all that was needed was information about the structure and function of the body and second, that the teacher was the only person who had a complete understanding of the health needs of pupils. As a consequence, the method of teaching was largely teacher-dominated and evolved into a procedure of having pupils memorize such things as the parts of the body and certain rules of hygiene which were thought best for good health. This method of memorization and repetition harkened back to medieval times, and as a result student interest was stifled and in many cases students were turned against any kind or type of health teaching.

Changing Concepts in Health Teaching Methods.—During the past few decades leaders in the field of education have placed more and more emphasis on the improvement of methods of teaching in all areas. As a consequence, teaching methods in most of the subject matter areas have undergone extensive study and revision in the attempt to assure more efficient and effective learning on the part of the school child.

Although the methods used in teaching in health education are not radically different from those employed in other areas, nevertheless, teaching methods in health have not kept pace with some of the long-established subject matter areas. This is perhaps due to a number of factors. In many cases health teaching has not been given status in the school curriculum on a basis comparable to most other subject matter fields. In other words, health teaching is at a distinct traditional disadvantage. Furthermore, the responsibility for teaching in health education has been somewhat on a "selected volunteer" basis from the viewpoint of teacher assignment. In addition, the atmosphere in health and hygiene classes is not always desirable. For example, when large numbers of pupils are brought together in a gymnasium for so-called "health instruction" it is readily understandable why so little is accomplished and why most students in such situations so thoroughly dislike it.

Perhaps another reason for the lag in teaching methods in health arises from the fact that, until very recent years, teachers in general have not been adequately prepared to teach health on a basis similar to other courses in the curriculum. The inadequate preparation of teachers in health, however, is gradually being overcome as a majority of the institutions preparing teachers are now offering preparatory education and training in this area.

With health education gaining more and more the status it deserves in the school curriculum, there are evidences of departure from the early methods which consisted predominantly of learning parts of the body and committing to memory and repeating a variety of health rules. As in many of the other subject matter areas, health teaching is being considered more from the functional point of view. In other words, health knowledge as an end in itself is slowly, but gradually, being replaced with the idea that health knowledge is a means of helping pupils cope intelligently with health problems. This concept indicates that health subject matter is not an end but a tool through which desirable health learning experiences may be provided. This implies that sources of criteria for health teaching do not come from subject matter, but from man and his environment. The newer concept of method in health teaching, then, recognizes the child as a living organism capable of sharing in the solution of problems which concern his health. In other words, modern health teaching based on these changing concepts provides for numerous learning activities designed to take into account individual differences and characteristics of the learner. When this procedure is followed emphasis upon teaching of health subject matter gives way to emphasis upon the optimum growth of pupils with respect to matters which influence their health. Furthermore, emphasis upon the teaching of health facts gives way to emphasis upon meanings which will function in improving living.

Some Factors Affecting Methods in Health Education.—It is a generally accepted theory that successful teaching should be based upon the needs and interests of pupils. The implementation of this theory may be dependent upon a variety of factors which may affect health teaching methods. In general these factors center around school personnel and school environment. In this regard experience has shown that the following factors exert considerable influence upon methods employed in health education.

1. The individual teacher
2. Time allotment
3. Equipment and materials
4. Classification of pupils

THE INDIVIDUAL TEACHER.—There are certain individual differences among teachers which will influence teaching methods. The fact that many teachers may have a limited amount of training and background in health teaching methods may cause them to resort to use of the textbook as a sole means of providing learning experiences.

Frequently a teacher may have much greater success with one particular method or set of methods than with others. This implies that there should be no ideal method or exact pattern of methods to follow. On the other hand, teachers should be encouraged to select and develop those methods best fitted to their individual special abilities.

TIME ALLOTMENT.—In a majority of schools too little time is devoted to health teaching. In those schools where health learning experiences are provided in the form of health units there appears to be a greater opportunity to preserve continuity and to utilize a variety of activities related to problem solving. Conversely, in those situations where health teaching is done on a haphazard or sporadic basis, it may be necessary to curtail the number of learning activities and resort to methods which do not provide for individual differences of pupils.

EQUIPMENT AND MATERIALS.—Until recent years the use of demonstration equipment and materials in health education has not been fully appreciated. This perhaps is due to the fact that the early purposes of health instruction were based on what the teacher felt the pupil should know about health. In other words, in the early days of health education teachers did not feel the need for equipment and materials so acutely as the main objective was to try to teach pupils an abundance of health facts, many of which were wholly unrelated.

With the modern trend in health education directed toward learning activities which are close to the everyday activities in the lives of students, there has been more widespread use of certain kinds and types of health equipment and instruction materials. In the absence of suitable equipment and materials some desirable learning activities which can take place through demonstrations, visual aids and the like, may have to be dispensed with in favor of other methods of teaching which are not likely to produce the desired results.

CLASSIFICATION OF PUPILS.—The relative merits of homogeneous and heterogeneous grouping of pupils have been discussed by numerous educators with regard to their effectiveness in teaching-learning situations. While it is not the purpose here to extol the merits of either of these methods of grouping, it should perhaps be conceded that classification and grouping of pupils will have an influence on the method of teaching. This may be particularly true when a wide range in variation of traits exists in a given classroom situation.

The problem of grouping occurs most frequently at the secondary school level in situations where health education is alternated with physical education class activities. When physical education class scheduling degenerates into a "catch all" basis it becomes inevitable that health education will fall into the same pattern if alternated with physical education classes. Consequently, faulty classification of pupils for physical education results in a duplication of faulty classification for health education. This situation amplifies the problem of method in health education in terms of providing for individual differences of pupils.

Sources for the Selection of Methods.—Teachers are constantly confronted with the problem of how best to provide learning experiences in order that the most effective and efficient achievement will result. A perennial question is "How can we teach best those things which children should learn?" The fact that there is no single simple answer to this question is readily discerned when one considers the variety of factors inherent in each specific learning situation. In other words, there is no single method which supercedes all others in every teaching-learning situation.

What sources then must we rely upon for the selection of methods? Considering the fact that progress is likely to be dependent upon the mutual action of experiential and experimental processes, there evolves two rather broad categories upon which we may draw as sources for the selection of methods in health education. The first of these is concerned with the use of our knowledge of psychology in the provision of learning experiences. The second source pertains to practices which have met with success in their application by teachers in the field.

One of the main purposes of using our knowledge of psychology as a source of teaching method lies in the fact that psychology should help us to keep from violating certain fundamental principles of learning. The paramount problem here is concerned with the application of psychology to the specific area of health education. Solution of this problem might be simplified if the teacher of health were also a specialist in psychology. In that the health teacher is not likely to be a psychologist, it may be considered entirely justifiable for teachers to rely to a certain extent upon the successful practices of others, because these successful practices more than likely will have as their bases the application of fundamental psychological principles of learning.

Some Principles of Learning Applied to Health Education.—There are certain fundamental facts about human nature with which educators of the present day are more fully aware than educators of other eras. These facts pertain to some basic aspects of the learning process which all good teaching should take into account.

As previously stated the older concept of health teaching was concerned predominantly with imparting information in the form of parts of the body, evils of alcohol and narcotics, and rules pertaining to health. The pupil who could commit this information to memory and then report to the teacher when called upon to do so was said to be receiving an education in health. In other words, pupils became the gramophone records upon which instructors recorded health information and at the desired time the information was reproduced through recitation or written tests.

Modern day teaching, for the most part, replaces this older mode of approach with methods which are based on fundamental facts of educational psychology. Outgrowths of these facts appear in the form of principles of desirable learning procedures. The following list of principles of learning accompanied by a discussion of each is intended to portray some of the reasons why the application of the principles is essential to efficient and effective learning.

1. LEARNING TAKES PLACE BEST WHEN THE INDIVIDUAL HAS HIS OWN PURPOSEFUL GOALS TO GUIDE HIS LEARNING ACTIVITIES.—To create a desirable learning situation teachers must be concerned with certain features of purposeful goals which guide learning activities. For example, the goal must seem worthwhile to the pupil. This involves such factors as interest, attention and motivation. Learning a variety of health rules may not seem a worthwhile goal to some pupils. This is especially true if the motivating factors are extrinsic to the extent that the rules are memorized only for the purpose of reciting them to the teacher or writing them down correctly in the form of a health test.

The goal must not be too difficult to achieve. It should present a challenge to the pupil, but at the same time it should be within his realm of achievement. On the other hand, it should not be too easy, lest the pupil lose interest. The degree of difficulty of goals presents a problem in the grade placement of health learning experiences. This is substantiated by the fact that pupils often feel that they may be repeating the same materials over and over again from grade to grade.

A purposeful goal gives direction to activity and learning, which means that after a pupil has accepted the goal he has a better idea of where he is going. In health education pupils are more likely to accept goals which are close to real life situations, and the subject of health provides unlimited possibilities in this respect.

Finally, it is necessary for pupils to find, and adopt or accept, their own goals. This means that they do not, or should not, receive them directly from the teacher. If the most effective learning is to accrue it is doubtful that one person can give another person a goal. This does not always mean that goals will not originate with the teacher. On the other hand, teachers can do a great deal to help the pupils find their own goal. This may be accomplished by planning the classroom environment in such a way that pupils with different kinds of previous experiences and interests may find something which appears to be worthwhile. This can be done and still be in keeping with the teacher's objectives. For example, health concepts may be considered as the teacher's goals. However, in a desirable classroom setting the competent teacher often influences in many ways the pupil's mental set toward possible goals. As a consequence, in a good classroom teaching environment pupils may adopt the health concepts which approximate the teacher's objectives as their own goals.

2. LEARNING TAKES PLACE BEST WHEN THE INDIVIDUAL IS FREE TO CREATE HIS OWN RESPONSES IN THE SITUATION HE FACES.—This principle implies that problem solving is the way of human learning, and that the individual learns largely through experience, whether direct or indirect. The validity of this principle is brought more clearly into focus when one considers experience as the interaction of the individual with his environment. In other words, the pupil is educated in accordance with the influence that the environment has upon him.

Another important factor to take into consideration in connection with this principle is that all pupils differ in one or more characteristics. While it may be true that children are more alike than they are different, they will perhaps always differ in what they know, and are able to do in any given class in health education.

Although the individual learns through experience, this does not mean that experience will always assure learning since it might possibly come too soon. For example, anatomy as taught at the higher grade levels, is not offered in the first grade, because children at that grade level are not ready for it. Conversely, experience can come too late, and this may often be in the form of repetitive experience. This may result in pupils being taught the same thing in the same way in the area of health over a range of grade levels.

Concepts of Methodology

When the individual is free to create his own responses in the situation he faces, individual differences are being taken into consideration, and generally, experience then comes at the right time for desirable learning. This situation calls for a classroom procedure which is flexible to the extent that pupils may achieve in relation to their individual abilities. It is evident then that one pupil may learn best through one specific activity while another pupil learns best through another activity.

3. LEARNING TAKES PLACE BEST WHEN THE INDIVIDUAL CAN ORGANIZE HIS OWN MATERIALS IN THE PROCESS OF SATISFYING HIS OWN PURPOSEFUL GOAL.— The implication of this principle has its basis in the thesis that a purposeful goal may at first be perceived only in a partially defined form. Consequently, the goal may change in the act of problem solving, or it may change as the pupil works toward it. When the individual is free to organize his own materials, complete definition of the goal is facilitated and problem solving is more readily accomplished.

Implementation of this principle requires freedom as a fundamental necessity in the teaching-learning process. This means that each pupil should be permitted as wide a range of selection as he is able to use wisely in determining how he shall go about problem solving. It becomes essential then that in the study of a specific health topic there should be basic core learning activities for a majority of the pupils, and also numerous optional learning activities. In this way all pupils should have an opportunity to express themselves through a medium of learning adaptable to their individual needs, interest and abilities.

When it is stated that "the individual should be free to make his own organization of materials", this should not be interpreted to mean that pupil-planning should dominate the health problem-solving situations. On the contrary, there should be maintained a proper balance between pupil planning and teacher planning. Moreover, a certain amount of teacher planning will have to precede pupil planning for best results to be attained.

4. LEARNING TAKES PLACE BEST WHEN THE INDIVIDUAL CAN SHARE COOPERATIVELY IN LEARNING EXPERIENCES WITH HIS CLASSMATES UNDER THE GUIDANCE AND DIRECTION, BUT NOT NECESSARILY THE CONTROL OF THE TEACHER.—The point of importance here is that, while learning may always be an individual matter, it is likely

to take place best in a group. In other words, pupils learn individually but the social setting is advantageous. Furthermore, it should be kept in mind that the group can serve as a motivating factor for individual activity, and that individuals in the group can learn through indirect experience by capitalizing on the direct experiences of other members of the group. Moreover, sharing in group activities seems an absolute essential in educating for democracy.

In health education it should not be too difficult to maintain a happy balance between individualization and socialization. For example, a class committee studying a phase of a health problem might gather data individually and then present findings as a group to the rest of the class. This type of activity involves a pooling and sharing of experiences and provides an opportunity for direct experience for one group of pupils and indirect or vicarious experience for another group.

5. LEARNING TAKES PLACE BEST WHEN THE TEACHER ACTS AS A GUIDE WHO UNDERSTANDS THE PUPIL AS A GROWING PERSONALITY.—This principle takes into consideration the fact that the teacher should view learning as an evolving process and not merely as instantaneous outward behavior. In that teaching may be expressed in terms of guidance and direction of behavior which results in learning, the teacher must judge when to speak and when to step aside and watch for further opportunities to guide and direct behavior.

The application of this principle precludes an approach which is teacher dominated. On the other hand, implementation of the principle is perhaps more likely to be realized in health classes which are pupil centered. For example, in the study of dairy products at the primary grade level, a number of pupils can participate in making butter. In this activity it is possible to provide a situation close to the lives of pupils to help them more fully realize the value of this particular kind of food. The pupils as well as the teacher are active participants with the teacher guiding and directing behavior at times when it appears feasible to do so. In this way the teacher attempts to help pupils discover direct pathways to meaningful areas of experience, and at the same time, contributes to the pupil's ability to become a self-directing individual.

6. THE PUPIL AGREES TO, AND ACTS UPON, THE LEARNINGS WHICH HE CONSIDERS OF MOST VALUE TO HIM.—By and large a majority of persons accept as most valuable

those things which are of greatest interest to them. This principle implies in part then that there should be a balance between health needs and interests of children as criteria for the selection of health course content. While it is of utmost importance to consider the needs of children in selecting the health content, we must not lose sight of the fact that we need their interest if learning is to take place. However, neither should pupil interest in health be the sole criterion for selecting health content. This is substantiated by the fact that *lack of interest may be synonymous with ignorance*. Also, the pupil may have a primary interest in health matters which are not significant. Moreover, there may be an interest in some phase of health that should be delayed until a later grade.

At the lower age levels the teacher is in a good position to know the health needs of children. It is part of the teacher's responsibility then to stimulate pupil interest in problems which concern their health. This is particularly important because in many instances pupils may not be aware of their own health needs. When the teacher can bring health interests and needs into proper balance there exists then the best opportunity for health education.

If a pupil acts upon the knowledge which he feels is personally valuable to him, it seems essential that health course content be considered from the viewpoint of psychological as well as logical organization. For example, psychological organization of material takes into account the fact that gaps may be left in the study of a specific health topic. These gaps are permitted because the material may be too difficult for the pupil to understand. Logical organization, on the other hand, which is based on an orderly sequence of material, may make it necessary for the child to try to comprehend too many things at once. Since the child is perhaps logical only within the limits of his past experience it is unwise to insist upon a too strict logical approach.

Some General Methods of Teaching Health.—Methods used in teaching health are largely the same as those used in other subjects. However, there are certain *specific* ways in which health may be taught. Furthermore, certain *intermediate* methods, such as demonstration, visual aids, and field trips have a definite type of application in the teaching of health. These specific and intermediate methods will be treated at length in subsequent chapters. The remainder of this chapter will be devoted to a discussion of certain methods used in health which may also be common to a number of subjects in the school curriculum.

All of the general methods presented here have a certain amount of value when properly applied by a teacher skilled in their use. Since certain extenuating circumstances must be taken into consideration in the use of general methods in health education, it may be safely stated that all of these methods are useful if applied in the right way at the right time by the right person. This is to say that any one general method should perhaps not be used to the entire exclusion of other methods. It should also be clearly understood that some of these general methods are very broad in scope and may require the use of a variety of sub-methods, procedures or techniques. On the contrary, the lecture method, for example, could be considered an entity in itself. These factors should be kept in mind with regard to the discussion of the general methods.

THE LECTURE METHOD.—The lecture method was perhaps one of the first formal methods to be used in health education. For instance, in the early stages of the teaching of hygiene, Harvard University offered a series of six lectures to young men on "what they should known about the human body."

In recent years the chief criticism of the lecture in the teaching of health has stemmed from the fact that it is an authoritative way of setting forth health principles. The validity of the objection arises from the fact that the teacher is likely to be the only active participant when the lecture method is used in absolute form. That is, when the teacher relies entirely on the lecture in developing health concepts there seems to be little possibility of capitalizing on real life experiences which have a wide range of application in health teaching. As a result, pupils are not likely to assume much of the responsibility for learning.

In that the lecture method is almost totally dependent upon listening as a medium for learning, the question arises with regard to the grade level where this method can be used most effectively. With the short attention span characteristic of the lower grade levels, listening activities in the form of health lectures will be less useful than at the higher educational levels. Consequently, other factors being equal, it seems advisable that the lower the grade level taught the less the lecture method should be used. As a matter of fact it is usually advised that the lecture method as such not be used at the elementary school level. This does not mean to imply that the converse is necessarily true. Therefore, irrespective of the grade level perhaps teachers should not resort to the "straight" lecture method in health teaching.

The previous discussion has emphasized the use of the lecture method on an absolute basis. The next inevitable question is, can this method be used most effectively in any phase of health teaching at the elementary and secondary school levels? Certainly a reasonble amount of listening is essential if worthwhile health learning experiences are to be provided. Therefore, the lecture method in the form of oral presentation can be used successfully in introducing new material and in summarizing the main points of a health lesson. If used wisely it can be a desirable way of communicating health information to pupils through brief explanation. However, experience has shown that health information in the form of eloquent verbosity may have little meaning and fail to hold the interest of pupils. This is a particularly important consideration for those teachers who use the services of resource people to talk to health classes. Oftentimes the resource person may deliver a fine talk without appropriately gearing it to the age level of the group.

THE TEXTBOOK METHOD. There are a variety of ways in which the textbook can be used in health teaching. Furthermore, there are a combination of factors which influence the way the textbook may be used. For example, in some states there are laws which require a specified number of minutes of hygiene teaching "from a textbook in the hands of the pupil."

Traditionally, teachers of most of the subject matter areas have looked upon the textbook as the foundation for any plan of teaching. The teaching of health is not an exception. Perhaps relatively few educators would advocate the elimination of the textbook as a source of study material in health teaching. However, the practice of relying on a single textbook without supplementing with other study materials is not recommended.

It has been postulated that health textbooks are needed because it would be difficult for teachers to find sufficient time to prepare all of their own study materials. This is especially true in small secondary schools and elementary schools where teachers have teaching responsibilities in many different areas of the curriculum.

In most cases health textbooks contain a suitable organization of materials for health teaching. Moreover, the textbook can be used as a common basis for all children in the teaching of health. Depending upon the resourcefulness and ingenuity of the teacher, the textbook in health can either become the unquestioned gospel of the health class, or it can be used wisely and supplemented with many other worthwhile health learning materials and experiences as seem necessary in the study of specific health topics.

THE RECITATION METHOD.—In its early form the recitation method consisted generally of having pupils recite on certain sections of the text which had been previously assigned for study. Early health teaching employed this method as a means of having children commit certain health facts to memory. The recitation method in its original form has been largely abandoned as a health teaching technique on the basis that it did not distinguish between learning and memorizing health rules. It should be emphasized that as far as health teaching is concerned, the recitation method in the modern school need not be considered as undemocratic. On the contrary, this method can be very useful in teaching health through the group process. The recitation method may serve as a valid means of estimating educative growth with respect to health knowledge. Another way that this method can be used is in the "health class quiz program" in a game type situation.

Question for recitation purposes can generally be used in all phases of a health lesson. They can be used to arouse and guide the thought process. Furthermore, questions and recitation may be important in previewing or approaching new health materials. In this way the teacher has a means of determining the current tone of the class and further identifying the needs of the class with regard to a particular health topic.

The usefulness of the recitation method in health teaching may be dependent to a large extent upon the ability of the teacher to formulate questions in such a way that worthwhile learning will result. In this connection, it will be to the advantage of the teacher to establish criteria for use in developing questions. For example, questions should be thought provoking and not the drill type of questions. Furthermore, questions should be of a problem-solving nature and well-adapted to the specific grade level. It is important that questions be addressed to the entire group and that the teacher accept and use worthwhile answers of pupils even though they may not have been the exact answers that the teacher wanted.

Teachers should give time and thought to the preparation of questions. Questions should be written out in the most logical and systematical order with sufficient latitude for flexibility.

THE INDIVIDUAL METHOD.—The rise of individualized instruction was perhaps a direct result of attempts to provide for the individual differences in intelligence of pupils. This method eventually developed into what is currently known as the unit method, which is discussed at length in chapter 8. The individual method is briefly presented here in the interest of continuity.

The individual method is based on the idea that learning is an individualized matter and that pupils should be permitted to proceed at a rate commensurate with their individual intellectual capacities. One of the early noteworthy attempts at a solution to this problem was the plan devised by Helen Parkhurst. It is sometimes referred to as the "contract plan" but is perhaps better known as the Dalton Plan. In substance this plan consisted of the pupil making a contract with the teacher covering a specified period of time. The pupil then divided his own time and did his own work with the help of the teacher.

Although it may seem that the most effective and efficient approach to the recognition of individual intellectual differences of pupils is through highly individualized instruction, nevertheless, it has been learned through experience that instruction can become too highly individualized. In the final stages of the development of individualized instruction it became so highly individualized that each pupil worked alone on his own work materials and projects entirely exclusive of other class members. It reached a point where there was practically no intercommunication between students in the same class. Pupils frequently lost all interest in each other and in the progress of the class as a whole. The humanizing and socializing effects of pupil participation in class activities, so important and desirable in developng democracy, were almost completely lost. As time went on the small group plan was introduced and developed to offset some of the ill effects of the individual method.

THE SMALL GROUP METHOD. The Small Group Method was devised and introduced to regain some of the highly desirable experiences and outcomes in education which were lost when the individual method became too highly developed. The Small Group Method is applied satisfactorily in health teaching at all grade levels by dividing a class into small groups for the purpose of attempting to arrive at the solution of a health problem. Pupils can work together in committees and then come together as an entire class to present their findings.

THE PROBLEM SOLVING METHOD. Although the problem solving method is frequently referred to as such in education, in reality it is not a specific specialized method for it is used in and throughout practically all methods of teaching even including the lecture method. For example, a good lecturer frequently poses questions or problems that the students must think through and solve in order to keep abreast of the lecture. One objective of the problem solving technique is to develop the ability to do reflective thinking. The readily evident need for reflective thinking in matters pertaining to individual and group health is indicative of the important place of problem solving in health education. Consequently, if a pupil has had the opportunity to engage in problem-solving situations he should be better able to cope with problems which involve his own health and the health of others.

Another reason why the problem-solving approach is so important in health education is that pupils seem to have a natural interest in problem solving of any type commensurate with their abilities and capacities. Therefore, problem solving should be used as much as possible in all methods of teaching in order to gain and hold the interest of pupils, provide for more meaningful learning, and develop the ability to do reflective thinking.

Questions for Discussion

1. How do health teaching methods differ from teaching methods in other subject matter areas?
2. Why has it been necessary to modify health teaching methods in recent years?
3. How does the individual teacher influence health teaching methods?
4. How does pupil classification influence health teaching methods?
5. What are some of the sources for the selection of health teaching methods? How valid are these sources?
6. What are some of the chief disadvantages of the lecture method in health teaching?
7. What is the place of the recitation method in health teaching?
8. How can problem solving be applied to health teaching?

Suggested Class Activities

1. Form a round table discussion group for the purpose of considering the importance of method in health education.
2. Write a brief summary on some of the early methods of health teaching.
3. Prepare a statement to a superintendent of schools recommending a specified time allotment for teaching health in the local high school. Justify the time allotment that you recommend.
4. Form a panel discussion group for the purpose of discussing the principles of learning which are presented in this chapter.

5. Write a brief report explaining how the lecture method can be used to advantage in health teaching.
6. Give an oral report to the class describing how you would use a textbook in a sixth-grade health class.
7. Form a panel discussion group for the purpose of discussing the advantages and disadvantages of the individual method and the small group method in health teaching.

References

1. Burton, W. H., *The Guidance of Learning Activities,* New York, 1944, Appleton-Century-Crofts, Inc.
2. Cushman, Wesley P., "Problem-Solving—An Effective Method for Teaching Health," *The Journal of School Health,* Volume XXIII, May 1953.
3. Douglass, Harl R., and Hubert H. Miller, *Teaching in High School,* New York, 1948, The Ronald Press.
4. *Heatlh Education,* Joint Committee on Health Problems in Education of the National Education Association and the American Medical Association, 4th edition, 1948, National Education Association, Washington, D. C.
5. Knight, Stanford S. and John M. Mickelson, "Problem vs. Subject", *The Clearing House,* Volume 24, September 1949.
6. Oberteuffer, Delbert, *School Health Education,* 2nd edition, New York, 1954, Harper and Brothers.
7. Rogers, James Frederick, "Supervision of Health and Physical Education As a Function of State Departments of Education", Bulletin 1940, Number 6, Monograph Number 14, Studies of State Departments of Education, Federal Security Agency, U. S. Office of Education, Washington, D. C., (Cited from Rev. school law. Approved March 24, 1866, sec. 55) p. 1.
8. Stiles, L. J., S. M. Corey and W. S. Munroe, "Methods of Teaching", Encyclopedia of Educational Research, New York, 1950, The Macmillan Company.
9. Turner, C. E., *School Health and Health Education,* 2nd edition, St. Louis, 1952, The C. V. Mosby Company.

CHAPTER 8

THE UNIT METHOD IN HEALTH EDUCATION

The Meaning of Unit in Health Education.—It is difficult to propose a universal definition for the term "unit" because at the present time it does not have a fixed meaning in the field of education.

The fact that the term "unit" has different meanings is noted when reading professional books and periodicals and when students convene to discuss this plan of teaching. The varying and different meanings surrounding the unit method is due in part to the fact that the unit idea in the field of education has had such widespread recognition in recent years. As a consequence, there has not been sufficient time for unit terminology to crystalize into common meaning and understanding among educators.

From the point of view of etymology the word "unit" (shortened from the word "unity") has been derived from the Latin word *unus,* meaning "one". In that the word "unit" may be used somewhat loosely in education there may be some merit in giving thought to its original derivation. This implies that the idea of oneness should prevail. In other words, there should be a union of component related parts evolving into a systematic totality. In health education this means that the health unit will consist of a number of interrelated learnings which are concerned with a specific topic or central theme. This is to say that the health unit involves a learning situation with respect to a certain area of health. Various types of experiences as well as subject matter areas are drawn upon for the purpose of enriching the learning medium for all students, so that desirable changes in behavior will be most likely to take place. Unity is more likely to be retained when provision is made for pupil-teacher planning and when there is a sufficiently wide range of learning activities to meet the individual needs of all pupils.

Development of the Unit Method.—Although the unit method of teaching has received widespread acclaim in recent years, unit organization should not be regarded as an entirely new development. On the contrary, for many years educators have been making contributions to method which were the seeds that have eventually grown into what is now generally referred to as the unit method. The following discussion is intended to show that the modern unit method is by no means a recent discovery, but a process of educational evolution.

The modern unit method is perhaps the product of certain changes that came about in the field of education around the turn of the century. At that time in our educational history the type of formalism which characterized the late years of the Nineteenth Century through the influence of Pestalozzi and Herbart began to recede in favor of the somewhat more progressive thought of such men as Dewey, Thorndike, the McMurry brothers and others.

As a result of some of the contributions of these men, the first two decades of the present century brought about some near-phenomenal changes in educational practice. Developments in educational psychology tended to create a situation which eventually led to the submergence of the earlier philosophic idealism in favor of a more scientific approach to education. Two prevailing concepts of formalism in education in earlier years emerged in the form of beliefs which held (1) that memorization should be replaced by a problem-solving type of learning, and (2) that a pupil should progress through school at a rate commensurate with his capacity and ability.

The implementation of the ideas of transition from memorization to learning through problem solving, and recognition of individual differences of children has not been an easy matter. As a consequence, there have been many and varied plans set forth in the last three or four decades in an attempt to provide desirable and acceptable learning experiences for the children and youth of America's schools. For example, as mentioned in a previous chapter, effort to allow for individual differences of pupils was carried to such extremes in some places that the important aspects of socialization were almost entirely lost. The fallacy of this practice was brought clearly into focus during the great financial depression of the early 1930's. At that time a greater need was seen for more stress on the social aspects of our society. If the public schools were to play a major role in the maintenance of democracy, then it became essential that attention be given to those factors which concerned living and getting along with others in a democratic society.

Consequently, many schools gave pupils an opportunity to learn to work together in groups, to share experiences, and to cooperate in problem-solving situations. At the same time individuality was retained to the extent that each member of the group engaged in learning activities in relation to his individual capacity. This practice, which emphasized individualized teaching and democracy in education, is one of the outstanding features in the modern unit method.

It becomes clearly evident that the unit method as practiced in many schools today has resulted largely from a continuous evaluation of procedures set forth by many American educators and scholars over a period of the past several decades. A few of the educators who have made significant contributions to the unit method include Dewey, the McMurry brothers, Parkhurst, Morrison, Washburne, Alberty, and Billett.

The fact that health teaching as such is a relatively new area in the school curriculum gives rise to the belief that health educators have a unique opportunity to incorporate a type of unitary teaching which could capitalize on past experience based on advanced thinking, experimentation and research. In other words, those persons responsible for providing the most acceptable health learning experiences for pupils should be in an ideal position to establish unitary teaching on a solid foundation of practices which have been improved upon through the years.

Types of Units.—There has been little progress made in standardizing the nomenclature of units. Nevertheless, there is substantial agreement with respect to terminology which describes the types of units with which all teachers should be familiar. The types of units referred to here are RESOURCE UNITS and TEACHING UNITS.

RESOURCE UNITS.—Resource units consist of collections of suggested health teaching materials and learning activities and experiences centered around specific topics. These units are to be used only as resources for teachers when teaching units are constructed. In other words, the teacher goes to the resource unit as a source of information in devising a teaching unit for a specific class.

Resource units may be devised by curriculum groups and published in courses of study or curriculum guides so that teachers may refer to them. They may also be devised in workshop groups, study groups and by students in pre-service or graduate training. In the latter case the resource unit is generally constructed on the basis of a hypothetical situation which the inexperienced teacher tries to visualize.

It should be kept in mind that the resource unit contains suggestions only and the teacher should consider it as such. Unfortunately, because of some existing confusion in unit terminology, some individuals have looked upon the resource unit as a teaching unit ready to be used without deviation in actual teaching. When this occurs the purpose of the resource unit is defeated. It should be kept in mind that the resource unit is more or less an outline of a unit.

TEACHING UNITS.—The teaching unit is sometimes referred to as the "learning unit." The latter may actually be a better term but the term "teaching unit" seems to have more widespread usage in the literature and is used here for that reason.

The teaching unit differs from the resource unit in that it is much more in detail and it contains those materials and learning activities to be used in a particular class. In building a teaching unit the teacher may wish to study resource units in state and local curriculum guides, taking out those items of the unit which can be useful in developing a teaching unit for a particular class.

The patterns or outlines for resource units and teaching units can be essentially the same, the main difference being in scope. For example, resource units offer as many suggestions as possible for use in a variety of situations, while teaching units should be limited to those procedures which would provide for the best learning in the specific situation.

Unit Patterns.—A few of the terms which the framework of the unit is called include, among others, "outline", "sequence", "guide lines", and "patterns." The term "unit pattern" is used here with the idea in mind that it is to be used as a framework guide or a pattern in the construction of the unit. It should be clearly understood that there is a wide variety of unit patterns. The examples that follow are submitted for the purpose of furnishing the reader with a small sampling of unit patterns. The reader should study these various patterns with a view to their similarities as well as their differences.

Johns[6] suggests the following guide lines for constructing the resource and learning unit in health education:

    I. Title of the Unit
   II. Overview of the Unit
  III. Objectives or Goals
  IV. Initiation of the Unit

V. Development of the Unit
   A. Content
   B. Experiences
   C. Instructional Materials
VI. Culminating Procedures
VII. Evaluation
VIII. Sources

Rash[7] recommends seven major headings as follows:

I. Name or Title of Unit
II. Expected Outcomes
III. Content
IV. Methods and Devices
V. Evaluation Procedures
VI. Teaching Aids
VII. References

Yeo[8], in devising a resource unit, outlines it in the following way:

I. Central Theme
II. Delimitation
III. Outline of Content
IV. Core Activities
V. Optional Activities
VI. Evaluative Activities
VII. Teaching Aids
   A. For teachers
   B. For pupils
   C. Visual and Auditory Materials

Billett[2] refers to the unit in terms of two sequences, the unit of learning and the unit of work:

Sequence I: Unit of Learning
   A. General Statement
   B. Itemized Statement or Delimitation
   C. List of Probable Indirect and Incidental Learning Products
   D. Materials and References for Teacher's Use Only

Sequence II: Unit of Work
   A. Unit Assignment—Overall tentative preliminary plan which the teacher makes for pupil activity
   B. Introductory Activities
   C. Core Activities—All pupils engage in these at some time to some degree
   D. Optional Related Activities—For fast learners and slow learners

  E. Evaluative Activities
  F. General Study and Activity Guide
  G. List of Materials for Pupil Use.

The following unit patterns have been selected at random from various courses of study and curriculum guides:

  I. Determination of Area of Health Education
  II. Determination of Objectives
  III. Pre-testing
  IV. Materials Needed
  V. Teacher's Plan and Procedure
  VI. Pupil Plan of Procedure and Activities Common to All
  VII. Optional and Related Activities
  VIII. Evaluation
  IX. References

  I. Introduction
  II. Objectives
  III. Basic Information to be Acquired
  IV. Suggestions for Initiating the Unit
  V. Pupil Problems and Activities
  VI. Evaluation of Outcomes
  VII. References for Teachers
  VIII. References for pupils

  I. Introduction
  II. Objectives
  III. Outline
    A. Recommended Common Basic Content
    B. Suggested Common Basic Activities
    C. Culminating Activities
  IV. Evaluation
  V. Materials for Teachers and Pupils Including References

  I. Introduction
  II. Objectives
  III. Teacher Procedure
  IV. Pupil Activities
    A. Common to All
    B. Optional
  V. Evidence of Mastery

A study of the various unit patterns presented here reveals that none of them are exactly alike. However, it should be noted that all of them contain certain constant features that are inherent in a valid teaching-learning cycle. These phases include (1) an introduction, (2) provision for learning experiences, and (3) evaluation.

Unit Construction.—In building either a health resource unit or a health teaching unit, the teacher should take into account two very important factors. First, there is the problem of how to organize the unit and second, there is the consideration of a valid teaching-learning cycle. It will be the purpose of this section of the chapter to show through discussion, illustration and example some of the important features that the teacher should consider when attempting to construct a unit.

The teacher should consider some sort of unit pattern as a guide for unit construction. In this connection it should be understood that the teacher is not obligated in any way to follow any pattern "to the letter." In other words, the unit pattern should serve only as a guide and the teacher should feel free to deviate from it if necessary. As a matter of fact the teacher should perhaps devise her own unit pattern if others do not suit her. The important factor to consider is that the pattern must include those features which make for good organization as well as the recognized phases of a valid teaching-learning cycle.

For purposes of discussion here the following unit pattern will be used:

  I. Overview
  II. Objectives
 III. Techniques for the Discovery of Needs
 IV. Introduction
  V. Learning Activities and Experiences
 VI. Evaluation
VII. References
   A. For the Teacher
   B. For Pupils
VIII. Materials Needed

OVERVIEW. The Overview consists of a general statement about the nature and scope of the unit. Sometimes a short description of the topic to be studied is included, along with the reasons why it is an important problem. The following example is an Overview of a unit on the "Common Cold" for a group of sixth grade pupils. (See complete unit at the end of the chapter).

  The common cold, for a long time a public enemy, remains a problem for all of us. Since the real cause has never been determined, the battle against the enemy has been a losing one and people continue to suffer and lose time from school and work.

In order that the suffering and loss of time from school be reduced to a minimum, we will try, through the study of the subject, to find out some things that can be done in our room that will help this situation. The problem is, "What can be done in our school room to help prevent colds and to prevent them from spreading if a member of the class does have one?"

Another example shows how the Overview was expressed for a sixth grade unit on "The Importance of Good Teeth."

When we consider the importance of the teeth in health it is very apparent that much attention should be given to the teaching of the basic facts of dental health. This unit will be concerned with the provision of those learning experiences for sixth grade children which should enable them to understand and conscientiously take good care of their teeth.

These examples are submitted to show what different teachers consider as the main purpose of the Overview. It should be pointed out that the first example is for a teaching unit, while the second is for a resource unit.

OBJECTIVES. Objectives of the unit may be stated in various ways. In some cases teachers prefer to state objectives in the infinitive form such as "To learn that milk is good for the body." However, when one considers objectives as valid health concepts it seems advisable to state them in the form of declarative sentences. The valid health concepts stated as objectives are, in reality, the teacher's goals. The provision of a good classroom environment and satisfactory guidance by the teacher should result in pupils adopting the objectives as their own purposeful goals.

In the unit on the "Common Cold" a few of the objectives were stated as follows: (See complete unit at the end of the chapter.)

1. The cause of the common cold has not been determined, but it is believed to be caused by certain viruses which may develop, particularly if body resistance is low.
2. Cold germs may be passed from one to another by direct contact, by droplets carelessly sprayed into the air from the nose or mouth of someone with a cold, or by improper use of, and disposal of tissue or handkerchiefs.
3. Colds are thought to be most communicable during the first two or three days.

4. When suffering from a cold, one should remain at home and away from others. If the cold is severe it is advisable to stay in bed for a few days.

When formulating objectives of the unit is is usually advisable for teachers to devise criteria for evaluating the objectives. When this is done the teacher should be in a better position to determine whether the objectives are suitable for the particular group. The following list of suggested evaluative criteria are submitted for this purpose.
1. Are the objectives adapted to the specific grade level?
2. Does the teacher understand the objectives?
3. Are the objectives measurable so that a suitable evaluation can be made?
4. Do the objectives contribute to the educational needs of pupils?
5. Is it possible to achieve the objectives through the health learning activities and experiences in which the pupils will engage?
6. Will there be sufficient time to achieve the objectives?

TECHNIQUES FOR THE DISCOVERY OF NEEDS.—If teaching is to be based on the needs and interests and specific problems of pupils, then there should be some way of determining what the needs are in a given situation. Teachers, for the most part, are familiar with the general health needs of pupils. For example, one can merely consult the national mortality rates to learn those things that are taking the lives of the school age population. Similarly, the morbidity rates can be studied to determine the types of illnesses that threaten the health and welfare of children and youth. Although such information is of utmost importance in building a unit, nevertheless it is equally important that teachers consider needs that are closely related to the local school and community.

The alert and competent teacher will be quick to discover such needs. This can be done in such ways as consulting the local school health service, studying health records of pupils, and by day to day observation of pupils. For example, in one school an eighth grade teacher noticed that an unusual number of pupils in her room appeared to have defective teeth. Several of the pupils were absent from school or had asked to be excused because of toothaches. A unit on "Dental Hygiene" was devised for the purpose of stimulating interest of pupils to learn how to take better care of their teeth. The teacher felt that she would like to find out what the dental defects of her pupils were and what the class members could do to help themselves. In order to gain a better understanding of the dental problem she circulated an anonymous questionnaire among the students and received the following responses:

		Per Cent	
		Yes	No
1.	Have you ever had a toothache?	83	17
2.	Have you ever been to a dentist?	94	6
3.	Have you had, or are you having your teeth straightened?	18	82
4.	Do you often have inflammed or bleeding gums?	40	60
5.	How often do you brush your teeth?	Once a day	70
		Twice a day	24
		Never	6
6.	How many of your teeth do you think you have had filled?	Total	173
7.	How many teeth have you had pulled in the last five years?	Total	92
8.	Would you like to find some of the causes of defective teeth?	90	10

With this information, and the fact that 90 per cent of the class wanted to "find some of the causes of defective teeth", the teacher and pupils set out to study the problem.

Another example of discovering needs is shown in the case of the teacher who observed the following cafeteria eating habits of her first-grade children.

1. All but one child drank milk.
2. Three children brought lunches from home despite the fact that the parents of two of them wanted them to buy their lunches.
3. About one-half of the children returned their plates with the brown bread untasted.
4. Only about one-fourth of the children ate the bread served them.
5. Some vegetables such as stewed tomatoes, string beans, peas, and carrots were scarcely touched.
6. Some children ate too fast while a few ate too slowly for the time allotted.

As a result of these observations the teacher decided that she would teach a unit on Foods with the idea in mind of (1) helping the first grade children to understand better why proper eating is necessary and important to them; (2) trying to develop interest in eating a variety of foods; and (3) trying to teach them to taste foods a number of times before they decide they do not care for them.

INTRODUCTION.—There are numerous ways of successfully introducing a health unit. In fact the methods of approaching a unit are almost unlimited if a teacher possesses a degree of resourcefulness and ingenuity. Some of the appropriate techniques for the introductory phases of the unit include, among others: the diagnostic pre-test, demonstration, discussion, audio-visual aids, free reading and field trips. An important factor for the teacher to keep in mind is that the entire success of the unit may depend materially on the way it is introduced. In this regard, there are certain fundamental features that the teacher should take into account when contemplating the introductory phase.

The introduction should ordinarily be problem creating in nature. Moreover, it should create a situation in which pupils may find purposeful goals. It should help pupils to get a standard of achievement in mind and it should be convincing enough so that they will feel that it is important to them and worth time and study. Perhaps the best approach will be one that is derived from the immediate environment. If this is not feasible it remains for the teacher to create a suitable environment for the proper approach.

Teachers should take care not to introduce a unit in such a way that the remainder of the unit will be "oversold." For example, if a health film is used for the introductory phase the film should be evaluated by the teacher in terms of its use. If the film contains certain features that "tell the whole story" the pupils may lose interest in subsequent parts of the unit. In other words, the introductory phase should give the pupils the desire to solve problems connected with the unit and provide them with an opportunity for creative thought.

The examples that follow are submitted for the purpose of illustrating the preceding discussion.

In beginning a unit on "Foods" for the first grade the story "The Hungry Little Bunny and What He Found Out" was read. In the story Baby Bunny refused to eat the carrots and lettuce which his mother had prepared for him. She told him to go out and find his own breakfast. He visited many friends on the farm and in the woods but none of the breakfasts appealed to him. When he returned home Mrs. Rabbit greeted him and asked if he had found any food that he liked. Baby Bunny said that he had returned home to eat his own kind of breakfast.

The story was discussed and from the discussion many desirable learning activities resulted.

In a third grade unit on "Vegetables" the unit was introduced with a visit to the local health department. The children brought back food charts for their room. From this field trip the discussion turned to foods. The pupils started their unit with a comparison of the two charts, "A Good House Needs" and "A Healthy Body Needs" by listing the materials necessary for both.

In introducing a unit on "The Process of Digestion" a high school teacher used a demonstration which consisted of showing how starch is broken down to a simple sugar. The materials used were two test tubes, Fehling's solution, Bunsen burner, matches, iodine and a soda cracker. Some thin starch was prepared by boiling the pulverized soda cracker in water. Some of the starch was placed in one tube, and water and a few drops of iodine were added. The resulting blue color showed the presence of starch, which is a carbohydrate. A member of the class then chewed some paraffin in order to make some saliva. A mixture of the starch paste from the soda cracker was placed in the second test tube with the saliva. Some water was added and it was heated and tested periodically with iodine. After a time there was no iodine reaction and the blue color was not present. Some Fehling's solution was then added to the mixture and heated. The resulting orange color indicated that the starch had broken down to a simple sugar.

This demonstration brought up such questions as: What were the reasons for the changes in color? Was digestion taking place? Is it necessary to chew your food? These and other questions resulting from the demonstration stimulated the class to try to learn more about the digestion of food.

While all of these unit introductions differed with regard to technique the ultimate purpose was the same. This is to say that the teacher should not depend on any one particular way to introduce a unit. On the other hand, the teacher should strive for the technique which presents the best approach for desirable learning as long as it is within the realm of the educational objectives of the unit.

LEARNING ACTIVITIES AND EXPERIENCES.—This part of the unit includes the bulk of the content of the things that might be learned. In order to provide for individual differences a variety of learning experiences should be provided. For example, there are various media through which desirable learning can take place by means of such activities as reading, observing, demonstrating, experimenting, constructing, creating, playing, singing, dramatizing, drawing, exploring, writing, and listening. Some of these media include reading materials, demonstrations, experiments, audio-visual aids, dramatizations, field trips and panel discussions.

Although the teacher should list as many varied learning activities and experiences as possible, pupils should also be given a part in planning the experiences. That is, they should be given an opportunity to decide on some of the things they might try to find out and some of the ways in which the problems of the unit might be solved. (See section on Teacher-Pupil Planning in sample unit at the end of the chapter.)

In order to be reasonably sure that the learning activities and experiences have a sufficient degree of validity it is recommended that the teacher subject them to critical evaluation. In other words, there should be certain standards that the learning activities and experiences should meet so that the teacher will be reasonably certain that the most desirable learning activities and experiences have been selected for the specific situation. The following list of suggested evaluative criteria is submitted as a guide for the teacher:

1. Has sufficient provision been made for problem solving experiences?
2. Has the economy of pupil time and energy been taken into consideration?
3. Is further teacher-pupil planning encouraged?
4. Do the activities and experiences provide for integration through use of school and community resources?
5. Are there possibilities for integration in relation to pupil's life aims, other subject matter areas and courses, extra-class activities, and out-of-school activities?
6. Has provision been made for individual differences through choice in required work, optional activities, encouragement of pupil suggestions?

EVALUATION.—A subsequent chapter will give a detailed analysis of the problems involved in the appraisal and evaluation of learning in health education. The discussion here should be sufficient to aid the reader in gaining an insight into the need and purpose of evaluation as it concerns unitary teaching.

There are a number of valid techniques which may be used for estimating the educative growth of pupils. Some of these include objective tests, observations, behavior records, anecdotal records, case study outlines and the like. In that health is concerned with attitudes and behavior as well as knowledge, the teacher is cautioned not to rely entirely on the health knowledge test as a means of measuring learning. The health knowledge test merely indicates the amount of knowledge that has been acquired, but it gives no indication that the knowledge has been put into practice. For this reason it is highly recommended that teachers give consideration to other evaluation techniques which indicate behavior changes.

REFERENCES.—It is desirable that there be two separate lists of references, one for use of the teacher and one for the use of pupils. If the teacher wishes she may give the exact page numbers in listing references for pupils. This is a good procedure if mimeographed study guides are to be distributed to pupils. The teacher then has sufficient specific references for study questions. Although pupils should perhaps be furnished with some specific references, this practice should be limited to some extent in the upper grades so that pupils may have the experience of finding information through exploration of general reference material.

MATERIALS NEEDED.—It is essential that the teacher have clearly in mind all of the materials that will be needed for a specific health unit. The possibilities of health learning experiences are so varied and extensive that the scope of possible materials is almost without limitations. The teacher should recognize that she must stay within the limits of the materials and resources that are accessible in a given situation. However, in order to make use of all available materials all of the resources of the school system and community should be explored.

As the teacher lists the learning experiences of the unit she should have clearly in mind the materials that will be necessary to carry out the unit successfully. However, during the process of pupil-teacher planning some pupils may wish to engage in an activity for which there are insufficient materials available. If the desired materials cannot be obtained the teacher may recommend an alternate activity of a similar kind. In some cases pupils have devised their own materials in carrying out an activity. This is a commendable practice in that it provides a creative learning experience for the pupils involved.

Length of Units.—A question often asked is "What is the ideal length of a health unit?" When one considers the many factors surrounding unitary teaching in health it becomes readily apparent that there can be no ideal standard in terms of a specified time allotment for a unit. For this reason the time allotted for teaching a unit should be considered in approximate terms. This is absolutely essential in order to assure the flexibility that is so necessary in unitary teaching.

For learning to be effective sufficient time should be spent on the unit to allow for an acquisition of knowledge that will form the basis of immediate or eventual improvement in health attitudes and behavior. The nature, scope and content of the unit will govern to a certain extent the amount of time spent on it. In addition, the length of the unit should give consideration to the characteristics of the pupils for whom it is intended. For example, experience has shown that shorter units are more advisable where slower learners have been grouped together. This same recommendation might be made for younger children due to the short attention span characteristic of the lower age levels.

Lesson Planning.—Regardless of the length of a health teaching unit most teachers make some provision for daily lessons planning. In other words, it is essential that the unit be broken down on a day to day basis. This does not imply that a lesson will cover only one class period. It is possible that a lesson will cover less than one class period or extend into more than one class period. The important consideration to keep in mind is that the continuity preserved from one class period to another should be such that the objectives of the health teaching unit are realized. This implies that in daily lesson planning the teacher should have a clear perspective of the total learning that is expected from the unit. In this respect it becomes necessary for the teacher to determine whether procedures in daily lesson planning are such that they are related to the inclusive teaching unit. With these factors in mind the following criteria are suggested for lesson planning:

1. Does lesson planning insure definite objectives for the lesson?
2. Does lesson planning insure proper continuity of one lesson with another?
3. Does lesson planning insure proper selection and organization of learning activities?
4. Does lesson planning give attention to the most desirable teaching procedures?
5. Does lesson planning insure provision for individual differences of pupils?
6. Does lesson planning provide for sufficient flexibility with regard to the total teaching unit?
7. Does lesson planning provide for suitable evaluation of the outcomes of teaching?

*The following is a description of a health teaching unit on the common cold.

I. OVERVIEW

The common cold, for a long time a public enemy, remains a problem for all of us. Since the real cause has never been determined, the battle against the enemy has been a losing one and people continue to suffer and lose time from school and work.

In order that the suffering and loss of time from school be reduced to a minimum, we will try, through the study of the subject, to find out some things that can be done in our room that will help this situation. The problem is, "What can be done in our school room to help prevent colds and to prevent them from spreading if a member of the class does have one?"

II. OBJECTIVES

A. The cause of the common cold has not been determined, but it is believed to be caused by certain viruses which may develop, particularly if body resistance is low.
B. Cold germs may be passed from one person to another by direct contact, by droplets carelessly sprayed into the air from the nose or mouth of someone with a cold, or by improper use of and disposal of handkerchiefs.
C. It is thought that colds are most communicable during the first two or three days.
D. When suffering from a cold, one should remain at home and away from others. It is usually advisable to stay in bed for a few days.
E. Colds are rarely a direct cause of death but long-continued colds may contribute to the development of diseases which do cause death.
F. The mouth and nose should be covered when coughing and sneezing.
G. To prevent self-infection or the infection of others, a disposable type handkerchief should be used.
H. Hands should be washed often and kept out of and away from the mouth.
I. To avoid chilling or overheating of the body, dress in clothes suitable to weather conditions.

---
*This unit was prepared by Miss Ruth A. Trice and used in her sixth grade class in Caroline County, Maryland.

J. The practice of good health habits will help keep the body in good physical condition and provide some resistance to germs.
K. A clean, well-ventilated room with sufficient moisture in the air may help prevent the spread of germs.
L. Dry sweeping and dusting should be avoided because harmful types of bacteria may be in the floor sweepings and dust.

III. APPROACH

In arithmetic we have done some work with graphs. As an activity we made a graph of our room attendance for the month of March. This graph showed that our attendance had been very good. When we compared this with the attendance of December, January, and February, we found it was higher than the preceding months.

In order to find the reason for this difference we made a quick survey of the class. We found the number of people who had missed one or more days during the school year and the number absent because of illness. The chief cause of illness we found to be the common cold. Next, and this time we depended entirely upon our memories, we made a check on those who had attended while suffering from a cold. The number in this instance was larger than the number of absentees.

Then we examined a chart showing causes for children's absences in per cent taken from a study made in California. This showed that almost one-half of the absences were due to respiratory diseases among which the common cold ranked first.

These findings left us with several questions unanswered so we formulated our problem—"What can be done in our school room to help prevent colds and to prevent them from spreading if a member of the class does have one?"

IV. LEARNING EXPERIENCES

    A. Teacher-pupil planning period
        1. Planning and listing questions
        2. Selecting material and arranging as a guide for study the following outline:

The Common Cold

    I. Causes
        A. What causes colds?
        B. Why do we have more colds in winter than any other time during the year?

Unit Method in Health Education

   II. How spread
  III. Prevention
       A. What can we as individuals do to prevent colds?
       B. What can we as a group do to prevent colds?
       C. What conditions in our room will help in the prevention of colds?
          1. What are the conditions over which we have control?
          2. What are the conditions over which the custodian has control?
          3. What improvements can be made?
   IV. Protection
       A. What can we do for our own protection if we have a cold?
       B. What can we do to protect others when we have a cold?

B. Reading—gathering information from books and pamphlets
C. Observing—films and film strips
   1. Pesky, the Cold Bug
   2. Controlling Germs
   3. Care of the Nose and Throat

D. Listening and reporting—pooling material and arriving at answers to our questions through class discussions
E. Writing—recording our findings
F. Constructing and creating
   1. Arranging the bulletin board using charts, pictures and posters
   2. Making posters to show some of the facts learned about colds
   3. Writing poems to stress some facts about colds
   4. Making a diagram to show the many contributing causes of colds

RECORD OF OUR FINDINGS

I. CAUSE
   A. The real cause is not known, but it is thought to be caused by certain viruses
   B. More people have colds in winter than any other time during the year probably because:
      1. In winter people stay indoors in warm and sometimes poorly ventilated rooms
      2. People get less exercise in the fresh air
      3. People get less sunshine

188 *Methods and Materials in Teaching Health*

II. HOW SPREAD
- A. Uncovered coughs and sneezes may spray droplets as far as twelve feet
- B. Drinking and eating after others
- C. Dirty hands and fingernails if put into the mouth
- D. Spitting
- E. Coming in direct contact with the breath of someone with a cold
- F. Flies and other insects
- G. Eating unwashed fruits and vegetables that have been handled by others

III. Prevention
- A. What we as individuals can do
    1. Cover the mouth and nose when coughing and sneezing
    2. Wash hands often and especially before eating
    3. Keep fingers and other things away from the mouth
    4. Wear enough clothing to keep warm when outside and remove extra clothing inside.
    5. Keep the mouth away from the spout of the drinking fountain
    6. Stay at home in bed as long as you have a fever
    7. Always have a clean handkerchief or soft tissue at hand (tissue is best as it can easily be disposed of)
    8. Get plenty of sleep and rest and eat the proper foods
    9. Practice all the good health measures so as to keep the body strong and healthy
- B. What we as a group can do
    1. Keep the room temperature from 68 to 72 degrees Fahrenheit
    2. Keep the room well-ventilated
    3. Use a vacuum cleaner on the floor
    4. Use a wet or damp cloth for dusting
    5. Remind each other of bad health practices that are noticed
    6. Clean your shoes before entering the building to keep the floor clean
- C. Conditions in our room that will help
    1. Conditions over which we have control
        a. Seven windows for ventilation and a ventilator

b. Shut-offs on radiators to control temperature
c. Sink for washing hands when necessary
2. Conditions over which custodian has control
   a. Keeping enough heat in radiators
   b. Keeping room clean
   c. Emptying waste baskets
3. Improvements that may be made
   a. More heat in radiators on cold days
   b. Clean floor with a vacuum cleaner instead of a brush
   c. Dust with a damp or wet cloth
   d. Keep the floor clean

IV. PROTECTION

A. For ourselves
   1. Stay at home in bed for a few days
   2. Keep warm, but get fresh air
   3. Eat wisely

B. For others
   1. Stay away from others when you have a cold
   2. Cover your mouth and nose when coughing and sneezing
   3. Do not lend belongings to others

V. EVALUATION

A. Children's attitudes and observations
   1. Discussion of what the work on the unit should have done for us and decide whether what we have learned from our experiences has changed our attitudes and actions
   2. Attitudes of some individual pupils
      a. A cold is serious and should be taken care of
      b. Other people have a right to expect protection from our colds
      c. When suffering from a cold we should try in every way to keep others from getting it
      d. Following good health rules is the best way to prevent colds
   3. Observations of some individual pupils
      a. Hands were washed when they were used to cover a sneeze

190   *Methods and Materials in Teaching Health*

        b. Pocket-sized packages of tissues are being kept in desks
        c. Tissues are being used to cover the mouth and nose when coughing and sneezing
  B. Teacher's observations of the behavior of individual pupils
      1. More frequent washing of hands other than before lunch
      2. Evidence of greater number of pupils supplied with some kind of handkerchief
      3. Increase in number of pupils using tissues in place of the cotton handkerchief
      4. Decided increase in those who cover mouth and nose with handkerchiefs when coughing and sneezing
      5. General understanding about room ventilation after coming in from physical education period
  C. Knowledge test
      1. True or false
        a. The common cold is one of several respiratory diseases
        b. A common cold is usually fatal
        c. Colds last only a short time so they are nothing to worry about
        d. A person who practices all the good health measures stands a good chance of not getting a cold
        e. It is believed that colds are caused by viruses
        f. A cold that is not properly cared for may contribute to the development of a disease which may be harmful to health
        g. Colds are contagious
        h. Cold germs are spread only by coughing and sneezing
        i. Droplets from the nose and mouth become harmless when they become dry
        j. The chief reason for using tissues instead of regular handkerchiefs is that tissues are soft to the nose which may be sore from much blowing
        k. It is unwise to sit before an open window when overheated
        l. Dust caused by dry sweeping and dusting may contain cold germs

2. Completion
   a. More people have colds in winter than any other time because:
      (1)
      (2)
      (3)
      (4)
   b. When suffering from a cold it is advisable to stay in bed for a few days because:
      (1)
      (2)
      (3)
   c. The conditions of the schoolroom may help prevent colds. It should be:
      (1)
      (2)
      (3)
3. Narrative
   a. Suppose you have symptoms which indicate you may be getting a cold.
      Write a paragraph telling what you should do.
   b. If we can cut down on the number of colds in our classroom, what may it mean to us as individuals and as a group?

VI. References for children
Brownell, C. L., et al.: *Fit and Ready,* (Health of Our Nation Series, Book Three), pp. 162-172; American Book Company, New York.
Brownell, C. L., et al: *Safe and Sound,* (Health of Our Nation Series, Book Four), pp. 93, 145, 165-169, 203-208; American Book Company, New York.
Brownell, C. L., et al: *Science in Living,* (Health and Safety Series), pp. 188, 189, 214; Rand McNally and Company, New York.
Burkard, W. E., et al: *Good Health Is Fun,* pp. 212-213, 214, 215, 223; Lyons and Carnahan, Chicago.
Charters, W. W., et al: *Habits, Health and Safe,* (New Health and Growth Series), pp. 30-33, 61, 64, 238, 55-58; The Macmillan Company, New York.

Charters, W. W., et al: *Health Secrets,* (New Health and Growth Series), pp. 77-87, 176-181, 104; The Macmillan Company, New York.

Charters, W. W., et al: *Healthful Ways,* (New Health and Growth Series), pp. 3-13, 57, 86-87, 107, 179; The Macmillan Company, New York.

Charters, W. W., et al: *Let's Be Healthy;* (New Health and Growth Series), pp. 13-14, 165-166, 188-189, 190, 191; The Macmillan Company, New York.

Jones, Edwina, et al: *Your Health and You,* (The Road to Health Series), pp. 102-105, 275, 282; Laidlaw Brothers.

Shacter, Helen, et al: *You and Others,* (Health and Personal Development Series), pp. 107-109, 140-141; New York, 1948, Scott, Foresman and Company.

John Hancock Mutual Life Insurance Company: *Home Care of Communicable Diseases,* pp. 5-11.

Metropolitan Life Insurance Company: *Colds, Influenza, Pneumonia.*

Metropolitan Life Insurance Company: *Respiratory Diseases.*

Metropolitan Life Insurance Company: *With a Cold You Never Know!*

VII. References for the teacher

Irwin, Leslie W.: *The Curriculum in Health and Physical Education,* 2nd edition; St. Louis, 1951, The C. V. Mosby Company.

Joint Committee on Health Problems in Education of the National Education Association and the American Medical Association: *Health Education,* 4th edition; Washington, D. C.

Turner, C. E.: *School Health and Health Education;* St. Louis, 1952, The C. V. Mosby Company.

Metropolitan Life Insurance Company: *Absent from School Today.*

Metropolitan Life Insurance Company: *First Steps in Health Education.*

Questions for Discussion

1. How can the unit method of teaching provide for varied learning experiences in health?
2. In what way is integration adaptable to the unit method of teaching?
3. What is the place of teacher-planning in the unit method of teaching?

4. What is the difference between a health teaching unit and a health resource unit?
5. What are some valid techniques for unit evaluation?
6. What are some of the factors that influence the time allotted for a health teaching unit?

Suggested Class Activities

1. Write a brief summary on the development of the unit method.
2. With a group of class members prepare a health resource unit for the third grade level.
3. With a group of class members prepare a health resource unit for the tenth grade level.
4. Prepare a health teaching unit for a specific grade at the elementary school level.
5. Prepare a health teaching unit for a specific grade at the junior high school level.
6. Prepare a lesson plan from the unit you constructed and teach a demonstration lesson to the other class members.
7. Devise an original unit pattern by using the patterns in this chapter as a guide.
8. Prepare several different introductory activities for a unit on fire protection at the upper elementary school level.

References

1. Alberty, Harold B.: *Reorganizing the High School Curriculum;* New York, 1947, The Macmillan Company.
2. Billett, Roy O.: *Fundamentals of Secondary School Teaching;* Boston, 1940, Houghton Mifflin Company.
3. Brubacher, J. S.: *A History of the Problems of Education;* New York, 1947, McGraw-Hill Book Company.
4. Butts, R. F.: *A Cultural History of Education;* New York, 1947, McGraw-Hill Book Company.
5. Caswell, H. L., and D. S. Campbell: *Curriculum Development;* New York, 1935, The American Book Company.
6. Johns, Edward B.: "Guide Lines for Health Education Unites", *Journal of the American Association for Health, Physical Education and Recreation, Volume* 24, November 1953.
7. Rash, J. Keogh: "Planning the Health Education Unit", *Journal of the American Association for Health, Physical Education and Recreation,* Volume 24, November 1953.
8. Yeo, J. Wendell: "A Sample Unit in Educational Guidance", Unpublished Materials.

CHAPTER 9

ORAL PRESENTATION IN HEALTH EDUCATION

The reaction against "lecturing" as a method of teaching in recent years has created a tendency among educators to overlook the very basic role that oral presentation plays in teaching. Although the lecture method as such has an important place in teaching at the college level and with advanced high school students who are capable of handling the abstractions of language, it becomes increasingly ineffective throughout junior high school and elementary school levels. However, "oral" presentation in the lower grade levels bears little relationship to the lecture method ordinarily used at the college and high school levels. Rather, oral presentation refers to that type of verbal communncation by which the teacher guides the pupils into and through learning experiences. Thus, it is a tool of major importance for it is one of the most successful means whereby thought is stimulated and tested, ideas are shared, and appreciation of the thinking of others is developed. Actually no instructional device or teaching aid reduces the importance of oral presentation. As a matter of fact, it may be said that the relationship of pupil to teacher and pupil to pupil rests to a considerable extent upon oral communication. It has been said that man lives "in a speaking world;" and thus it is important that close attention be given to the role of oral presentation in the teaching-learning situation at all grade levels.

The Role of Oral Presentation.—Exclusive of lecturing, oral presentation usually takes the form of: (1) brief statements or exposition by the teacher, (2) question and answer sessions, (3) pupil presentations, and (4) one or another type of group discussion.

In practice, oral presentation is commonly employed in the following ways:

    1. As an introductory activity used by the teacher to do such things as introduce new units of instruction and audio-

visual aids and to plan field trips and school visits. In using oral presentations in these ways emphasis should be upon orientation of thought, relating old material and experience to new, and rousing interest by relating the new material to the life interest of the pupils. Oral presentation of this kind should be as brief as possible and usually should be supplemented by other forms of introductory activities such as demonstration and films.

2. As a means of determining the present level of knowledge of a class. Before actual teaching begins it is sometimes desirable to ask a series of questions which will reveal not only what the pupils already know about the new unit but how their thinking is organized in relation to their existing knowledge, and what application and implications they see in what they know.

In the process of determining the extent of knowledge the pupils have about a new unit, the teacher can also find out what they want to know as well as what they think they need to know. If this is the case, specific questions may be asked in order to determine needs and interests of pupils.

3. As a means of clarification and illustration.

4. As a means of evaluating progress during the course of a unit. Again, by means of class discussion and questions, it is possible for the teacher to determine the extent and effectiveness of learning. When oral presentation is used in this way it becomes to some extent an evaluative procedure in that it reveals achievement on the part of pupils and also it measures the effectiveness of teaching. Other results of oral presentation of this kind are that it may indicate the need for more audio-visual aids, more question and answer sessions to clarify health concepts, and it may help to identify pupils in the group who are learning and progressing very rapidly and need extra work and assignments. Also, the slow learning pupils who may need extra assistance can be identified through oral presentations.

5. As a means of encouraging pupil participation. This may take several forms, including individual pupil reports, class discussions, presenting demonstrations, panel discussions, and the like. It may also take the form of pupils responding to questions posed by the teacher with the intention of "drawing the class out" on subjects about which they have some awareness.

Questions and Answers.—The question and answer technique is one of the oldest of pedagogical procedures. It was highly developed by Socrates in the fifth century B. C. as a means of leading his students to higher levels of thought. It should be used ordinarily as a device for discovering, enlarging upon, and integrating what is known rather than what is *not* known, although in some cases its use in finding out what is not known can be justified. Skillful use of questions and answers is an excellent way to develop and maintain good teacher-pupil and pupil-pupil relationships in addition to stimulating desirable verbal exchange among the pupils.

Question and answer periods must be used correctly and at advantageous times for the best results to accrue.

Some of the advantages of the question and answer techniques are: vagueness and uncertainty can be corrected immediately; synonyms for unknown or doubtful vocabulary can be supplied on the spot; the thinking of pupils can be stimulated, guided and challenged; and known areas of knowledge can be quickly differentiated from unknown. Moreover, questions and answers can be utilized to good advantage at all stages of the instructional sequence.

Experience in the use of the question and answer technique shows that the best results are obtained when careful thought, planning and organization are given to building and constructing sets of questions. The haphazard, "inspirational" types of questions frequently used by some teachers, especially when they are not properly prepared for the daily lesson, are usually inefficient and ineffective. As a general rule question and answer periods and sessions should be planned in detail and in advance as carefully as any other teaching procedure. Moreover, it is well to improve upon questions immediately after they have been used and to keep them for future use.

Some Considerations in Developing and Utilizing Questions.— Questions should be definite, concise, and thought provoking and they should be carefully adapted to the grade level of the group. When utilizing a series of questions, the teacher should take care that their unity be evident. That is, that one question and answer builds upon or is related to another for some definite purpose. A barrage of questions and counter questions is unlikely to be effective although it may seem so, particularly to the inexperienced teacher.

A series of questions and answers may be framed in such a way that they constitute a problem solving device. A specific problem may be posed (questions may also be used to define the basic problem itself) and solved by the group, as in the illustration "A Typical Class Discussion" which appears later in this chapter and which has to do with solving problems related to food selection under special circumstances.

However, care must be taken that question and answer sessions of this type not be permitted to become time-consuming beyond their importance.

It is important for teachers to learn how to deal with the responses that pupils make to questions. Such a question as, "Now let us review what should be done if a playmate is badly hurt while playing some distance away from home?" may elicit a variety of responses ranging from the proper and best answers to excited accounts of accidents that individual pupils have observed. The teacher's task is to keep the attention of the pupils directed to the purpose of the lesson so that it will constitute a learning experience; but it also is important that pupils not be discouraged or embarrassed because of inept responses. A personal account may be interrupted in such a way as, "Tell us about your experience after we have reviewed these basic ideas, and then we'll see how well the accident you saw was handled." Thus, instead of rebuffing the pupil, allowance is made for his contribution, and instead of his story being merely an exciting episode it is made a desirable part of the lesson.

The teacher should avoid letting talkative, aggressive or superior students monopolize the question and answer sessions, and she must do this courteously and without stifling initiative and interest. Quiet and less aggressive individuals should be encouraged to contribute their share of responses. Also, all pupils should be made conscious of the need to deliberate before answering and to make well-thought-out and well-stated responses.

Types of Questions to Avoid.—The following list gives several types of questions which generally speaking, should be avoided.

1. Questions requiring only "yes" or "no" for an answer, such as, "Is milk pasteurized to prevent the spread of disease?"
2. Leading questions which suggest the answer, such as, "Is the World Health Organization concerned with health problems in Africa?" or, "The oxygen-carrying cells in the blood are for what purpose?"
3. Alternative questions in which the teacher has done most of the thinking, such as "Which mineral is used chiefly in the hardening of bones, calcium or iron?"
4. Irrelevant questions upon which no essential information depends.
5. The "who-can-tell-me" type of question which tends to invite a free-for-all response from the class.

6. "Catch" questions, except as they may be employed deliberately to alert pupils to verbal deceptions which are sometimes used in the advertising of health products and treatments.

7. Ambiguous questions for which there are several acceptable answers, such as "What *one* thing must we do to become healthy and strong?"

8. Vague questions which frequently are prefixed with the phrase, "what about", such as "What about vitamins in this day and age?"

9. Question addressed to younger pupils, low ability groups, and others with little health background, that contain abstract terms and concepts, such as "What is health?" Such questions are likely to elicit responses such as: "Health is open the window at night," "Health is when you drink milk," or "Health means swat a fly."

Oral Presentation as an Introductory Activity.—Regardless of the age level involved, in principle, the introductory activity entails setting the stage for what is to follow. This is usually done by means of recalling known related experiences, materials or problems before venturing into the unknown. For example, a unit on grooming at the 7th grade level might begin in something like the following manner:

Teacher: "You remember in our animal feeding experiment that when the rat did not get the proper food, a number of things happened to him. What were some of those things?" (The class enumerates the symptoms.)

Teacher resumes: "Isn't it interesting that so many things having to do with the rat's appearance had to do with the kinds of food that he ate? Do we have any reason to believe that what is true of animals and their food might also be true of human beings?"

Thus from such a starting point related to work that has gone before the teacher is in a position to develop the various concepts of grooming and personal appearance.

It should be emphasized that regardless of the grade level of the class, introductory activity is most successful which goes directly to the life interests of the particular students involved and moves on from there to new concepts. It is for this reason that many successful teachers of health explore the numerous leisure time interests of young people as a point of departure for many units of teaching. These interests include nature, farm life and animals, the zoo, camping trips, games and sports.

One third-grade teacher likes to introduce the subject of rest and sleep to her pupils by talking about the resting and sleeping habits of various animals. She begins by describing the odd sleeping positions of her own cat which sometimes lies with its feet directly in the air. This description almost invariably stimulates some of her pupils to want to tell about the sleeping habits of their pets, including fishes, turtles, and birds. It is often a surprise to children to learn that horses sleep standing up. Also, hibernation of such animals as bears, is a source of considerable curiosity.

Having aroused interest in this way, this teacher finds it a simple matter to begin the proper consideration of sleep and rest for human beings and especially children. Many comparisons are made between animal and human sleeping needs, sleeping positions and the kinds of "beds" each uses. This teacher finds that her approach rarely fails to make her pupils more sleep conscious and more receptive to learning about the importance of good sleep habits.

Oral Presentations by Students.—Some commonly noted advantages of pupil presentations are that: (1) pupils ordinarily present and describe experiences with which other children of their age and grade level are familiar; (2) usually, the illustrations and examples pupils give are of interest to the group; and (3) the vocabulary used by pupils tends to be on a level with and understandable by the other children.

Some common disadvantages of pupil presentations are that: (1) children may select extreme or fantastic illustrations; (2) they may select examples which are not entirely pertinent to the subject under consideration; (3) their information may not be entirely accurate; and (4) their presentations may not contribute materially to the learning of the group. It is readily apparent that the disadvantages do not necessarily invalidate pupil presentations but merely underscore the need for the teacher to exert some guidance and control over them.

Discussions among the pupils as well as between teachers and pupils can be a very desirable means of sharing experiences and expanding knowledge in health.

When group discussions, panels, forums, and the like are employed, they should be preceded by periods of study on the subject under consideration. Otherwise, the discussions are likely to degenerate into a pooling of ignorance and a random intermixing of truth, half-truth, and untruth which in the areas of health and safety can be very harmful. Discussions not preceded by study are likely to be of value only if the teacher is using them as a means of: (1) showing how fruitless and frustrating the exchange of uninformed opinion on any subject is likely to be, or (2) as a means of dramatizing the need for facts and understanding if value is to be derived from discussion, or (3) as a means of showing the limits of present knowledge and of making plans for extending it.

Discussions or panels may also be used as culminating activities which engage all pupils in the process of outlining and appraising the status of their knowledge and of making applications of their knowledge. In this way the pupils are in the position of having to defend their ideas and they are under pressure to marshal their facts and clarify their thinking. Emphasis is thus upon getting at the facts and their meaning rather than upon pleasing the teacher or just meeting specified requirements.

The discussion approach may readily be adjusted to the proper academic level of the students. At the upper elementary school level they should deal largely with basic concepts. At this level the teacher usually finds it necessary to give considerable guidance to the discussions in order to keep attention focused upon the concepts under study and consideration.

The Discussion Leader.—A few considerations relative to discussion leading should be noted. Certainly, before turning the duties of discussion leader over to the pupils, the teacher should prepare them for the task if they have not had such training. Essentially, the leader's role is to make the discussion as fruitful as possible. The leader's first responsibility is to orient the group as to the direction and scope of the discussion.

Ordinarily, he states any rules which seem necessary, such as limiting individual contributions to a specified amount of time, particularly when verbal exchanges become heated and not particularly productive.

Usually, the leader should not take too active a part in the discussion. Rather, his job is to get a maximum amount of thoughtful and orderly participation from the group. If there is any doubt as to a contributor's meaning, the leader may re-state that point of view briefly as he understood it and ask the speaker whether that was as he had intended it; or he may ask the speaker to re-state his own position briefly for clarification purposes. In either event, he should avoid seeming partial in any argument. He reacts quickly to any speaker's tendency to become diverted from the agreed-upon subject, but in doing so he remains tactful. Finally, the leader is responsible either to summarize the ground covered and conclusions reached in the discussion, or else to appoint a summarizer to assume responsibility for the task.

A Typical Class Discussion.—The following illustrates a sixth-grade class discussion in progress.

Teacher: Let us see how we can use the knowledge we have gained about food in deciding some things of importance for ourselves. Suppose you are in a summer camp, and you are asked to plan a menu to use on a three-day camping trip for the eight boys or girls in your Tribe. How would you go about it?

Pupil 1: My Father gave me that job when we went camping last summer. First you have to figure out what to take and how much of each thing so that there will be enough for everybody.

Pupil 2: I like stew and pancakes on camping trips.

Teacher: If you need to decide what foods and how much of each thing let us think about *what* foods first. How will you decide?

Pupil 3: We know there should be a balanced diet; so you should plan a balanced diet.

Pupil 4: You should include foods from all of the Basic Seven Groups.

Teacher: Now, what are the basic seven foods?
(The basic foods are re-stated and illustrations of each are given.)

Teacher: When you are on a camping trip, will you be living an easy life or a vigorous, active life?

Pupil 1: Camping in the woods is a very active life.

Teacher: Well now, we know that camping will be a very active life and that it will help you to build up your muscles. What does a very active, outdoor life mean in regard to the foods you will select?

Pupil 5: Plan plenty of energy foods to keep you going.

Teacher: What energy foods do you have in mind?

Pupil 2: The things it is most fun to eat but that you should not eat.

Teacher: That is not quite right, is it?

Pupil 2: No, I mean starchy foods such as pancakes and sugars, and the syrup you put on your pancakes. Foods like that are all right just so you leave room for plenty of other foods with vitamins and minerals in them.

Teacher: But how about the muscle builders?

Pupil 6: Proteins.

Pupils 7: Meats and cheese and milk and beans and soybeans and nuts.

Pupil 1: You have to travel light when you go camping in the woods.

Pupil 8: Dried foods are light. Canned food is heaviest but canned milk is worth it because of its food values and because you can make other things of it.

Pupil 6: You do not want a lot of fancy stuff. Who wants to spend all of his time cooking?

Pupil 9: And you had better ask the other kids if there are foods they just do not like. I know you wouldn't take shrimp, but if I had to eat shrimp I wouldn't want to go. My sister likes it.

Teacher: That is a good point, too. I think we can start listing foods that would be suitable and then we can make a menu. Martha, will you come to the blackboard and write down the suggestions?

The class then proceeds to plan a menu for what is to these children a real and interesting adventure. Perhaps a professional camp leader is finally invited in to check their plans and to give them ideas from his own experience and possibly from his knowledge of how Indians prepared for long camping trips.

In some situations where camping is very popular or where a school or school system has access to a camp for actual camping experiences, this type of work can be very real in that pupil-planning is actually utilized in the outdoor situation.

The Lecture.—The limitations of "straight lecturing" as a teaching procedure are so well known that it is not necessary to elaborate on them. Regardless of the grade level in question, the basic problem seems to be that in the lecture method active participation is centered in one person.

Although the lecture method is relatively ineffective below the advanced grades in the secondary school, it is widely used in the upper high school grades and in colleges. Therefore, as pupils progress throughout the elementary and junior high school grades they should gradually develop the ability to profit from the lecture method.

Oral Comprehension.—As the child grows older, certain of the oral presentations which precede and follow the various learning activities may be gradually extended. In this way, the child's ability to comprehend sustained oral presentation may be increased in a manner that is comparable to his increased ability to learn during periods of uninterrupted reading. For example, in time, pupils should become able to listen to speeches and round table discussions by experts on various health subjects with real comprehension of the information and points of view presented.

Critical Listening.—Just as it is essential that the young be taught to read critically, they should also be taught to listen critically as well as carefully. We know that communication is an active, two-way process, and that it is essential to develop the ability to listen intelligently as well as to speak effectively.

In the field of health all manner of claims are made by advertisers. Some of these claims are factual and responsible. Others are concerned solely with selling a product. Most claims are probably relatively harmless; but some are quite misleading and harmful. The teacher of health should, of course, help pupils to become cautious in their acceptance of advertising and other claims, whether they are by printed or spoken word. Specific instruction on this subject seems essential. However, excellent practical experience can be acquired by means of listening critically to class presentations. For the most part, of course, lectures should be devoted to the development of concepts that are based on the established facts in the field. On the other hand, on some occasions the class may be forewarned to be alert for misleading or false statements. The teacher may sometimes deliberately include false statements in oral presentations in order to test the ability of the students to detect them. After long years of being urged to accept and obey authoritative statements and commands at home and at school, it often comes as somewhat of a shock to pupils to realize that authority can actually be trying to trip them. In the present day perhaps even more than in the past, a doubting and skeptical attitude towards authoritative statements, particularly those dealing with health, seems desirable.

The teacher should have little difficulty in locating misleading and false statements, arguments, and misconceptions. For example, a miraculous cancer curing machine was recently used to cheat hundreds of desperate people of their money. The teacher could report the machine as a new weapon in cancer fighting in the same terms used by its inventor, telling just enough about it to cast doubt on its authenticity. In challenging the value of the machine the pupils can be led to state what they would need to know about such a thing before putting their faith in it.

Evaluation.—Whatever instructional technique is employed, whether discussion, film, demonstration, or lecture, it is essential that suitable evaluation take place. In many instances this may take written form, but more commonly it is in the form of oral exchanges which are calculated to "take the experience apart" for its meaning and uses. The evaluation may include a summary of major points usually by one or more pupils and interpretation and application of the concepts involved. Since thought is primarily in terms of verbal symbols, and since the communication of ideas is based upon verbal symbols, oral evaluation of educational experiences may be regarded as a most essential phase of health education in terms of both: (1) checking the effectiveness of the teaching-learning experience, and (2) cultivating in the learner the habit of systematically evaluating his experiences for their significance. Thus, for example, pupils may not only grow in their ability to grasp the content of oral presentation of health concepts but also they may form the habit of evaluating what they hear in terms of sound criteria.

Questions For Discussion

1. What are some important relationships between the capacity for oral communication and the mental development of children?
2. What are some major uses of oral presentation in health education?
3. What are some advantages and limitations of the lecture method?
4. How can pupils be active participants in oral communication? Discuss a number of ways.
5. What are some important considerations to be taken into account in preparing questions for class discussions?
6. In what ways is oral presentation important in relation to teaching aids?
7. What is meant by "critical listening?" Of what importance is critical listening when information on health is presented by way of the popular media of communication?

Suggested Class Activities.

1. Prepare a talk on a health topic which is designed to challenge the critical thinking of the group.

2. Outline ways in which pupils at specific grade levels may be participants in oral presentation of health subjects.
3. Prepare a sequence of questions for use in a question and answer session on some phase of health. Specify the grade level for which the questions are intended and specify where and why they should be used.
4. Prepare a list of visitations, field trips, and other activities which can form the basis of oral presentation by pupils.
5. For a week, collect examples of advertising which are concerned with health. As a class activity, analyze each in terms of its likely influence upon the health concepts of those who see it.

References

1. Bogert, L. J., *Nutrition and Physical Fitness.* Philadelphia, 1949, W. B. Saunders Co.
2. Duker, S., "In an Age of Communication, Are We Listening?" *The Educational Forum,* **18**:405-408, May 1954.
3. Dzenowagis, J. G. and L. W. Irwin, "Prevalence of Certain Harmful Health and Safety Misconceptions Among Fifth and Sixth Grade Children," *Research Quarterly,* **25**:150-163, May 1954.
4. Rasmussen, C., *Speech Methods in the Elementary School,* New York, 1949, The Ronald Press.

CHAPTER 10

MATERIAL AIDS TO LEARNING IN HEALTH EDUCATION

The term "material aids to learning" is difficult to define because of its extent and breadth in the field of education. Learning material in the school program is said to be concerned with any material that is used directly with pupils. Moreover, it has been postulated that everything in the pupil's environment which contributes in any way to the learning situation may be considered as an aid to learning. Defined in these broad terms material aids include all things that teachers and pupils use in enhancing the learning process.

Although the term "material aids" is in reality extremely broad in scope, it has come to have a more or less colloquial meaning to most teachers. In other words, its meaning will perhaps be dependent upon the limitation of the use of material aids in a particular school system. For example, in some localities such items as pencils, paper, chalk and the like might be considered as material aids in that these standard items are the only material aids used. On the other hand, some school systems go far beyond the use of the usual equipment found in the average classroom. In such cases the items previously mentioned may not be considered as material aids, but merely as standard equipment in every classroom.

For purposes of discussion in this chapter material aids will be considered as specific types of aids to learning which may be used in addition to the standard traditional equipment which is a part of almost every classroom. Consequently, such things as pencils, paper, chalk, blackboards, textbooks and the like are in reality material aids but they will not be discussed here. The purpose at this point will be to consider the use of certain specific material aids to learning in health teaching which are not commonly found in all classrooms. Material aids to learning are defined in this manner so that the reader will not become confused with respect to certain other chapters in this book. For example, full chapters have been devoted to field trips and audio-visual aids which are material aids in the real sense yet they are broad enough in scope to require much more detailed consideration.

Attention is called to the fact that the material aids to learning discussed in this chapter consist of a combination of various sensory aids and materials used by pupils. It should be understood that the material aids presented and discussed in this chapter do not cover the field as far as health teaching is concerned. Those presented here are submitted as examples and as a sampling of the numerous possibilities.

The General Nature, Purpose and Use of Material Aids to Learning in Health Education.—It has been mentioned in various places throughout this volume that health teaching has not kept pace with other subject matter areas with respect to method. It has been postulated that the reason for this may be due to the uncertain status that health has had in the school curriculum and the fact that relatively few teachers receive sufficient, actual pre-service training in this area. As a result many teachers who have been assigned to teach health classes have resorted to verbalism and textbook reading as the chief method of teaching. One reason for this may be that because of an insufficient background of training in the specific area of health teaching, teachers perhaps have not known how certain material aids can contribute to the teaching-learning situation in health.

In that health teaching is concerned with an accumulation of knowledge that will favorably influence attitudes and behavior, it is apparent that such expected outcomes will be difficult to accomplish if the teacher relies solely on verbalism and textbook reading. Therefore, it is readily obvious that certain material aids are practically indispensable if the most desirable learning is to accrue.

Living in modern society presents many complex problems for the growing individual, not the least of which are the problems which influence the individual's health. In teaching for health all possible measures should be taken to help pupils learn about principles of health which will influence their present and future well-being. Consequently, those material aids to learning which will help pupils gain a more complete understanding of abstract health principles should be thoroughly explored.

There are various kinds of material aids to learning in health education and each kind serves a more or less general purpose. One type is designed primarily for the development and improvement of the basic tools of learning such as reading and writing. Practice materials like health workbooks and health study and activity guides may be conveniently placed in this classification.

A second type is one which serves the purpose of furnishing pupils with direct experience through use of material aids. That is, the material may appeal directly to one or more of the senses. In the study of foods that are good for health, actual vegetables may be used as material aids to learning. For instance, a carrot provides direct experience for the pupil in that he can see, feel and taste it.

Another classification of learning aids is the type that is used for the purpose of having pupils receive an indirect experience. This type is generally used when those materials which give direct experience are not readily accessible. For example, a picture of the object under study might be shown to pupils.

In the use of any of the various types of material aids to learning it should be kept in mind that as much variety as possible should exist. Moreover, material aids to learning in health instruction might be selected on the basis of their appeal as multi-sensory aids. This is particularly important because of individual differences of pupils in a given health class. While many class members may learn best with a visual aid to learning there are also those who may gain a better insight through the sense of hearing or being able to touch and handle the materials. It remains for the teacher to know the pupils well enough so that the best possible material aids to learning may be selected for health teaching. Regardless of the range of capacity among pupils in a class the possibilities for material aids to learning in the area of healthful living are such that some type of aid can be found that will make the specific health topic more meaningful.

In using material aids to learning in health teaching there are certain basic procedures which should be taken into consideration if the best results are to be obtained. In this regard the following suggestions are submitted to guide the teacher in the proper use of material aids.

1. The material aids should be readily accessible. There is nothing more disconcerting for a class than to have to wait for the teacher to locate materials that have been misplaced.

When this occurs continuity and interest in the lesson are often lost.
2. It is important to remember that the material aids are to be used and not just shown. The teacher must know just how a particular aid to learning fits into a specific situation. The material aids themselves will not do the teaching for the teacher. They should be used as tools in such a way that they will give the lesson more meaning.
3. If there are a number of different material aids to be used it might be well to use them one at a time in sequence. When it becomes necessary to show relationships with graphs or charts it is then feasible that more than one be displayed at a time.
4. Material aids, when used in a logical sequence, should be such that they complement each other. In other words, the teacher can use a phychological approach within the logical limits of the class.

Bulletin Boards.—Every classroom should have one or more bulletin boards. The types of materials that can be placed on the bulletin board to stimulate pupil interest are almost unlimited. For example, it may be desirable to display pictures, charts, maps, specimens, current news clippings and other related materials during the study of a specific health unit. These displays can serve as a very desirable supplement to the unit.

Many teachers find the classroom bulletin board a very useful medium in introducing a health unit. For instance, a unit on foods may be introduced by having a suitable bulletin board display of pictures of various kinds of foods, food charts, and the like. In many cases bulletin board displays stimulate the interest of pupils to the extent that they will raise questions and problems helpful in initiating a unit.

It is of paramount importance that meticulous care be taken with regard to the organization, arrangement and selection of bulletin board material. Too often the school bulletin board is a "catch-all" for unorganized, unattractive, unrelated and non-essential displays.

Careful attention should be given to the length of time materials are left on the bulletin board. Ordinarily two or three days is the limit for most materials. Otherwise the students seeing the same things displayed day after day become bored with them. Usually it is better to leave a bulletin board blank than to leave materials displayed on it past the psychological limit of attention holding. However, in cases where pupils make and prepare materials for bulletin board displays the material does not need to be changed as frequently. Children like to see their own materials day after day for longer periods.

Cartoons.—When properly used, cartoons are an excellent medium for conveying health concepts to pupils. However, great care must be taken lest the cartoon be associated merely with entertainment rather than learning. Teachers must consider that by their very nature cartoons are generally associated with "comic strips", and that material of this kind is extremely popular with most pupils. Therefore, it seems wise to capitalize on a medium that has the advantage of being interesting to a majority of pupils.

Teachers should select those cartoons which are appealing to pupils and at the same time make a contribution to their learning. Many cartoons pertaining to health and safety are available for distribution by both voluntary and commercial organizations. Also, health and safety cartoons constructed by children are very effective. Designing and constructing cartoons can be a desirable learning experience for pupils who have an aptitude for drawing.

In using cartoons in health and safety teaching the teacher should always consider the need for critical appraisal and evaluation of the material. The following standards may be helpful in appraising and evaluating health and safety cartoons:

1. Will the pupils fully understand the implication for health or safety that the cartoon is supposed to portray?
2. Does the cartoon present an accurate treatment of a health or safety concept or is it exaggerated to the point where the idea may be lost?
3. Does the cartoon present the health or safety concept in such a way that the pupils can react intellectually toward it?
4. Does the cartoon emphasize humor over and above the health or safety concept, or is a proper balance maintained?
5. Is the cartoon unique, appealing and easily understood?

Charts.—Charts can be used in health teaching to help pupils visualize relationships. Among others the data chart, diagrammatic chart, flow chart and genealogical chart have been used successfully as material aids to learning in health education.

DATA CHART.—The data chart is perhaps more commonly used than others. This kind of chart is useful in presenting health data to pupils in an understandable way. For example, one teacher conducted a survey in her eighth-grade class to determine the dental health status of the class. After the data were compiled, she devised a chart so that the pupils could get a more complete understanding of the status of the class with regard to defective teeth. Figure 1 is an example of a data chart.

DENTAL INFORMATION CHART

SECTION A	NUMBER OF PUPILS			NUMBER OF TEETH			TREATMENT SINCE MARCH 1		
	BOYS	GIRLS	TOTAL	BOYS	GIRLS	TOTAL	BOYS	GIRLS	TOTAL
Pulled	4	8	12	27	15	42	2		
Filled	9	6	15	62	35	97	2	2	
Cavities	7	10	17	25	20	45			
Perfect	4	2	6						
SECTION B									
Pulled	5	9	14	10	16	26			
Filled	7	10	17	29	72	101			
Cavities	8	7	15	18	17	35			
Perfect	0	0	0						

Fig. 1

DIAGRAMMATIC CHART. The diagrammatic chart provides an effective means of presenting health information through diagrams. The diagrams may or may not be labeled. Some teachers prefer to use those that are not labeled and have the pupils label or fill in as the case may be. The teacher mentioned above used a diagrammatic chart as a measure of reliability in obtaining the necessary data on dental defects by asking the pupils to fill in the chart shown in Figure 2.

FLOW CHART. The flow chart is useful in depicting the functional relationships of an organization. This type of chart is almost essential in the study of a local health department or any type of health organization in that it helps pupils to see the various responsibilities of the officials of the organization.

GENEALOGICAL CHART. The genealogical chart is very useful in showing growth and development. An example of this is in the study of health topics related to heredity. Genetic influences on individual traits and characteristics can clearly be shown by this type of chart.

TOOTH CHART

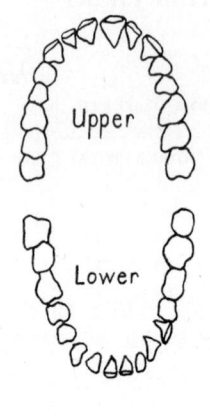

Mark the tooth chart as nearly as you can remember
Pulled -- Red
Filled -- Green
Cavity -- Black

Fig. 2.

Genealogical charts are also valuable in tracing a certain material from its origin to its present status. For example, a step-by-step process of how milk is made ready for human consumption can be charted in this manner.

Flash Cards.—This technique has been used for many years at the elementary school level as a means of helping children learn words and memorize factual material. The flash card in health teaching perhaps has its greatest use as a method of teaching children to recognize certain objects. Some teachers have used flash cards as a means of testing certain areas. It is not, however, widely used as a measurement device in health education.

Flash cards are valuable in health and safety teaching in that they are likely to make a favorable impression on pupils with respect to certain factors which might jeopardize their health and safety. For example, experience has shown that flash cards can be used very satisfactorily in a unit on summer safety by having pupils acquire practice in quickly identifying such things as poisonous plants, poisonous insects, poisonous snakes and other harmful agents. The idea here is to help children to learn to react quickly to situations which could be harmful to them. Flash cards containing both harmful and harmless agents can be mixed together and flashed to pupils for short periods of time so that they may gain experience in quick observation of the harmful agents.

Flat or Still Pictures.—The terms "flat" and "still" pictures are ordinarily used interchangeably. They refer to several kinds of pictures such as photographs, paintings, magazine pictures, advertising brochures, slides and film strips. Slides and film strips are for projection purposes only, while the others may be used with or without a projector. However, in order to project still pictures other than slides or film strips, it is necessary to have an opaque projector.

The popularity of still pictures as an aid to learning stems from the fact that they are easy to obtain, entail little or no cost, and they may be used over and over again.

The list of still pictures that can be used in health and safety teaching is almost unlimited. However, one of the most common ways that they are used is to have pupils cut them out of magazines and arrange them in word pictures related to health and safety concepts, or to use them in a health or safety scrapbook. Selecting, cutting out and preparing series of word pictures and scrapbooks on health and safety concepts are excellent and desirable activities particularly for elementary school children as they seem to hold the pupils' interest.

In using flat or still pictures in health instruction, teachers should take certain precautions so that pupils do not fall victim to erroneous conceptions. One very important consideration is the fact that different pupils may view a picture in a different light. Although pictures are largely for the purpose of being "seen and not read", it may be difficult to keep pupils from "reading" certain meanings into a picture. The meaning a picture conveys to a pupil depends largely on the past experience the pupil has had with the health or safety idea that the picture is intended to convey. For example, a picture depicting a certain bicycle safety practice may have an altogether different meaning for a pupil who owns and rides a bicycle than for one who does not.

Another consideration to keep in mind is that pupils should be given sufficient time to view a picture so that they may gain maximum value from it. It is also important that pupils be given the opportunity to view a picture at close enough range so that they may gain a full understanding of it.

As in the case of some of the other material aids to learning in health instruction, the teacher should devise standards for critical appraisal and evaluation of still pictures. The following list of criteria is suggested as a guide for the selection and use of still pictures:

1. Does the picture help in achieving the purpose of the lesson?
2. Does it give a true picture of the health or safety concept to be conveyed?
3. Is the picture technically correct with respect to health or safety concepts?
4. Does the picture have the proper amount of detail?
5. Does the picture stimulate the imagination, thus helping to stimulate thought?
6. Is the size of the picture such that it is large enough to show sufficient details and small enough to be handled and used effectively?
7. Is the picture suited to the age level and abilities of the pupils?

Graphs.—Graphic materials can be used most effectively in health and safety teaching to show something of a statistical nature or to show comparisons and relationships. Where statistics and figures are concerned they will be much more meaningful to pupils if shown in graphic form. Graphs may also be an effective aid to learning in health and safety when they are used to illustrate those things which cannot be seen, such as vitamins, or action of acids on food in the body.

Experience has shown that there are three kinds of graphs which are of special importance in health and safety instruction. These include the area graph, bar graph, and pictorial graph.

AREA GRAPH.—Among the various kinds of area graphs the circle graph, sometimes referred to as the wheel or pie graph, has been found to be very useful in teaching health and safety. This kind of graph gives pupils a concept of the relative size of quantities. At the upper elementary level an opportunity is provided to integrate health and safety with arithmetic because the circle graph is often used in the study of simple fractions.

A good example of the circle graph in health and safety instruction is the circle which is divided by hours into a twenty-four-hour day. On this circle pupils can graph their activities for a one-day period, or for longer if necessary. The circle graph is useful in the introduction of units on food, exercise, or rest depending on where the greatest need is shown by the pupil-made graphs. Figure 3 illustrates a circle graph.

BAR GRAPH.—The bar graph has the advantage of being easily understood. The bars may be drawn vertically or horizontally. The horizontal arrangement is recommended because it follows a natural

CIRCLE GRAPH SHOWING AN INDIVIDUAL PUPIL'S ACTIVITY OVER A TWENTY-FOUR HOUR PERIOD

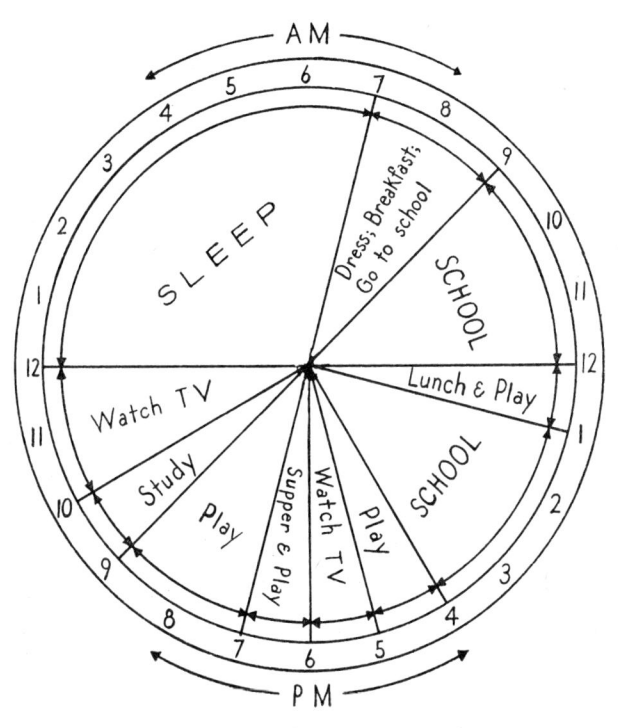

Fig. 3.

left to right reading pattern. Pupils are more likely to understand a distance or "from here to there" relationship more than an "up and down" height relationship. Figure 4 illustrates a graph of this type which was used to accompany a class discussion in the introduction of a unit on dairy products.

216 *Methods and Materials in Teaching Health*

Many bar graphs are suitable for use with upper elementary school pupils, largely for the purpose of making comparisons.

PICTORIAL GRAPH.—The type of graph illustrated with pictures combines the graphic and still picture idea. This kind of graph is particularly useful with slow learners because it shows number concepts in a pictorial relationship.

WHICH ONE IS BEST FOR OUR BODIES ?

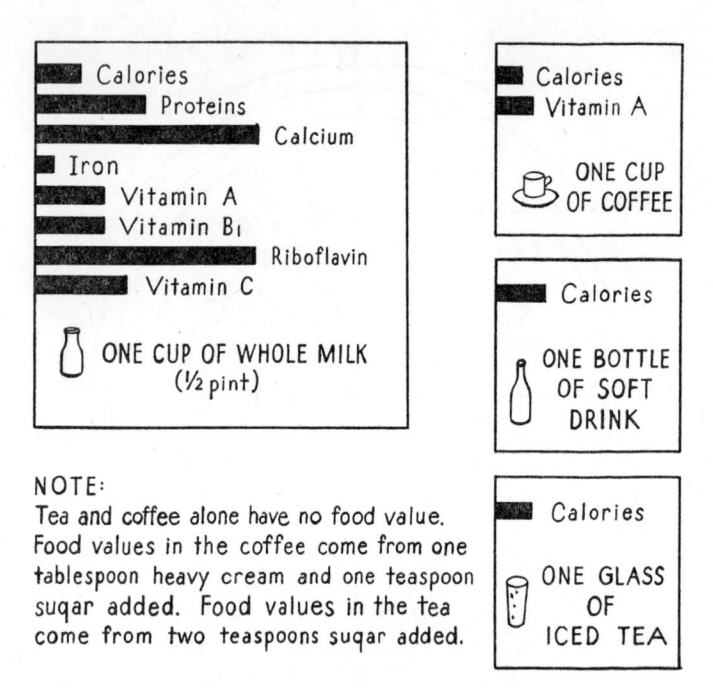

```
┌─────────────────────────────────┐  ┌──────────────────┐
│ ■ Calories                      │  │ ■ Calories       │
│   ■ Proteins                    │  │ ■ Vitamin A      │
│      ■ Calcium                  │  │                  │
│ ■ Iron                          │  │      ONE CUP     │
│   ■ Vitamin A                   │  │      OF COFFEE   │
│   ■ Vitamin B₁                  │  │                  │
│      ■ Riboflavin               │  └──────────────────┘
│   ■ Vitamin C                   │  ┌──────────────────┐
│                                 │  │ ■ Calories       │
│    ONE CUP OF WHOLE MILK        │  │                  │
│         (½ pint)                │  │     ONE BOTTLE   │
└─────────────────────────────────┘  │     OF SOFT      │
                                     │     DRINK        │
 NOTE:                               │                  │
 Tea and coffee alone have no food   └──────────────────┘
 value. Food values in the coffee    ┌──────────────────┐
 come from one tablespoon heavy      │ ■ Calories       │
 cream and one teaspoon sugar        │                  │
 added. Food values in the tea       │     ONE GLASS    │
 come from two teaspoons sugar       │     OF           │
 added.                              │     ICED TEA     │
                                     └──────────────────┘
```

Fig. 4.

At the elementary school level simple forms of the pictorial graph may be made by the teacher and pupils. An illustration of a pictorial graph appears in Figure 5. In preparing for a unit on milk a teacher decided to survey the milk-drinking habits of her class by observing them in the school lunchroom for a period of one week. She found that out of her class of thirty pupils, approximately 50% drank their milk, 20% took milk but gave it away, and 30% did not take the milk at all. The pupils cut out figures and arranged them in graphic form to show the milk drinking practices of the group.

Maps.—One of the most important features in the use of maps as a material aid to learning is that they help pupils gain an awareness of spatial relationships. Through the use of maps pupils readily learn about the location of different areas as well as their size and shape. In addition, maps can be used to portray the contours of the terrain and the economic resources in a given locality.

HOW OUR CLASS USES MILK

ϪϪϪϪϪϪϪϪϪϪϪϪϪϪϪϪ
Drank Milk

ϪϪϪϪϪϪ
Took milk but gave it away

ϪϪϪϪϪϪϪϪϪϪ
Did not take milk at all

Fig. 5.

Specific examples of how maps may be used in health and safety instruction include (1) showing where various kinds of food are grown, (2) showing those areas where different diseases are most prevalent and (3) showing where the greatest number of accidents occur.

The outline or blank map, sometimes referred to as the "problem map", may also be used for these purposes. The outline map merely presents a boundary outline and pupils fill in the specific information required.

Objects, Specimens and Models.—Objects are considered as "the things themselves", specimens are referred to as "parts of objects", and models are "replicas of objects."[3] When possible, objects or specimens should be used because they furnish the real thing under study. However, in many instances this is not possible as in case of the study of certain vital organs of the body such as the heart and lungs. When it is obvious that an object or real thing cannot be used the model may be the next best material aid to learning.

An object, specimen or model is used in health teaching so that pupils may have first-hand experience by direct personal contact with these items. In general the more direct the experience the more meaningful it is to pupils. This means that in the case of objects, specimens and models provision should be made for pupils to view, hear, touch, taste, or manipulate them as the case may be. In other words, objects, specimens and models should be used and not just shown.

There is an almost unlimited range of possibilities for use of objects and specimens in health and safety teaching. One or two examples here should suffice to give an idea of these possibilities.

In the study and discussion of foods, such things as apples, carrots, cereals, oranges and the like should be displayed. Although all children are familiar with such foods, nevertheless, they retain the visual image of these objects in connection with their study much longer than they would if just a verbal description or discussion occurs without them. Another example is that of collecting specimens injurious to health. One way that this can be done is to place a test tube containing a small amount of culture medium in a certain place in the school over night such as in a gymnasium locker, corridor or the like. The collected specimens placed under a microscope can serve to give the pupils a clearer understanding of the prevalence of germs when they see how the specimens have collected in the culture medium.

Models have two types of uses in health education. They can be used to substitute for objects and specimens for the purpose of creating a visual image, or they can be constructed by pupils to assist them in a clearer understanding of the subject being studied. Pupil-made models serve a definite purpose for the pupils who learn best through constructing and making things. This procedure may also provide for possibilities of integration with other departments of the school such as the fine arts department or industrial arts department. More complex models may take the form of a class project. For example, a third grade group studying vegetables worked together in the development of a model of a garden. This was accomplished by planting seeds in a window box and caring for the vegetables as they grew.

Posters.—When used correctly health posters can be desirable aids to learning in health and safety. The value of posters in health education is directly related to the period of time that they are displayed. If they are displayed for too long a period it is quite possible that they might become boresome to pupils to the extent that they will "grow" pencil drawn beards and moustaches. When this occurs it is likely that a poster will detract from rather than contribute to learning and retention. An exception to this rule concerns those health posters that are made by pupils. Pupil-made posters may remain on display for longer periods of time because pupils, particularly those at the elementary school level, receive a great deal of enjoyment and satisfaction from having their own work displayed in the room.

Posters may be obtained from numerous voluntary and official health agencies at little or no cost. Also, many commercial organizations distribute health and safety posters to schools free of charge. Posters of this nature that are of greatest value in health and safety instruction are those that attract immediate attention and convey one principal idea related to health or safety.

Teachers often find posters a practical and satisfactory means of introducing a health or safety unit. This is accomplished by displaying numerous posters for the purpose of stimulating the interest of pupils in the problem of the unit.

Scrapbooks.—The making of scrapbooks is a popular activity with many pupils at the elementary and junior high school levels. When health scrapbooks contain collections of items which are related to a particular health unit they become desirable aids to learning. However, if the compilation of a scrapbook is conducted merely for the purpose of keeping pupils busy, the time spent is not likely to be justifiable.

Some teachers find it valuable for pupils to keep a record of a health unit in scrapbook form. This may be done to show how a unit was planned and developed. This type of scrapbook may be a cooperative venture of the entire class or each pupil may make his own.

Items that may be collected for health and safety scrapbooks include, among others, magazine articles and pictures, newspaper articles and pictures, photographs, pictures from catalogs and pamphlets, letters, poems, jingles, and drawings by pupils.

Study and Activity Guides.—The study and activity guide is a kind of work material, usually in mimeographed form, that is distributed to pupils when they begin work on a health or safety unit. One of the main purposes of the study and activity guide is to present pupils with questions and problems that will guide them in the study of the unit.

Study and activity guides may be divided into the two broad categories of general study guides and special study guides. The general study guide is broader in scope and it is usually a guide for the entire unit. The special study guide is concerned with directions or explanations needed to guide pupils in performing a certain phase of the unit.

Approximate estimates indicate that about 50% of the teachers, particularly at the junior and senior high school levels, use study and activity guides to some extent. This material ranges from a few copied textbook questions to the well-planned study guide. Lack of use of study guides is generally attributed to: (1) mechanical preparation involved, (2) failure of teachers to recognize their value, and (3) confusion as to the time when pupil-teacher planning takes place.

In the sample study and activity guide which is presented here it will be noted that references are not furnished for all of the questions. It is felt that a few direct references should be given to assist pupils in finding materials. However, they should also have the opportunity to locate material by searching for it themselves.

Although study and activity guides are perhaps used more frequently with junior and senior high school students, they can be very effective if prepared properly for upper elementary school pupils.

The following sample study and activity guide has been constructed for secondary school students:

SAMPLE STUDY AND ACTIVITY GUIDE FOR A UNIT ON THE PROCESS OF DIGESTION

Questions and problems.—Find the answers to the following: It is recommended that you write in your notebook the materials and findings that may be essential to show the conclusions for each. Underline all new words that appear in the study guide. Look up the meaning of these words.

Material Aids to Learning 221

Note: A number of books and textbooks should be available. The teacher should list some of the page references in the books where the answers to questions can be found.

1. What is the function of saliva in digestion?
2. What is the function of the gastric juices in digestion?
3. What are carbohydrates?
4. What are proteins?
5. How can one detect the nutrients known as carbohydrates, fats, and proteins?
6. What is the function of the mouth and teeth in the process of digestion?
7. What is the function of the pharnyx and esophagus in the process of digestion?
8. What is the function of the stomach in the process of digestion?
9. What is the function of the small intestine in the process of digestion?
10. What is the function of the large intestine in the process of digestion?
11. Why must food be digested?
12. What is the function of the digestive juices?
13. Are there any foods which are not digestible?
14. What is the peristaltic wave which aids digestion?
15. How long does it take food to digest?
16. Is it necessary to have food in the mouth for the salivary glands to function?
17. What happens when you smell a freshly baked apple pie?
18. What parts of the digestive system are used for the mechanical phase of digestion?
19. What are the factors which influence the chemical phase of digestion?
20. How do the mechanical and chemical digestive changes work together?

Select one of the following activities—
1. Keep a record of your diet for one day. List the foods and tell where in the digestive tract the greatest amount of digestion takes place.
2. Go to the school cafeteria and get a copy of the weekly menu from the dietitian. Write down all the foods and tell which organs of the digestive system would do the most work in digesting these foods.
3. Go to one of your local restaurants and procure a menu and follow the above procedure.
4. Follow the above procedure if you bring your lunch to school.

5. Make a collection of pictures of food advertised in a magazine. Write down where in the digestive tract the greatest amount of digestion of these foods takes place.

Optional activities*—Pupils should obtain the approval of the teacher for optional activities which they wish to select.

1. Visit your physician and find out some of the causes of "indigestion". Report to the class on how these causes might have been eliminated.
2. Write a report on the use of dehydrated foods and digestion.
3. Write a report about how the cooking of food influences digestion.
4. Interview a war veteran about rations. Report to the class on this interview.
5. Report to the class on one of the following topics:
"An apple a day keeps the doctor away."
"You are what you eat."
"Eat Wheaties the breakfast of champions."
6. With two or more other members of the class form a panel group to discuss either of the following:
Is beef easier to digest than pork?
Which is more important mechanical or chemical digestion?
7. Draw a cartoon which shows the digestive system as a factory.
8. Write a humorous song or poem which describes the process of digestion.
9. Write a short play in which the characters are the various organs of digestion.
10. Make a poster which indicates the various phases of digestion.

Workbooks.—The workbook is of relatively recent origin as an aid to learning and it is generally considered as an outgrowth of the laboratory manual. Health workbooks are usually one of two types. One may be referred to as the general type which is planned for use without a textbook, or it may accompany any health textbook. The other is known as the specific type and it is designed to parallel and supplement a particular textbook.

---

*Some teachers maintain a card file available for pupil use in optional activities. A 4 × 6 or 5 × 8 card with the title of the activity, key questions and suggested reading will aid the pupil in pursuing the optional activity.

The question often arises as to which of these types of health and safety workbooks is best. Although teachers in general appear to prefer the specific type, each form has its advantages. For example, if the textbook material is valid and up-to-date, the accompanying workbook should be useful provided it contains sufficient enrichment and supplementary materials. On the other hand, if the textbook is out of date, until such time as it can be revised, a good general type of health workbook might be provided as an aid to learning.

The teacher should keep in mind that the health or safety workbook is only one aid to learning and its use should not preclude other desirable health learning experiences that are not included as workbook activities. In other words, the teacher should not hold the pupils within the bounds of the material in the workbook. This is to say that the content of the health workbook should be viewed as basic material for class work, and that further pupil planning should supplement the learning experiences provided by the workbook.

To be of value as an aid to learning, the health or safety workbook should be organized in such a way that the teacher can use it to best advantage in meeting the individual differences of pupils. A workbook that includes nothing more than a list of drill questions harkens back to mere fact memorization in health and, therefore, cannot be considered a desirable aid to learning. Workbook activities should be of a problem-solving nature.

If the workbook is such that it makes possible individual adaptation to rate of learning the teacher should not lose the opportunity for this by having all pupils go through the workbook material in the same sequence and at the same rate.

Evaluation of Material Aids to Learning in Health Education.—The material aids to learning in health education are of such great importance that they should be subjected to continuous evaluation. When this is done means are provided for the improvement of present practices.

Criteria for evaluation of certain particular aids to learning have been discussed under the appropriate headings in this chapter. However, it seems advisable that there be some general criteria which are common to most of the material aids. The following list of suggested criteria for evaluation is given with this purpose in mind.

1. Does the aid represent a sufficient degree of accuracy?
2. Provided the aid is accurate in every detail, is it relevant to the particular learning situation?
3. What degree of realism does the aid present?
4. Does the aid have a high degree of comprehensibility?
5. Are the pupils able to use the aid effectively?
6. Are the pupils interested in the aid?
7. Do the pupils display a good attitude toward the aid?
8. What are the reactions of the slow learners to the aid?
9. What are the reactions of the fast learners to the aid?

Questions for Discussion

1. What are some of the main purposes of material aids to learning in health and safety education?
2. How can material aids to learning in health instruction be classified?
3. In what ways can cartoons be used satisfactorily in health teaching?
4. How can flash cards be used in health teaching?
5. What are some advantages of the use of still pictures in health teaching?
6. What is the place of the "fill in" map in health teaching?
7. How can health scrapbooks be used in health teaching?
8. What procedure would you use in evaluating a health workbook?

Suggested Class Activities

1. Prepare a list of ten material aids to learning and tell where they might be used to advantage in health education.
2. With other members of the class, prepare a class bulletin board for an introduction to a unit on nutrition.
3. Collect some health data on various members of the class. Prepare a chart which interprets the data.
4. Devise a flow chart which shows the functional relationships of an official community health agency.
5. Prepare an original area graph for a specific health topic.
6. Prepare a bar graph for a specific health topic.
7. Bring a health poster to class. Use this poster in giving an oral report telling how you would evaluate the poster.
8. Prepare a general study and activity guide for use in a health teaching unit on "professional health services".

References

1. Department of Audio-Visual Instruction, Instructional Aids Committee, "Flat Pictures", *National Education Association Journal,* Volume 43, April 1954.
2. Edwards, N., "Helpful Resource Materials for Teachers", *Elementary School Journal,* Volume 52, February 1952.

3. Koon, C. M., "School Use of Visual Aids", *Bulletin Number 4*, Office of Education, Washington, D.C., 1938, p. 12.
4. Lajoie, J. K., "Keys to Faster Learning", *The Instructor*, Volume 63, April 1954.
5. Larrick, N., "Finding the Right Materials for Each Child", *Education*, Volume 74, January 1954.
6. Lawler, M. R., "Institute on Materials for Instruction", *School Executive*, Volume 71, November 1951.
7. Musial, J. S., "Comic Books in Teaching?" *Phi Delta Kappan*, Volume 33, January 1952.
8. Robertson, W., "Teaching Aids for Today's Needs", *Childhood Education*, Volume 27, October 1950.
9. Schreiber, R. E., "Non-projected Teaching Materials", *Audio-Visual Guide*, Volume 19, October 1952.
10. Simpson, A. P., "Children Learn by Using Materials", Pennsylvania University Schoolmen's Week Proceedings 1951.
11. Stonecipher, J. E., "Contemporary Problems in Instructional Materials", *North Central Association Quarterly*, Volume 24, April 1950.
12. Woelfel, N., "How to Start a Teaching Aids Program", *The Nation's Schools*, Volume 47, February 1951.

CHAPTER 11

THE PLACE OF AUDIO-VISUAL MATERIALS IN HEALTH EDUCATION

Although modern educational literature dealing with audio-visual aids abounds with comparatively new terms such as "visual aids", "visual instruction", "audio-visual aids" and "auditory-visual aids", the use of visual material is not new. Early educators such as Froebel, Comenius, Rousseau, and Pestalozzi recognized the value of and emphasized the need for visual aids in the educational process. Aids such as blackboard illustrations, drawings, pictures, maps, charts, and graphs have been used in the classroom for decades. Modern developments in sensory aids during the past two or three decades have been so rapid, however, that many look upon them as something relatively new in the school program. Inventions, discoveries, and developments in the field of motion pictures, radio, photography, television and related areas have given strong impetus to the development and use of sensory aid in health education.

The scope of audio-visual and sensory aids in the modern school program includes blackboard illustrations, bulletin board displays, radio and television programs, field trips, dramatics, pictures, graphs, maps, models, charts, motion pictures, posters, slides, and film strips, as well as many other visual and auditory means utilized in teaching.

The Place of Audio-Visual Aids in Health Education.—Audio-visual aids neither supplant nor eliminate the need for the usual basic procedure in teaching, including oral and written methods of instruction. They primarily serve the purpose of supplementing and enriching other methods of teaching. They are materials and ways used to facilitate the meaning and understanding of oral and written presentations. They are means by which the teacher uses more than one sensory channel in clarifying, interpreting, and correlating materials of instruction. They are not intended to be methods or ways of eliminating the need for work and thought on the part of the students. Rather, they should be used for the purpose of varying activity and making learning more interesting and meaningful, as well as for stimulating creative thinking and exploration.

Sensory aids have an important place in health education because of the great need for supplementary means of instruction. Because of the factual and uninteresting nature of much of the health content materials they are more likely than most other school subjects and activities to become boresome and uninteresting to the child. Therefore, audio-visual aids are very important in the field of health education, particularly from the viewpoint of motivation, gaining and holding interest, varying activity in a meaningful way and clarifying subject matter.

The Purposes of Audio-Visual Aids in Health Education.— Much of the teaching in health and hygiene in past years has been limited largely to oral or printed words or symbols. As a matter of fact it has been limited more to the oral word which has frequently taken the form of nagging and preachment on the part of parents, teachers, and others who come in contact with the child. Modern developments in psychology and education indicate clearly that there must be sensory experiences of a visual and auditory nature beyond the usual oral and written presentations, if health knowledge gained by the child is to be most effective and functional in terms of habit formation, attitudes, practices and appreciations. Sensory experiences must be arranged and provided as a background for understanding and interpreting the oral and written word. An example of this might be that in which the child is first studying and learning about bacteria. Although he may gain some understanding as well as many misconceptions of bacteria through a teacher's oral discussion and description and through reading in a textbook about them, his conception and proper understanding of bacteria can hardly be real and complete until some type of visual aid is used to give him a correct visual image. The correct visual image can be given to the student through such aids as drawings, illustrations, still pictures or motion pictures. However, perhaps the best and most logical approach in this case would be for the child to actually see living bacteria under a microscope.

In health education teachers should be fundamentally concerned with facts and concepts for it is upon facts and concepts that desirable health attitudes are built. Acceptable and effective teaching in health and safety requires that concepts be carefully defined and that sensory experiences be provided which will help to develop the most desirable outcomes. Experimentation and research in the field of audio-visual aids has shown beyond question of doubt that they greatly facilitate and enhance the development of desirable outcomes in health and healthful living.

It is now generally recognized that the interest of students is of primary importance in the learning process. Research in the field of psychology has shown that there is far greater efficiency in learning when children are interested in the knowledge they are expected to acquire. Although children may learn even though they have only a mild interest or practically no interest whatever in health and safety materials yet, it is a well-known fact that learning under such circumstances is too often incomplete and usually it is inefficient and highly wasteful of time. The opinions and beliefs held by early teachers and educators in this country, that subject matter should be pursued in a manner disregarding interest and that the children should do things which they do not like to do but which are supposed to be good for them, are no longer acceptable. The older methods of teaching which were more or less limited to oral and written presentations, drill and memorization, did not assure efficient and effective learning because they were not conducive to developing, gaining, and holding the interest of the pupils. The addition of audio-visual aids in the teaching of health and safety has done much to increase the effectiveness and efficiency of learning through the added interest of the pupil.

Motivation in education is closely related to interest. There are many ways of motivating, not all of which are fully acceptable in modern educational methods. Formerly, motivation was largely of the negative type. That is, the child was required and compelled to pursue specific subject matter and rigidly assigned tasks regardless of how uninteresting or unpleasant the task might be. The motivation in this case was frequently based on fear. The child pursued the task primarily to escape punishment of some type. In health and safety the fear factor was sometimes that of sickness, injury or death. Naturally, the child learned some things but the process was highly inefficient and ineffective in terms of final outcomes. The effects on the mental attitude and the emotional development of the child were often devastating. Children frequently rebelled in the process and many disciplinary problems were created.

Positive types of motivation which are frequently used are marks, awards, verbal recognition, prizes, privileges and various kinds of honors. Although these means are considered positive when compared to fear and compulsion they are not fully accepted as the best means of motivation in health education. The underlying theory is that the attention of the pupil is divided between the pursuit of knowledge for its own sake and the award or reward to be gained. It is postulated that the student fails to recognize that the pursuit of knowledge is the most important element in the situation. Experience in the field of health education shows that artificial stimulation of this type is not conducive to retention of things learned nor to the best application of knowledge. An example of this might be in the case where a classroom teacher offers awards and recognition of various types to children who brush their teeth regularly. When the awards and recognition are discontinued or withdrawn, the children may cease to be interested in brushing their teeth.

A main purpose of motivation in modern education is to develop the inherent interest of the student to the point where the pursuit and accomplishment of a worthy task provides sufficient personal satisfaction to justify the pursuit of knowledge, rather than to escape punishment or to gain extrinsic rewards. Through motivation, the interest of the child should be such that he is carried on by inner drive toward ultimate goals of achievement which are the most effective and lasting forms of education. When the inner drive of the child is such that he is spurred on to accomplishment for the sake of the personal satisfaction involved, not only is the learning process more efficient and lasting but the chances of establishing the proper health attitudes, practices, and appreciation are much greater.

How Audio-Visual Aids Contribute to Motivation and Interest in Health Education.—Experience in the use of audio-visual aids with students of all ages shows that they gain and hold their attention. In the first place they provide variety in the program which is highly essential to gaining and holding attention. Also, they help in breaking the monotony of the usual more or less formal schoolroom routine. Visual aids are usually easier to understand because they are concrete. A verbal description of an object, process, or thing may be highly uninteresting and difficult to understand especially if the child lacks related background with which to associate the description. An object or demonstration to accompany the verbal description provides first hand experience which promotes interest, understanding, and possible mastery. An example of this is that in which an instructor may be teaching the use of the reef or square knot in bandaging in first aid. The children would gain practically nothing from a mere verbal description a teacher might give of the way the knot is tied. Also, they would likely lose all interest immediately because of the intangible features of the description regardless of the skill of the teacher in presenting materials. If the teacher gives the verbal description step by step as she demonstrates the tying of the knot with a triangular bandage, the children are far more likely to be attentive and interested and certainly they will learn far more from the presentation. This example may be carried further to illustrate another factor involved. There is a natural tendency for children to manipulate. This tendency seems to be more or less a part of the original nature of the child. The opportunity to touch, manipulate, and handle gives an added interest and appeal. When the teacher announces in advance that following the description and demonstration sufficient triangular bandages will be provided for the children to actually practice and learn to tie the square knot, the interest and appeal of the lesson are much greater.

Basic Factors Involved in the Efficient and Effective Use of Audio-Visual Materials in Health Education.—The use of audio-visual materials in health education the same as other types of techniques, devices, and procedures, has been developed somewhat on a trial and error basis. Although some of the audio-visual aids such as the radio, motion pictures, and television are relatively new, the recent strong emphasis on them as aids in education has crystallized certain basic procedures which may be capitalized upon to help eliminate certain mistakes and errors in their use. Therefore, the teacher of health education should think through and have clearly in mind the best and most logical approach to such things as: 1. the selection of audio-visual aids; 2. adequate preparation in the use of audio-visual materials; 3. the program of audio-visual aids; and 4. evaluation of audio-visual aids in health and safety education.

The Selection of Audio-Visual Aids.—A consideration of the many kinds of sensory materials available in health education indicates at once that there must be careful selection of the types to be used in the varying situations and circumstances arising in the educational process. Also, it is clearly perceptible that each type of aid has a particular function. That is, each aid usually can be used to the best advantage with some particular type of presentation. An example of this is that of the teacher using the demonstration method in teaching the square or reef knot which was previously cited. It is readily evident that the actual demonstration of the tying of the knot along with the verbal description given by the teacher is a far more logical and effective means of presenting this than could be done through showing it in still pictures or even on television. One main advantage of the actual demonstration of the square knot is that the teacher can stop at any point to answer questions, retrace the steps or start over again. The selection and use of one type of audio-visual aid when some other would be more effective may be both inefficient and uneconomical.

Although it is highly important that the teacher of health education give ample time and thought to the selection of the aid best adapted in a particular situation, the proper selection of the type of aid best suited however, is only one phase of the process. The teacher must be able to use them intelligently, efficiently and profitably after the selections are made. There are certain acceptable techniques and approaches in using the different types of sensory aids the same as in other methods and procedures in teaching.

Another highly important point in the proper selection of any audio-visual aid is its suitability and appropriateness for the age, maturity, background, and experience of the children with whom it is to be used. A teaching aid is most valuable only when it provides the maximum aid. Consequently, if an aid is unsuited to the level of maturity, background, experience, interest, and needs of a particular group, it cannot provide the maximum aid. If an aid is too advanced and difficult for a group its use cannot be justified. If it is below the maturity level of a group, it may create adverse psychological reactions and unfavorable attitudes as well as stifle interest. An example of this would be in a case where an elementary school classroom teacher attempted to use a complicated graph to try to clarify a point in foods and nutrition. Because most graphs are not recommended for use with elementary school children the teacher's attempt to use the graph would likely result in a lack of attention and interest on the part of the group as well as a failure to clarify the points intended.

Adequate Preparation in the Use of Audio-Visual Materials.— In order for audio-visual materials to be used most efficiently and to render the most effective results, there must be adequate preparation on the part of both the teacher and the pupils. One undesirable tendency in the trial and error development of the use of some visual aids was that of merely showing them without attempting to devise ways and means of assuring that the students derive the greatest benefit from their use. As a matter of fact, some types of sensory aids such as motion pictures and television have often been used more for entertainment rather than for their contribution to the learning process. This does not mean to imply that aids should not be interesting and even entertaining. It does mean however, that usually visual aids cannot be justified in health education solely on the basis of entertainment. The tendency to use some sensory aids and particularly motion pictures largely as entertainment has perhaps been greater in the teaching in health education than in most other fields. This has been caused in part by the comparative irregularity of the time schedule for health teaching in the school program and because elementary school classroom teachers and health education teachers often lack sufficient training in proper health teaching methods.

It should be remembered that most teaching aids are more or less abstract. That is, they deal with representation of reality rather than with reality itself. Consequently, the teacher should have a very clear purpose in mind when aids are used and she should convey this purpose to the children. There is usually a need to clarify some visual aids through the use of other aids or through discussions and demonstrations. In the use of health education aids particularly, there is a greater tendency for children to be unduly attracted by the comical, unusual and morbid phases and thereby fail to gain the main points of the lesson or theme.

It should be clearly evident then, that preparation for the presentation of sensory aids on the part of the teacher is extremely important. Naturally, the kind and extent of preparation necessary will vary with the type of aid to be used. For example, the preparation for the use of a set of charts to show the relative nutritional value of different foods would be quite different from the preparation needed for the showing of a motion picture dealing with vitamins or the planning and conducting of a field trip to study foods. In the first case the charts present a limited and pointed lesson. In the case of the motion picture a much wider area would be covered with a good chance that the children might miss many of the main points in the lesson and even fail to understand the connection with past and future presentations. In the case of the field trip, it would likely turn out to be largely an excursion or vacation from school if the teacher and students failed to make careful plans to observe and study the important elements pertaining to the lesson. It is the responsibility of the teacher to be certain that the time given to visual aids is used most economically and advantageously.

With some types of visual aids such as motion pictures, slides, and film strips, lesson plans and teachers guides are often supplied. In most cases though it is necessary for the teacher to make adaptations for her own specific use even though teachers guides are provided. It is a good policy for teachers to gradually develop their own techniques and procedures in the use of all types of audio-visual aids. The main reason for this is that teachers vary greatly in their ways of teaching. Consequently, a teacher must fit the sensory aid to her particular style and way of presenting materials.

Pupils must be prepared for some types of sensory aids if they are to gain the most from them. In some cases there is no need for advance preparation on the part of the students. For example, a teacher may show still pictures or graphs for clarification purposes in the routine teaching of a lesson. In this case, advance preparation on the part of the pupils likely would be largely premature and unnecessary. This case is quite different though from one in which a motion picture is used. In this case the teacher might review the important points of the film to be used and she might even give the children a mimeographed set of questions to be answered or problems to be solved after viewing the film. In this way the teacher helps to direct the attention of the pupils to those points of the lesson which are most important and in harmony with past and future presentations. Also, preparation of this kind helps to develop and create the proper attitude and readiness to learn. Too, the pupils are more likely to recognize a need for the aid in learning the lesson.

The proper preparation on the part of both the teacher and the pupils helps to avoid passive receptivity on the part of the children. It has been mentioned previously that, in the past, many aids have been used more or less indiscriminately and as entertainment rather than primarily as an instrument of instruction. School children have, to some extent, come to accept this view especially in the case of motion pictures and television. They are in the habit of viewing commercial entertainment films at the theatre and seeing television at home. Consequently, the entertainment idea and attitude is likely to carry over into the school especially when motion pictures and television are involved. Discussions, questions, reports, and tests covering the aids used help to develop a spirit and attitude of active participation on the part of the children.

The Program of Sensory Aids in Health Education.—At the present state of development it is difficult to determine accurately just what might be considered a well-balanced program of audio-visual aids in health and safety education. In past years insufficient aids were used. It is quite likely that most teachers do not as yet make use of sufficient aids. One main reason for this is that there has been, and continues to be, a lack of *suitable* aids. With the present strong emphasis on their use in education it seems safe to predict that teaching aids will develop very rapidly in the next decade or two. With a more rapid development of health and safety audio-visual aids there is some danger that they will be used indiscriminately. It should be kept in mind that the haphazard, indiscriminate, and untimely use of sensory aids in health education cannot be justified. As a matter of fact they may do positive harm. The indiscriminate use of visual aids in the field of health and safety education particularly, may even detract from learning and have an adverse effect upon the development of habits, attitudes, practices and appreciations on the part of the children.

It is not known at the present time just how many aids can be used successfully in a health education course or even in a unit of a course. Questions of this kind can be answered only with further research, experience, and experimentation. At the present time the matter of the kinds and number of aids to use must be left largely to the individual teacher. A general rule for the teacher to follow, until such time as there is advanced development in the field, is that a variety of aids be used and that proper emphasis be placed upon them.

The emphasis on different types of aids is extremely important in order to recognize the individual differences of children. It is readily apparent that all children are not likely to react the same. For example, one child may react most favorably to a health radio program but gain little from a motion picture. On the other hand, another child may have practically no interest whatever in the radio program but gain much from the film. Then, too, a variety of aids is needed because of the different purposes for which each is intended. Some aids are used best for individual study while others serve best in group situations. For example, the microscope lends itself best to individual study and certain motion pictures to the summarizing of materials with all children participating.

Evaluation of Audio-Visual Aids in Health Education.—There are at least two main reasons for evaluation in the use of aids in health education. First, the aids should be evaluated in terms of their value and contribution to the educational process. Second, the teacher should continually evaluate techniques and procedures in the use of the various aids in attempting to make them contribute most to the education of the child. Reliable and objective means of evaluating the sensory aids program in health education do not exist at the present time. Therefore, it is necessary for teachers to evaluate largely on a subjective basis. Both teachers and pupils can participate in the evaluation on the basis of such things as interest, attitudes, general reactions and tests of various kinds.

Other important phases of evaluation include such items as the accuracy and authenticity of the material, suitability in terms of the lesson involved, gradation in terms of age, background, and experience of the particular group, and value in view of the effort, expense, and time involved.

Questions for Discussion

1. What are some factors which have influenced the recently increased use of audio-visual aids in education?
2. What are some major purposes for using audio-visual aids in health education?
3. What is the basis of the argument that audio-visual aids reduce the importance of the teacher in the learning process? How valid is this argument?
4. What are some implications of audio-visual aids for more efficient learning?
5. What are some factors which should influence choice of audio-visual aids?
6. What are some means whereby the maximum value may be gained from given audio-visual aids?
7. Why should the teacher assume the major responsibility for determining the kinds and number of audio-visual aids to be used?
8. What are some major considerations to be taken into account in evaluating audio-visual aids?

Suggested Class Activities

1. Prepare a list of major sources of audio-visual aids which are commonly available to schools.
2. Assemble a variety of audio-visual aids. Discuss each in relation to its most suitable uses in health education.
3. Prepare a list of criteria to be used in evaluating audio-visual aids.

4. Devise a check list which might be used as an objective means of evaluating audio-visual aids.
5. Describe the audio-visual aids program of a school with which you are familiar.

References

1. *Audio-visual Handbook for Teachers,* Trenton, N. J., State Department of Education, 1954.
2. Cross, E., et al, *Audio-visual Handbook,* Oklahoma City, Okla., State Department of Public Instruction, 1954.
3. Dale, E., *Audio-visual Methods in Teaching,* New York, 1946, The Dryden Press.
4. Hass, K. B., *Audio-visual Education,* New York, 1950, Prentice-Hall, Inc.
5. Huseby, H., "Mass Media in the Classroom," *Education,* October, 1953.
6. Kelley, G., "Results of a Nation-Wide Survey: Audio-visual Activities of State Education Departments," *Audio-visual Guide,* October, 1954.
7. Kinder, J. S., *Audio-visual Materials and Techniques,* Dallas, 1950, The American Book Company.

CHAPTER 12

MOTION PICTURES, RADIO, AND TELEVISION
IN HEALTH EDUCATION

It is difficult to comprehend the extent to which the living and thinking habits of the American people have been influenced by motion pictures, radio, and television in recent years. However, statistics give some idea of the role that they now play. There are approximately 36,000 radio broadcasting programs per day in the United States at the present time. There is evidence that some children spend more time in watching television each week than in attending school. Also, it has been found that there are more television sets in some heavily populated areas than there are bath tubs. Furthermore, it is estimated that motion pictures of various kinds reach over one hundred million people weekly.

In attempting to reckon with motion pictures, radio, and television, educators have been concerned with at least two basic problems: (1) how to gain access to and use these media of communication so that they might contribute most to the teaching-learning process? and (2) how to develop the discriminating abilities of young people so that they will select the superior programs? Both of these general problems are important in health education and each will be discussed in some detail in this chapter.

Without doubt motion pictures have a psychological advantage as teaching aids because most people have long been accustomed to regarding them as pleasurable and entertaining. Thus, when a film is begun, the audience is usually psychologically ready to receive it simply by virtue of earlier associations and unless it is very dull, the flow of pictures and sound tend to hold observers' attention. These circumstances, among others, undoubtedly underly the marked success of films used as instructional devices during World War II and the Korean War. Other factors which contributed greatly to the success of military films but which are ordinarily lacking in the educational situation are: (1) virtually limitless resources in the way of money and equipment in producing films to meet specific needs, and (2) access to the necessary technical assistance in film production as well as in educational methodology.

Developments in education during the last few years have made it clear that our problem is not *whether* mass media such as radio, motion pictures and television should be used in the classroom, but *how* and under what circumstances they should be used. For as we adjust ourselves to the time in which we live we must grow in ability to handle our problems, and to do this, we must learn more effective and efficient means of bringing information and ideas to pupils in vivid, realistic and meaningful ways. Therefore, it is highly important that teachers make use of the many modern devices and media of communication at their command.[12]

The results of surveys indicate that more than one-half of the state departments of education in this country are engaged in concerted audio-visual activities. Motion picture films ordinarily constitute one of the largest single audio-visual budget items in most state departments of education. An example of the extent of this is one particular state which provides more than 8,000 films for distribution. Furthermore, at least eleven state departments of education are involved, to some degree, in educational radio and television broadcasting. Partly in anticipation of a need and partly in recognition of an existing need, numerous teacher education institutions now require, or at least highly recommend, that teachers take college courses in audio-visual education in which the mass media play a prominent part.

Although state department of education leadership in audio-visual activities indicates a modern trend in this area, it cannot be taken as an entirely accurate reflection of total state interest in audio-visual education. In some states the plan of decentralization relegates the state department itself to a relatively minor role. For example, in some states, the state department of education provides guidance and certain films to various distribution centers in the state. This plan guarantees a certain equalization of audio-visual offerings throughout the state; but at the same time localities are encouraged to go beyond this basic offering and as they become more aware of the advantages of these teaching aids, to add to the resources of their audio-visual center. A number of state departments of education provide free and inexpensive audio-visual handbooks which are intended to serve as guides to the uses and sources of audio-visual aids.

Silent and Sound Motion Pictures.—Although some teachers feel that silent films are now obsolete, others argue that under certain circumstances they are actually superior to sound films. The two major advantages of silent films are: (1) they cost less, and (2) they involve no spoken words which might be unsuitable for the vocabulary level of a particular group. Although silent films may include a written vocabulary that is not properly graded for a particular group, the teacher may compensate for this by verbalizing and simplifying the reading material when necessary.

Although silent films remain highly useful and effective in education, sound films have certain advantages in some cases:

    1. Sound may be used to enhance the effectiveness of the presentation in ways other than verbalization. For example, a film on the heart may include amplified heart sounds, thus adding an auditory experience to the visual.
    2. Sound films do not require a reading proficiency and thus are more suitable for groups which may be retarded in reading.
    3. Teachers inexperienced in using films, lectures and oral explanations are probably helped more by sound films.
    4. Continuity of the film need not be broken by interruptions of the teacher in explaining titles and elaborate descriptions.
    5. Sound films are of special value for inferior students who usually have difficulty handling the more abstract symbols of other forms of communication.

Motion Pictures in Health Education.—Some authorities consider motion picture films one of the best mediums for presenting health problems in easily recognizable terms. For example, the results of studies show that health films have increased the health knowledge and interest of large numbers of people.[16] Health films have been found effective in influencing thought and behavior from the primary grades through college and into adult life, because they tie words and thought to the emotions and to action, and tend to encourage participation in the action of the film. By way of illustration, a film in which a physician teaches women self-examination for breast cancer seems to be talking directly to the individuals in the audience. Also, people viewing the film, "Human Reproduction," are very likely to identify themselves with one or another of the actors. Obviously, this kind of approach makes for personalized and emotional as well as logical appeal.

In the field of health education a large number of films are available and their subjects are sufficiently diversified that virtually any unit of instruction may be supplemented by at least one film. Very generally speaking, when making a decision as to whether or not to employ a film, questions such as the following should be considered:

1. Does the film make a contribution to learning that other, less expensive or more easily accessible aids such as film strips, field trips, or visiting speakers cannot make?
2. Is there a need to show a process in which motion is an important feature?
3. Would a slow motion presentation of a process facilitate comprehension?
4. Are microscopic details or animations desirable for understanding?
5. Would eye witness observation of some public or other health problem situation, or some corrective action, make the health problems under consideration more real?
6. Would a dramatic presentation help to establish desirable concepts upon which good attitudes are built, regarding such subjects as health fads and superstitions, venereal disease, mental health and illness, wise food selection and cancer?

In recognition of the fact that numerous health units benefit greatly by carefully selected films, the discussion which follows will be concerned with: (1) film sources, (2) standards for selecting health education films, and (3) using films as teaching aids.

STATE DEPARTMENTS OF EDUCATION AS FILM SOURCES.—As was pointed out earlier, most state education departments have some form of audio-visual aids program of which motion pictures usually constitute a major aspect.

An audio-visual aids director or a health education supervisor should be able to inform teachers as to readily available health films that are provided by the state, city or county education department. One person, frequently the school librarian, is in charge of all of the school's audio-visual information material. This individual should be useful in helping to locate desired health films, and in providing extensive listings of films available from education and health departments, professional groups, and industrial and commercial organizations. In some states, audio-visual materials including films, are concentrated in a special department or bureau of the department of education headquarters. In others, a policy of decentralization has been adopted such that audio-visual materials are concentrated at the county department of education level or are available through branch libraries in the state. Some large city school systems maintain extensive film libraries for the use of their teachers and oftentimes films need to be scheduled only a few days in advance.

In some states, the state university has assumed responsibility for acquiring and distributing films and other audio-visual materials; also in some states, private colleges and universities furnish many visual aids to schools. In any event, principals, librarians, or health or general supervisors can usually provide information for teachers concerning the most readily accessible health film sources in the particular educational system.

Most established audio-visual organizations prepare listings of their films by subject matter areas. If health supervisors are available they should make every effort to inform teachers as to suitable films which they may use. In the absence of such assistance, teachers can request the health listings from those responsible for audio-visual aids in their schools.

In addition to listings of film titles, some established audio-visual departments also provide descriptive material on each title. Thus, it is possible to learn the grade level or type of group for whom the film is intended, some details as to subject matter coverage, the approach taken, and something about the quality of each film. Service of this kind simplifies the problem of film selection for the teachers. Many health departments and commercial organizations also provide descriptive literature with their film listings.

Many films provided by education and health departments are designed especially to be shown to adults for purposes of improving school health programs. "School Health in Action," and "The School that Learned to Eat," are illustrations of this kind of film.

DEPARTMENTS OF HEALTH AS FILM SOURCES.—Local, county, and state health departments are frequently good sources of health films. However, care should be taken in evaluating health department films because many of them are selected for adult and professional groups, and may not be well suited for classroom use, especially in the lower grades. On the other hand, some health departments provide films which are quite appropriate even at the elementary school level.

Descriptive information on each film title offered does much to guide the teachers' choices. Another source of guidance is the school nurse. Nurses are advised of audio-visual materials available through their health departments and usually they are eager to make suggestions to teachers and even to make the necessary arrangements for obtaining suitable films.

The health department may prove to be an excellent source for films on such subjects as: wise food selection, principles of weight control, the digestion of foods, dental health, first aid, the effects of alcohol and narcotics upon human beings, cancer, tuberculosis, heart disease, human reproduction, menstruation, mental and emotional health, and principles of sanitation.

After exploring the possibilities of the departments of education and health, teachers may find that virtually all of their film needs can be met from these sources. It is only necessary to schedule sufficiently in advance so that films and other audio-visual materials may be available when desired. As has previously been stated, the school nurse is frequently of invaluable assistance in scheduling and sometimes in presenting films.

VOLUNTARY AGENCIES, INDUSTRIAL AND COMMERCIAL ORGANIZATIONS AS SOURCES OF FILMS.—A great many voluntary, industrial and commercial organizations and groups prepare and distribute audio-visual aids of various kinds, including motion picture films on health subjects. In the past, many films prepared by industrial and commercial organizations have been advertising media, with health instruction largely if not entirely incidental. Consequently, most of these films did not qualify as teaching aids. However, at the present time many films from industrial and commercial sources are unquestionably of high quality because ranking authorities in various health education areas frequently have been utilized in research and film production. They frequently emphasize desirable health instruction, and they do not intrude advertising into the subject matter. In fact, many of the films listed in education and health department offerings have been prepared by industrial and commercial groups.

Another reason for calling attention to industrial and commercial films is because they frequently are available to teachers by way of local non-school channels. In some cases, these films may be obtained quickly with little or no advance scheduling, whereas the major school sources available to the teacher sometimes require scheduling months in advance, and may not arrive as planned. However, when these outside sources are utilized, the teacher should be careful to clear them with the constituted education department authority, perhaps the audio-visual department, and to preview them so as to be confident of the suitability.

STANDARDS FOR SELECTING HEALTH EDUCATION FILMS.—It seems desirable to evaluate films in terms of their contribution to a specific learning situation. Like any other instructional technique, film values depend upon whether or not they increase the individual's knowledge of a particular subject and his awareness of the uses and significance of that knowledge.

A basic consideration in the evaluation of a film is whether it materially assists the pupils in progressing toward the desired learning goals. Of course, technical matters of film making and mechanical matters of visibility, sound, and the condition of the film should be taken into account in determining the value of a motion picture.

Following are some questions which should be considered when selecting a health educational film.

1. Is it interesting and appropriate to the age and grade level?
2. Does it convey the desired facts and concepts, and is it likely to contribute to the formation of desirable attitudes?
3. Is it accurate and up to date?
4. Can it be correlated with and integrated into the course of study at the particular grade level?
5. Is the language well-suited to the intended audience?
6. Is it likely to be understood by pupils?
7. Does it meet reasonable standards of technical excellence in terms of good quality pictures, satisfactory sound, and natural acting?
8. Is the film of suitable length?

Many teachers find it desirable to keep card files or folders of evaluation of the individual films that they have used. For evaluation purposes, cards or sheets of paper may be mimeographed to include standard information on each film such as the following:

Film title: .... Source: ....
In color? .... Showing time ....
Condition of film: .... satisfactory: .... unsatisfactory.....
Photography: ..... satisfactory: ..... unsatisfactory.......
Sound: .... satisfactory: ....unsatisfactory: ....

Useful in what unit(s) of instruction? ....
Best used to: ...... introduce unit; ...... put across facts;
put across concepts: ...... evaluate or follow-up. Other ......
      New vocabulary (specify). ....
Did the pupils like it? .... yes; .... no; .... so-so.
Effectiveness as teaching aid (as evaluated by testing, etc.):
..... very effective; ..... fairly effective; ..... not effective.

Comments :

One group of teachers developed the following film evaluation report for use in their classes. It is shown here to illustrate how the basic information may be modified to meet the needs of particular individuals:

FILM EVALUATION REPORT
NAME OF SCHOOL ....
Film Title ....
                                Year
..... Sound Length: ..... min. Produced ..... B&W .....
..... Silent   ..... fast Color ....

Description of Content:

Intended teaching purpose (s):

Main ideas and/or skills presented:

Production rating:
                (encircle)   Contents rating: (encircle)
Photography Good   Bad   Accurate and authentic Yes No
Sound   Good   Bad   Correlated with the cur-
Vocabulary   Good   Bad   riculum   Yes No
Acting   Good   Bad   Presents needed facts   Yes No
                           Stimulates pupil activity Yes No
Types of Learning: (check)
Developing   Forming   Molding   Critical
Skills .... Concepts ..... Attitudes ..... Thinking .....
List particular strengths or weaknesses:

Of course, much more extensive and detailed evaluation devices may be employed than the above, but to most teachers brevity is important. A short evaluation card is usually ample to recall the film to mind and to refresh the memory as to the essential factors.

USING FILMS.—Each subject matter unit in health instruction may be visualized as being composed of three aspects as follows: (1) the introductory or orientation aspect; (2) the learning activities aspect which is sometimes termed the "unit assignment" and (3) the evaluation aspect.

As in the case when using all audio-visual aids, it is necessary to make a decision as to when in this sequence the motion picture might most profitably be used. Sometimes, the nature of the film makes it especially valuable as an introductory aid because it arouses interest in and provides an overview of the subject under consideration. In other instances, the film is more intensive or specialized and may be deemed more suitable in the second aspect of the sequence. Films that are good for introducing a subject are also frequently good in evaluation, because they may help to retrace the ground covered. Indeed, one film is sometimes shown at the beginning and at the end of an entire unit or a particular portion of it, with the result that much fuller meaning is derived in the second showing because of intervening study.

PREVIEWING AND SCHEDULING THE FILM.—Teachers should have an opportunity to preview even superior films if they are to make best use of them. It is also essential that teachers know just when a given film will be available for use. Both of these things are essential for getting proper use from films as teaching aids. However, in the practical situation it is frequently impossible to preview and schedule properly. Administrators and audio-visual aids department personnel should give this problem very careful consideration because the value of films and other audio-visual aids is known to depend to a considerable degree upon whether they are used at the proper time in teaching.

If there is no opportunity to preview films prior to the first time that they are used, the teacher must be guided by descriptive information about them, and by information from other teachers. Once having seen a film, the teacher can henceforth be guided by her own evaluation card or sheet.

If there is doubt as to whether a film will arrive as scheduled, or if it is not possible to adjust the teaching of given material to the date of the film's arrival, it is usually wise to plan the entire unit without depending upon the film. It is better to have the film added to the unit preparation than to have the unit incomplete or poorly integrated because of its absence.

It has been mentioned previously that the person designated as coordinator of audio-visual aids, the librarian or a teacher, takes care to post the dates when films are scheduled to arrive at the school. Guided by this information all of the teachers who wish to use them can frequently adjust their teaching in such a way that films will fit reasonably well into the unit or lesson. Of course, if the schedules are not reliable, such planning is useless, and administrative action is necessary if audio-visual aids are not to lose a great part of their value.

SHOWING THE FILM.—As is the case with entire health teaching units, the showing of a film may be regarded as a three-phase sequence, consisting of: (1) an introductory or orientation phase; (2) the showing of the film; and (3) a review and evaluation phase. These phases are discussed in other parts of this volume, but they should be restated here in relation to motion pictures because of the rather universal tendency to regard films as "things in themselves," capable of standing alone without aid from the teacher. It must be emphasized that even the best of films need proper usage.

Before the film is shown, the class should be prepared for the subject under consideration. For example, let us suppose that a film on dental health is to be shown. The introductory phase may be devoted to a brief discussion period in which various factors related to dental health are reviewed with the class. It is possible that teaching has not yet taken into account the role of proper diet in dental health and the film is intended to introduce and outline the principles involved. In this event, the teacher may point out that a very important new factor is to be introduced, namely, diet. The teacher may also introduce or review vocabulary that is used in the film, possibly such words as enamel, dentine, calcium, prophylaxis, and the like. The teacher may ask the class to make a special note of types of foods and specific foods which are important to dental health. In brief, the teacher tries to make certain that the class approaches the film psychologically ready to profit from it.

In showing a film, consideration should be given to the physical conditions of the room. It should be a properly darkened and ventilated room, the screen visible to all, the projector properly situated and the sound correctly adjusted. It is usually unwise to require pupils to take notes during film showings because of the darkened condition of the room and because their concentration may be diverted from the film to the notes. Sometimes, however, it is useful for pupils to record individual words or phrases for reference in later discussions.

The final phase is to review and evaluate the content of the film, primarily for the purpose of integrating it into the learning activities under consideration. In some cases, this may take the form of a brief written "quiz" in order to determine the effectivness of the film in teaching and establishing facts and concepts to the particular group. Brief oral review by pupils is important and is more frequently used than written evaluation. Continuing with the example of the dental health film, a pupil may be asked to go to the blackboard and with the aid of the class, list the recommended types and specific examples of foods stressed by the film as essential to dental health.

If the film is produced by a company with a commercial or other bias, the teacher may forewarn the class to be on the alert for indications of a slanted approach, perhaps unjustifiably favorable to a product. During the evaluation period, this possibility may be reckoned with, and it may be used as an incentive to further study in order to discover whether certain of the film's contentions are valid.

It seems apparent that the review and evaluation aspect of film-showing has a three-fold value as follows: (1) to recapitulate the contents of the film; (2) to weigh the value of the contents of the film by testing it against other evidence; and (3) cultivating the discriminative powers of the pupils to the end that they may be cautious in accepting information presented to them, particularly when it is presented by what may be a prejudiced source.

The literature dealing with motion picture films in education is replete with a central idea which also deserves emphasis here. That is, films in no way reduce the importance of the teacher. In fact, using films, like using books and other educational tools, adds to the complexity and responsibility of teaching. Films are a teaching aid. It is possible to judge their value only on the basis of the use to which they are put and the way in which they are used. Moreover, they should be used only when they can contribute more to learning than other readily available and less expensive and time-consuming means.

RADIO AS A TEACHING AID IN HEALTH EDUCATION.
—A number of cities have made extensive use of radio as an educational tool. A few schools saw the possibilities and initiated pioneering programs as long as thirty years ago. Typically, commercial stations have sometimes made time available to schools and have assisted in the technical aspects of program production. However, in some instances school systems have developed such high regard for the educational possibilities of radio that they have purchased their own stations and, as in the case of the Cleveland Public Schools, they broadcast programs for several

hours every school day. In these situations, schedules of programs are distributed to all teachers so that they may incorporate suitable broadcasts into their teaching plans. Teachers and pupils, as well as outside specialists and the various necessary radio technicians, participate in the planning, preparing, and presenting of these programs.

Most communities which have made use of radio as a teaching aid have not gone beyond using the facilities of commercial stations. In some cities, regularly scheduled educational programs are beamed into classrooms and auditoriums, and on the week-ends, into the homes. Thus, radio has helped to bring the world into the classroom and to teach the community what is going on in the classroom. Obviously, there are grave difficulties in attempting to meet the unique program needs of many different teachers at any particular time, even in one school system. Difficulties of this kind have been solved in some cases by recording superior local or even national broadcasts and then making them available as needed by individual teachers.

Radio has been used extensively as a means of educating the general public on health and safety topics and as a means of familiarizing the public with the history and drama of the medical profession. The American Medical Association has been broadcasting programs for many years. Educational, medical, and commercial groups have presented innumerable programs dealing with the general fields of health and safety including some highly informative interviews with health and safety authorities, and round table discussions by specialists on various health topics. Major diseases, public health problems, and personal health subjects have been prominent in these presentations. In recent years, radio has been used increasingly to clarify and point up the problem of mental health.

In those cities where radio is used extensively as a teaching aid, health and safety programs have commonly been included in the general offering. Usually, planning is in cooperation with commercial radio, programs being utilized at the time of broadcast when possible, but recordings of outstanding programs being made available for later use when necessary. Regular programs are prepared with the cooperation of individual teachers and their students.

As in the case of other mass media, emphasis should be placed upon: (1) making radio a teaching aid rather than an end in itself; (2) integrating information of the broadcast into the instructional material under consideration; (3) employing suitable build-up and follow-up activities in order that fullest value may be derived from the experience; and (4) developing the critical listening ability of the pupils to the end that they may exercise judgment and caution when listening to claims and possibly biased reports.

The possibilities of television as an audio-visual aid in health education should not blind us to the fact that radio has not been as fully utilized as its value and availability would indicate that it should be. Advocates of educational radio point out its value as a means of stimulating the imagination of children. Opportunities for bringing significant and dramatic health events into the classroom, such as activities of the World Health Organization, medical research, events in the history of world and national health and stories about healthful living for children, can do much to vitalize the teaching of health. Moreover, numerous schools are equipped already to use radio as a teaching aid and need only leadership to develop this possibility more fully.

THE USE OF TELEVISION IN HEALTH AND SAFETY EDUCATION.—Although television is relatively new, it is already of major concern to education and gives promise of becoming a teaching aid of major importance. Like motion pictures, television appeals to two senses and tends to capture an undivided kind of attention that is not so evident in radio. It can take its audience as eye witness anywhere that a television camera can be taken and it can utilize virtually every other type of audio-visual aid, from demonstration to chart, and from diagram to model, and it can simulate the best of field trips and interviews. Still, major difficulties confront television as an audio-visual aid in schools. Such matters as high costs of stations, program production, and of receiving sets, difficulties in previewing programs, adjusting schedules to meet the needs of teachers, and other matters, constitute a formidable series of problems. In spite of these difficulties, progress to date has been such that it seems safe to predict continued rapid growth in educational television.

Certain basic factors, in addition to its obvious advantages as a medium of communication, account for the rapid and accelerating growth of educational television. For example, the Federal Communications Commission requires that a certain amount of broadcasting time be devoted to educational and other public service programs and has set aside over 200 channels for non-commercial and educational use. Still another basic consideration is unquestionably the fact that a large segment of the American public finds many educational subjects intrinsically interesting when they are skillfully presented. It is noteworthy that the most successful of educational telecast producers are meticulous in their planning for popular appeal. For example, one large university's science review is carefully planned in terms of what its producers describe as, "time, thought, tempo, theater, title, and talent."[84] This indicates that merely an interesting subject alone is not enough.

The interest of the public in educational television is indicated by the fact that, as the Joint Committee on Educational Television reported recently to the Federal Communications Commission, in this country ten educational television stations were in operation and nearly as many again were under construction. More than twelve million people are now within range of educational television stations and this number is expected to increase to forty million within a very few years. Money for financing educational television has come from several sources, including some state legislation appropriations, school budgets, foundations, and private business.

A recent study of United States Army trainees gives some indication of the values of educational television. For example, it was discovered that normal instruction time in an electronics course was cut in half when the course was presented on television and included visual aids such as cutaway models. Students who received instruction by television remembered what they had learned as well as and sometimes better than students taught by the traditional method. Men with low intelligence benefited most; they made much better grades on examinations than groups of equally low intelligence who were taught in regular classes.

TELEVISION IN HEALTH EDUCATION.—Apart from considerations of costs and technical matters, health educators have been profoundly concerned as to how best to utilize television as a teaching aid. Following are some suggested objectives of television in health education:

1. To provide an aid to teaching.
2. To supplement and broaden the health education program.
3. To motivate learning and stimulate interest.
4. To inspire teachers to better planning and teaching.
5. To enable parents and others to better understand the school health program.
6. To stimulate changes in pupil behavior in terms of basic concepts of healthful living.
7. To present important aspects of school health in a more effective way.

With these objectives in mind it would seem that for health education by television in the school to be effective the televised programs should:
1. Have an educational purpose and be educationally sound.
2. Provide continuity, be pertinent, and be a part of units of instruction.
3. Be built upon the health needs and problems of a potential audience.
4. Be a means of growth and development for the individual.
5. Allow the viewer to identify himself with the participants.
6. Extend the health experience of the viewer by stimulating him to think, to act and to make his own decisions.
7. Present material that is authentic and unbiased and that neither arouses fear nor leads to complacency.
8. Communicate clearly and effectively.
9. Be conducive to the best visual health of the pupils.
10. Reach reasonable standards of technical excellence in production and photography.
11. Be a good educational investment in terms of time and money.

In addition to the criteria of the program offered, it is well to determine whether television is the best medium for presenting the subject under consideration.

The above criteria should not only provide a guide for the organization of educationally sound television programs but should also serve as a measure used for health education in the school.

The Philadelphia Public School System has been among the most active in bringing health and other educational television into the classrooms and homes of its pupils. Working closely with commercial television stations, which provide regular telecasting hours and technical assistance and with citizens groups, which, for example, have provided many schools with television sets, this school system has demonstrated a realistic way of utilizing television at this particular point in its development. Each month schedules are published of programs which are: (1) prepared by the schools' television staff, with the cooperation of many teachers and pupils, and (2) part of the stations' non-school offering which is judged to qualify as educational. Typical health program titles which have appeared in the past include, "Your Carriage, Madame!" "Fit as a Fiddle," "Happy Play," "Community Health," "Water and Sewage," and "Food Control." The schedule describes the content and purpose of the various programs, indicates the grade levels for which they are intended, and makes suggestions as to how they might be utilized by the teacher. Equipped with this information, individual teachers are able to make their plans well in advance so that television programs may be fitted most advantageously into teaching plans.

Although the development and use of television in the schools is in its infancy, the following things should be kept in mind: (1) television provides a most promising opportunity to vitalize the teaching of health in both the school and in the community; (2) it should be used according to the criteria of other teaching aids which, if wisely used, contribute to but cannot replace or reduce the importance of good teaching at all grade levels; (3) as it grows, it will need continuous and deliberate evaluation on the part of individual teachers and professional groups in order to keep its great potential power harnessed to the aims of education, and (4) television will remain one of numerous audio-visual aids and it should be used only when it meets educational needs better than other available media.

Questions for Discussion

1. What are some of the arguments presented in favor of extensive use of films in health education?
2. What are some hazards to be reckoned with in relation to using films in health education?
3. What considerations should guide the teacher when she is deciding whether or not to use a particular film or other audio-visual aid?
4. What are the most commonly available film sources in your locality?
5. Under what conditions can teachers best utilize films provided by commercial and industrial groups?
6. What are some criteria of good health teaching films?
7. To what uses might films evaluation sheets or cards be put?
8. To what extent is radio used as an educational aid in the communities represented by this particular class?
9. In what ways can radio be used as a means of teaching health?
10. What provisions are made by the Federal Government to encourage educational television?
11. How is television being used as an educational aid at the present time? As an aid in health education?
12. What are some criteria for television programs for health education in schools?

Suggested Class Activities

1. Make an analysis and evaluation of all film sources available to the schools. What major sources are not being utilized, if any? Explore additional sources suggested in this chapter and elsewhere.

Motion Pictures, Radio, and Television

2. Show a film on health. Evaluate it in terms of its suitability for classroom use.
3. Using the evaluation card suggested in the text as a starting point, construct an evaluation card or sheet for actual use in teaching.
4. Study and discuss ways in which fuller use might be made of radio and television in health education in your community. Explore the possibilities with commercial radio and television authorities and school administrators.
5. Work up specific plans for improving the discrimination of pupils in their choice of radio and television programs. Discuss the problem: how can you teach pupils to look and listen more critically?

References

General

1. *Audio-visual Handbook for Teachers.* Trenton, New Jersey: State Department of Education, 48pp., 1954, 50c.
2. Cross, E. et al, *Audio-visual Handbook,* Oklahoma City, Oklahoma: State Department of Public Instruction., 1954, free.
3. Dale, E., Audio-visual Methods in Teaching. New York: The Dryden Press, 1946.
4. Duker, S., "In an Age of Communication, Are We Listening?" The Educational Forum, May, 1954.
5. Haas, K. B., Audio-visual Education, New York: 1950. Prentice-Hall.
6. Hazard, P. P., "The Humanities, The Mass Media and The High School," *Education,* October, 1953.
7. Huseby, H., "Mass Media in the Classroom," *Education,* October, 1953.
8. Kelly, G., "Results of a Nation-Wide Survey: Audio-visual Activities of State Education Departments," *Audio-visual Guide,* October, 1954.
9. Kinder, J. S., *Audio-visual Materials and Techniques.* Dallas, 1950, The American Book Co.
10. Lottick, K. V., "How Schools Can Teach Discrimination Through audio-visual Analysis," *Education,* October, 1953.
11. "New Tools for Learning" (motion picture), 19 min., sd., b&w, Chicago: Encyclopaedia Britannica.
12. Schuller, C. F., "...so that the scarecrows can be taken out of Wisdom's Gardens," *Education,* October, 1953.
13. U. S. Dept. of Agriculture, "What Research Shows About Audio-visual Aids". Washington, D. C.: U. S. Government Printing Office, 1949.
14. Wittich, W. A. and C. F. Schuller, Audio-visual Materials, *Their Nature and Use.* New York, 1953, Harpers & Brothers.

Films

15. Bell, R. et al, *Motion Pictures in a Modern Curriculum.* Washington, D. C.: American Council on Education, 1941.
16. Creer, R. P., "Movies that Teach Health," *Today's Health,* October, 1954.
17. Dale, E. and J. Morrison, *Motion Picture Discrimination.* Columbus, Ohio: Ohio State University, Bureau of Educational Research, 1951, 41 pp. 50c.

18. Nichtenhauser, A., et al, *Films in Psychiatry, Psychology, and Mental Hygiene,* New York: Health Education Council, 1954.
19. "The Teacher Utilizes a Motion Picture Film," filmstrip, 30 frames. Norman: University of Oklahoma.
20. "Using the Classroom Film," 21 minutes, sd., b&w, Chicago: Encyclopaedia Britannica Films.

Radio

21. Bauer, W. W., "Radio Health Broadcasts," *Hygeia, The Health Magazine,* October 1944.
22. Braun, E. C. and F. J. Stanley, *Let's Broadcast* (A Textbook on the Use of Radio Broadcasting as an Educational Tool.) Minneapolis, Minn., Northwestern Press, 1948.
23. Bureau of Health Education, *Radio Handbook.* Chicago 1946, The American Medical Association.
24. *Journal of the Association for Education by Radio.* 228 N. La Salle, Chicago 1, Illinois.
25. Levenson, W. and E. Stasheff, *Teaching Through Radio and Television.* New York, 1952, Rinehart.
26. Philadelphia Public Schools, "Radio-TV News," 1954-55.
27. *Teaching With Radio.* Washington D. C.: U. S. Office of Education and the Radio Television Manufacturer's Association, 1953.

Television

28. Barg, B. "The Science Telecast in the Classroom," *Education,* October, 1953.
29. Bureau of Health Education, *TV Handbook,* Chicago: The American Medical Association, 1951.
30. Dunham, F. and Lowdermilk, "Television in Our Schools," Bulletin No. 16, Washington D. C.: U. S. Government Printing Office, 1952.
31. Ingalls, L. (ed.) *The Use of Television in Education.* Albany, N. Y., 1953, Argus Co.
32. Laurent, L., "Educational TV's Progress Baffles Prophets of Doom," Wash. Post and Times Herald, Sunday, October 24, 1954.
33. Philadelphia Public Schools, "Radio-TV News," 1953-54.
34. Poole, L., *Science via Television.* Baltimore: Johns Hopkins University, 1950.
35. Rones, B., "Does Television Damage the Eyes?" N. Y. 1953: National Society for the Prevention of Blindness, Inc.
36. Schreiber, R. E., "Let's Look at Television," *Phi Delta Kappan.* April, 1953.
37. Teicher, J. D., "Teachers and Television," *Health Education Journal,* April, 1953.
38. *Television in Education,* Washington D. C.: American Council on Education, 1952.
39. *The Modern School Looks at Television.* Camden, New Jersey, 1953, Radio Corporation of America.
40. Zankan, L. "The Eye Doctor Looks at Television," *Health Education Journal,* December 1952.

CHAPTER 13

DEMONSTRATIONS IN HEALTH EDUCATION

An old Chinese proverb points out that one picture is worth a thousand words. A picture constitutes a visual experience which may convey a meaning as directly as the reality that it represents. On the other hand, spoken or written words are abstractions which often require complex interpretations if their meaning is to be correctly conveyed. From birth to maturity and beyond there is a more or less gradual growth in the ability of the individual to correctly interpret verbal symbols. Experience in teaching shows that sensory aids of various kinds are helpful to students of all ages and grade levels in interpreting and understanding verbal descriptions and symbols.

Although demonstrations are among the most useful of sensory experiences which may be employed in health education, they have not been developed and used to any great extent by a majority of the teachers in the United States who are responsible for health teaching. In recent years however, both health educators and elementary school classroom teachers are slowly but gradually developing and using demonstrations in teaching health and safety.

Demonstrations of a wide variety may be prepared as a means of showing how things are done or how they work in the various units of health instruction. The discussion which follows is concerned with describing how demonstrations may be used as valuable teaching devices in health. It will be noted that although a number of the demonstrations used as illustrative examples involve some technical knowledge and skill, such as in the case of preparing bacteriological cultures or going through a physical examination, the greatest emphasis is upon demonstrations which involve inexpensive and more or less commonplace materials.

Comparison of Individual Laboratory Work and Demonstrations.—Individual laboratory work has not been developed in the field of health education on a basis comparable to the field of science. In the future, individual laboratory work in health education may be developed to some extent at the junior and senior high school levels, but a general trend in this direction seems quite unlikely at this time. There is some controversy even in the field of science concerning the value of individual laboratory work in comparison with demonstrations. Some of the arguments in favor of the individual laboratory method are that it encourages learning by actually doing, that there are some indications that the material is better retained, and that pupils benefit by learning how to handle equipment properly. On the other hand, some of the arguments in favor of the demonstration are that both superior and retarded students are likely to learn more from demonstrations; demonstrations take less time and cost less; there is better control over each student during the demonstration and retention of knowledge is greater following demonstrations. Generally speaking, whatever benefits the laboratory technique in the elementary and secondary schools may have, it is not clearly justifiable in the minds of some educators in terms of the effort and expense involved.

Regardless of whether individual laboratory work or demonstration or both are used, there should be a properly located and equipped special room for health teaching which includes laboratory-like arrangements as well as facilities and arrangements for both temporary and permanent exhibits. Such a health laboratory should be equipped with running water, Bunsen burners, test tubes, pipettes, beakers, funnels, forceps, asbestos sheeting, tripods and other standard laboratory equipment. At the present time most schools throughout the country do not have the special health laboratory-exhibit type of classroom. In such cases it is recommended that a properly located classroom in the school be selected and remodeled as a special health classroom. In the construction of new school buildings the newer type of special health room should be included. Any new school building being constructed in the present day and age that does not include a special health classroom is outmoded before it is completed.

In some high schools it may be possible to use the science laboratories for demonstrations and recitations. However, experience has shown that most school science laboratories are in use the greater part of the day with the various science classes, which leaves little or no time for health classes. Furthermore, science laboratories ordinarily do not have sufficient space nor are they properly arranged for both temporary and permanent health exhibits.

The Role of the Demonstration.—Although demonstrations in health education can be used to advantage in practically all stages of a lesson and with most methods of teaching, they are particularly effective as a means of introducing new units.[4] The use of demonstrations in introducing new units of instruction are somewhat in contrast to the way they are usually employed. That is, demonstrations are perhaps most frequently used to illustrate something already learned rather than as a means to challenge the pupil's skill in putting his learning to use and as a stimulus to his quest for knowledge. In the latter case, demonstrations should be of such nature that they raise problems in the minds of the pupils and at the same time they should be closely related to the core activities of the unit being studied.

Regardless of how demonstrations are used in an orderly plan of teaching in health education it has been learned through experience that they are one of the best means of vitalizing, clarifying and bringing to life the subject matter of health which otherwise often becomes tiresome, boresome and frequently highly uninteresting to the pupil.

Teacher Demonstrations.—The teacher should keep in mind certain principles of demonstrating which apply regardless of where or how the demonstration is used in the learning experience. Major considerations are outlined as follows:

1. The demonstration should work; obviously, if it does not, children tend to lose confidence as well as interest.

2. Adequate preparation should be made. The demonstration should be rehearsed before the class arrives.

3. If possible, all equipment should be arranged on the demonstration table before rather than after the class arrives.

4. Equipment should be large enough and the demonstration on a large enough scale to be easily seen by all pupils.

5. Demonstrations should be as simple and speedy as possible.

6. Equipment should be stored away intact until it is to be used again.

7. Pupils should be prepared ahead of time for the demonstration. Perhaps problems and other materials may be mimeographed and distributed for use following the demonstration.

The following are some common errors frequently made by teachers in utilizing demonstrations:
1. Failure to show how the demonstration fits into the health unit being studied.
2. Failure to direct the student's attention to the important health facts of the demonstration.
3. Failure to adjust the health vocabulary to the particular grade level.
4. Failure to allow pupils time to record data.
5. Failure to stimulate pupils to ask questions.
6. Failure to emphasize major health and hygiene facts over minor ones.
7. Failure to require pupils to make generalizations and reach conclusions.
8. Failure to encourage pupils to suspend their judgment until adequate data on the problem has been reached.

Pupil Demonstrations.—The preparation and presentation of demonstrations in health education provides pupils an excellent opportunity to "learn by doing." Work groups may be appointed to study specific health subjects and topics and then to report their findings to the entire class. In many cases, a demonstration can be a most valuable part of the report. For example, in a 9th grade class which was studying community hygiene, one group visited a dairy, another a water purification plant, and another a sewage disposal plant. Each group was responsible for giving a full description of the operation of these plants to the entire class, and each developed a demonstration as part of its presentation.

DAIRY DEMONSTRATION.—Several simple demonstrations were suggested by members of the group. These had to do with separating cream from milk, the principle of homogenization, and heating as in pasteurization. The teacher asked whether it would be possible to show the class what actually happened to the milk as a result of the heating. This question led to microscopic examination of the milk before and after pasteurization and the development of bacteriological cultures. Two especially interested boys eventually stained some slides. The class demonstration also included a sample of contaminated milk for microscopic examination in order to show the effects of careless handling.

WATER PURIFICATION.—The second group studied water purification and visited the city water works. For a demonstration they considered two possibilities: a mechanical filtering system and chemical treatment of the water to destroy bacteria. They decided on the filtering system; and following the design of the large filters, they filled a metal box with layers of sand, gravel and rock. The demonstration then consisted of pouring dirty water into the filter and observing the clear water which flowed from an outlet pipe at the bottom.

SEWAGE DISPOSAL PLANT.—This group decided upon a demonstration having to do with destroying bacteria by chemical means. During the presentation, the class had an opportunity to examine some swamp water under a microscope and a second sample of this same water after it had been treated with chlorine. This demonstration was used as the basis for describing how it is possible to make sewage safe for use as fertilizer after it has been treated by various means to kill the microorganisms in it.

Preparation for Demonstrations.—It is important to bear in mind that whoever prepares the demonstration—work groups, individual pupils, or the teacher—care should be taken that it is pre-tested and that it will work. If the demonstration does not work properly, its whole point may be lost and the class will very likely lose interest.

As a matter of fact, particularly when pupils are putting on the demonstration it is advisable to require them to rehearse all parts of the demonstration prior to presentation before the class. During the rehearsal attention should be given to the selection of the best location from the point of view of the best visibility for all class members. The equipment or material to be used should be located so as to be easily seen from all parts of the room. The demonstrator should be coached as to where to stand and how to present his work in such a way that he can be seen and heard easily without blocking the class's view of the demonstration.

The demonstrator should be encouraged to give a full account of of his demonstration and related information, including the scientific principles involved. For example, in the demonstration of the pasteurization of milk, Pasteur's pioneer work or at least detailed pertinent aspects of it might be described; a diagram or picture of the actual dairy equipment might be presented to show how the basic idea is utilized in a modern dairy if it is not possible for the entire class to visit the dairy. Information as to the nature of bacteria and how they are prepared for scientific investigation might also be introduced. Thus, the significance of a relatively simple process may be greatly expanded in terms of many new concepts, appreciations and applications.

Utilizing Pupil Ingenuity.—It has been stated previously that many units of study may profitably be introduced by presenting a demonstration. In such cases the teacher may choose to do the preparation and presentation. For example, a rubber syringe, a plastic tube system and colored water could be used to introduce a unit on the circulatory system. Thus, it might be desirable to employ a demonstration before the class has progressed far enough to participate in the preparation. Among young school children it may be that a desired demonstration is too difficult and complex for them to prepare or construct in the available time. In such cases the teacher may find it necessary to prepare the demonstration without pupil assistance.

Perhaps it should be repeated and emphasized again at this point that one of the most helpful and valuable aspects of demonstrations is the opportunity that they provide for utilizing the creative thinking, ingenuity, and talent of pupils. Although demonstrations have long been recognized as one of the most effective teaching devices by teachers, the pupil-demonstration has not been so widely used. Pupil-demonstrations deserve much more widespread recognition as they can be utilized to achieve many desirable ends including the development of language skills and the ability to express ideas in a variety of ways.

If the teacher can succeed in stimulating the imaginations of her pupils in health education, she will frequently be surprised at the quality of the results of their individual and group work. Illustrations of this point are instances in which: (1) a seventh grade boy in a rural school prepared a model at home which demonstrated how pollution from an improperly placed privy can eventually seep through the ground and substrata into the water supply of a farm; and (2) a tenth grade boy, using clay and string, prepared a model of the stomach and neural connections with the central nervous system including lower levels of the brain in order to demonstrate how surgeons may cut sympathetic nerve fibers so as to eliminate emotionally induced digestive turmoil. In both of these instances, the information dealt with and the concepts elaborated went considerably beyond the scope intended by the teachers. But, in both cases, the classes were able to grasp the processes involved with interest and the individuals who had conceived and made the demonstrations had added greatly to their knowledge of new scientific areas and how to find information on them.

Some elementary school teachers find ingenious means of providing informal individual laboratory experiences for children. For example, in order to vitalize certain information in anatomy and to convey basic concepts of bodily movement, one teacher obtained a chicken leg for each child in her fourth grade class. Under her direction, the pupils carefully dissected the joints, examined and identified the bony and cartilaginous parts and the connective tissue. Very effective activities of this sort suggest other possibilities of a similar kind which provide individuals or small groups an opportunity to examine animal structure and function at first hand.

Assigning Demonstrations.—Some teachers prefer to regard demonstrations as voluntary assignments, of the nature of the "optional related activities" included in some unit plans. This point of view is usually based upon the idea that such work must be well done if it is to be effective as a teaching device; consequently, some teachers feel that only the exceptional students are qualified to design and develop demonstrations. Of course, it is recognized that sometimes students who are not considered exceptional will take a keen interest in some phase of the work, and because of special knowledge or manual skill produce quite satisfactory demonstrations. Thus, a not particularly academically minded high school girl put on a very satisfactory demonstration of the latest methods of artificial respiration. Her instructive performance was an outgrowth of her experience in camping and her personal plans to be a waterfront specialist in a summer camp.

On the other hand, demonstrations may be regarded as being too important a part of health teaching to be left to the chance interests and talents of class members. In such cases the teacher may assume full responsibility for the demonstrations or she may assign them to superior individuals as regular class responsibilities in order to assure presentation of those deemed essential.

A third possibility, and one that seems to deserve serious considerations, involves requiring the preparation and presentation of demonstrations by all students, but doing so primarily on the basis of their interests, in so far as possible. Some aspect of the health education curriculum may be counted upon to interest virtually every student if a skillful job of teaching is done. Considering the range of the subject, extending as it does from a study of nutrition, exercise, and rest, to disease, mental health, human reproduction, personal grooming, and the like, there should be no great difficulty in helping each pupil to find a health subject upon which to concentrate special effort, either as an individual or as a small group member, as the case may be.

Examples of Demonstrations.—Following are a few examples of demonstrations which may help to illustrate the possibility of fitting demonstrations into the broad range of health education, and to show the kinds of things from which students may choose. These possibilities are not intended to be in detailed form but merely to suggest ideas and to stimulate thought as to further work of this kind.

1. SOME SIMPLE FOOD TESTS AS ELEMENTARY DEMONSTRATIONS. The following simple experiments may be used to identify the content of various foods and are often effective means of introducing lessons on the role of various foods in the diet.*

a) Testing various foods for the presence of starch.—Soften, crush, or dissolve various foods in water. Place this material in a test tube with a small amount of water, and add a drop of well-diluted iodine (about 1% solution). If the solution turns blue, starch is present. This demonstration may be used to illustrate a simple method of food analysis, may help to identify the main starch foods, and may provide an opportunity to become familiar with and use basic laboratory techniques. Further discussion may deal with the role of starch in the diet.

b) Test for fat in foods.—Place various foods on pieces of paper. Remove the foods, then place the papers on the radiator to heat. Observation of the paper should then reveal which foods contained fat. Such foods as sugar, flour, skim milk, fruit, and lean meat should leave very little mark; but fatty foods such as butter, bacon, cream, and pastry should leave appreciable grease spots. Milk, rich in butter fat, may be compared with skim milk in the same manner. (In such an experiment, small amounts of milk must be allowed to dry on the paper in order to allow a grease spot to form.)

c) Test for proteins.—Burn various foods in the direct flame of a Bunsen burner. Protein foods (including raw lean meat, cheese, dried beans, and dried milk) will emit the odor of burning feathers; other foods which contain little or no protein, such as sugar, bread and pastry, will not. In some cases it may be necessary to begin this experiment by burning a feather so as to familiarize the pupils with the odor.

d) Test for mineral content in foods.—Burn various foods on a small asbestos or metal plate. Non-mineral foods such as corn starch

---

*"The National Dairy Council's "Taking Milk Apart" is a useful source of food experiments. The reader may refer to this source for more detailed presentations of experiments.

and sugar will burn almost completely leaving only a small residue of black carbon. Others of relatively high mineral content (including dried milk, beans, peas and egg yolk) will leave a gray ash containing one or more minerals, such as calcium. Tests for specific minerals are for advanced students.

e) Test for the presence of water.—Fruits, leafy vegetables and other foods of high water content may be exposed to the air for sufficient time for them to become shriveled. Dried foods, sugar, meal and flour may also be exposed but it will be observed that they undergo little if any change since they contain very little water. The foods may be weighed before and after dehydration in order to determine just how much water is lost. A fresh fruit, such as a plum, may be compared with a dried fruit, such as a prune, in terms of what happens to them when they are exposed to the air for a period of time. Drying certain foods as a means of preserving them may thus be introduced.

2. DISEASE CONTROL: MALARIA.—As a part of a unit on control of disease or public health, swamp or other stagnant water containing mosquito larvae may be obtained. It will be observed that the larvae rise occasionally to the surface for air. A small amount of oil is dropped into the water. The oil will be seen to form a thin layer over the water. The mosquito larvae cannot penetrate this film to breathe and soon die. The demonstration thus shows one of the commonest and most simple means of mosquito control which is used throughout the world where malaria is a threat.

3. RELAXATION DEMONSTRATION.—In addition to teaching the young to keep pace with the fast-moving and rapidly changing times, schools should assume increasing responsibility for teaching children how to find respite from pressure and how to relax. A series of relaxation exercises may be presented by pupils, with care being taken to emphasize the principles involved and the correct procedures.

4. DEMONSTRATION OF ACTIVITIES TO IMPROVE BODILY EFFICIENCY.—Select and demonstrate a series of simple exercises which employ the major muscle groups of the body. Discuss the effects of regular exercise upon muscle efficiency; and discuss the importance of such activities as walking, bicycle riding, and play for the health and efficiency of the heart and circulation. Demonstrate the kinds of movement which bring the various muscle groups into action.

5. MEDICINE AND FIRST AID KIT DEMONSTRATION.—Following appropriate study and guidance pupils may demon-

strate a properly equipped medicine chest and first aid kit. They may describe and in some cases demonstrate, the proper uses of the various first aid articles.

6. FIRST AID DEMONSTRATIONS.—It is common procedure for teachers to demonstrate specific first aid procedures before pupils practice them. In addition to demonstrations and practice on such first aid procedures as bandaging and splinting, correct and incorrect ways of handling emergency situations may be demonstrated. Emergency cases can be very effectively presented by means of acting out desirable and undesirable ways of handling the situation and then calling upon the class for analysis and evaluation of each. For example, an untrained person can be portrayed as he comes upon an accident. The untrained person is likely to show uncertainty and confusion as to what to do. He usually becomes panicky, moves the victim roughly and administers first aid incorrectly or ineptly. The portrayal of faulty behavior of the untrained person should be analyzed step by step and followed by a demonstration of the right way to give first aid.

7. DEMONSTRATION OF TOOTH DECAY.—When bacteria attack sugars in the mouth, an acid is formed which commonly dissolves tooth enamel and thus initiates tooth decay. This process has been demonstrated by means of a large model of a tooth. The model tooth is made of a substance which is soluble in water, or better, a water-resistant material which is soluble in a suitable acid. A few drops of solvent are applied and deterioration of the surface material sets in. If a relatively hard substance is used for the tooth and an acid for the solvent, it is possible to show how the dissolution of the tooth may be stopped by simply rinsing the tooth with water in a way similar to rinsing the mouth after eating candy and other sweets.

It is also a simple matter to demonstrate the proper way to brush teeth by means of brush and tooth models.

8. THE FEET AND THEIR CARE.—Proper use and care of the feet are of great importance because of the close relationship of the feet to the efficiency of walking and running, to comfort while on the feet, and to many serious cases of foot, leg, and back pain. A number of demonstrations on this subject can be used to emphasize certain critical points to students such as: (a) Using old shoes with holes worn through the sole to show how the transverse arch "falls" into this low spot if a new sole is merely nailed over the old one. (The old sole should

of course be removed before a new one is put on.) (b) Demonstrate improper handling of the feet; e.g., walking with toes pointed outward which modifies the position of the bones of the ankle and leg. (A skeleton or jointed wooden model is useful in this demonstration.) Also, shows how walking or running with toes pointed out reduces the distance covered at each stride. (c) Demonstrate the correct mode of standing, walking, and running. Show exercises to strengthen the feet and improve the arches. Demonstrate how to massage the feet and lower legs to increase circulation and reduce foot fatigue and pain.

9. DEMONSTRATION OF LUNG ACTION.—It is sometimes difficult for people to visualize how the lungs work. (a) For young pupils use a large balloon or ball bladder to demonstrate the action of inhalation and exhalation. Another possibility is to make the model in such a way that a board or metal plate representing the diaphragm and fastened to the bottom of the bladder causes the bladder to inflate when it is depressed. (b) Perform a demonstration of osmosis to illustrate the principle of how oxygen is transmitted to the blood through the membrane of the lungs and how carbon dioxide is exchanged.

10. DEMONSTRATIONS OF LIGHTING.—Demonstrate the reflection of light from surfaces of varying textures and colors. Use a light meter (obtainable from public utilities companies if not available in your school) to make accurate measurement. Using a chair, lamp, and a pupil, demonstrate good and bad lighting arrangements for reading, studying, and other work in the home. With the children working in pairs, have them watch each other's eyes ("pupils") dilate and contract when they pass from a brightly lighted place to a dimly lighted one. Also have them observe one another when they attempt to read or do close work where the light is inadequate or otherwise bad; evidences of strain should be noted on their faces as they attempt to see. Source of lighting in relation to right and left handedness may be demonstrated and discussed. The similarities between the eye and a camera may be demonstrated and discussed.

11. DEMONSTRATIONS INVOLVING VISION.—A number of demonstrations may be developed to "vitalize" the eye and vision unit. For example, eye dominance may be demonstrated by having an individual sight with both eyes open along a gun barrel or ruler's edge, at an object several feet away. While continuing to sight, the pupil is instructed to close first one eye, then the other. It will be found

that only his dominant eye will actually be sighting on the target. (It is for this reason that many shooting instructors recommend that both eyes be kept open when aiming, especially when doing fast shooting; the dominant eye will do the seeing anyway.) This same experiment may be done by sighting at some object with both eyes through a small hole in a piece of paper. It will be found that by closing first one eye and then the other that only the dominant eye is actually seeing the object; the other eye is seeing nothing but the paper on one side of the hole.

Several other vision experiments, including simple demonstrations of color blindness, peripheral vision, the blind spot in the field of vision, and the inversion of images by the lenses of the eyes, which can be used as demonstrations may be found in the *Popular Science Monthly* of September, 1954.

12. REPRODUCTION DEMONSTRATIONS WITH INSECTS.—There is a tendency among some thoughtful teachers to begin sex education early in the grades but not as a "subject" labeled sex education. On the contrary, it is dealt with as it occurs quite naturally in the child's environment, and can form a realistic basis for future education of this kind. Various insects provide an easy source for reproduction demonstrations. Suitable glass containers, such as aquariums, may be obtained, and partially filled with sod. In the early autumn grasshoppers may be caught (the females have four pointed spikes at the end of the abdomen which are used in digging the hole in which eggs are deposited) and placed in the container. The mothers will eventually lay eggs in the soil and during the winter, in the warmth of the classroom, the younger grasshoppers will emerge and may be studied as they grow.

13. DEMONSTRATION OF A PHYSICAL EXAMINATION.—A joint committee of the National Education Association and the American Medical Association suggests an excellent demonstration to be conducted in the classroom by a physician. This demonstration can be geared for any age level, but in simple form it is highly recommended at the elementary school level.

Using a volunteer, perhaps a younger child who is not embarrassed by the situation and who is dressed only in swimming trunks, the physician-demonstrator takes the class with him, step by step, through an examination. Objectives of such a demonstration are specified as:

    1. To dramatize a careful physical examination for both pupils and teachers.

2. Through improved understanding, to help overcome or prevent fears of being examined.
3. To teach some basic anatomy and physiology.
4. To teach some of the basic principles of good health.
5. To teach something of disease control.

It is well to consider that although all physicians may be qualified to give a good physical examination, not all are qualified to do a skillful job of teaching or presenting a demonstration of this kind. When arranging for this demonstration, the teacher should take into account the ability of the physician to teach and to deal effectively with the pupils in a way that is appropriate to their age level. In many cases it is necessary for the teacher to make suggestions to the physician as to how to adjust his presentation to the particular group.

A somewhat similar demonstration can be conducted in the classroom by a dentist. Demonstrations of this kind can be instructive and can help to reduce children's fear of visiting the dentist.

Animal Experiments as Demonstrations.—Some of the most successful demonstrations reported are those involving animal experiments. White rats, guinea pigs, mice and hamsters are the most commonly used animals. In one situation, for the last several years first grade children as well as older children have been taken to the biological laboratory of a nearby college to observe the results of feeding experiments conducted for their benefit. This approach was found to be very effective from the point of view of learning, presumably because of the intense interest of the children in animals. Some of the concepts of differential feeding become perfectly clear when children see their rat friend Sammy show the effects of poor diet at the same time their little Andy abounds in vigor and good health on a good diet. In one of these experiments one rat regularly received soft drinks instead of milk in his otherwise good diet. As was anticipated his growth became slower than that of his litter mates. Unexpectedly he suddenly died of unknown cause or causes. It had not been intended that the animal would be killed in the experiment. The primary teacher and biology professor did not know quite what to do under the circumstances in that many of the children were distressed because they felt that the rat had been very cruelly treated.

Numerous teachers provide their own demonstrations by raising animals, usually rats or mice but sometimes guinea pigs or hamsters, in the classroom.

Responsibility for Animals in the Classroom.—The teacher and pupils are obliged to provide humane living conditions for the animals. The class should make plans as to how the animals should be cared for and where they should be kept in the room before they obtain them. Thus, not only will the animals be more likely to receive proper care, but the children will learn how it should be done and can apply this knowledge at home if they have pets.

The small animals mentioned previously may be handled. Gentle care will assure their remaining tame.

THE CAGE.—A number of satisfactory designs for inexpensive animal cages are available.[10] The most important consideration in selecting a design is whether the cage can be readily cleaned. The greatest single objection to raising animals in schools or homes is that they sometimes create an odor which is noticeable in distant parts of the building. This unpleasantness is, of course, unnecessary if the cages are properly made and maintained. The animals will keep themselves clean if given the opportunity. It is recommended that not only should droppings and urine be removed each day (a simple matter if the floor of the cage is ¼ inch wire screen and constructed so that a newspaper can be easily inserted under it to catch the droppings), but also that the screen and wood of the cage should be washed with soap and water each week.

SOME SAMPLE ANIMAL EXPERIMENTS ARE:

1. Studies of Inheritance.—A variety of inheritance experiments may be performed which will help to supplement and clarify class studies of the subject. Some of these may readily be suited to the maturation level of the pupils. Black rats may be crossed with white in order to observe the coloring of the resulting young. Of course the color ratios of the young are highly unlikely to follow those indicated by Mendelian ratios, but some of the basic points, including the variability of white and black proportions, may be made. Among older pupils, experiments of this kind may be used to show that acquired learnings and injuries of the parents are not transmitted to the young. Injuries may take the form of small clippings in the ears. Demonstrations of this kind are valuable in helping to teach the kinds of things that are inherited and the kinds that are not inherited.

2. Feeding Experiments.—Animal experiments have been found suitable for demonstrating the effects of good and poor diets upon the growth and health. These can be highly effective means of clarifying basic concepts related to food values. Experiments of this kind can be handled in such a way as to be suitable for virtually every grade level. For example, in the primary grades, it may be quite sufficient to record developments on the basis of observations of gross changes in the rats. Each child may keep a record of the observations, and thus the situation may be used as a means of improving and practicing writing skills. Also, weekly weighing of the animals can provide the basis for more precise study, and may be an interesting source of data for arithmetic problems.

In the upper grades, experiments can be developed in which established "optimum diets" can be used and varied with careful measurements of different foods in very much the same way in which scientific experiments on the subject are conducted. With guidance, perhaps sometimes by university scientists, interested high school and college students can employ scientific methodology and help to bring such techniques into the classroom in a highly interesting way. Thus, a demonstration of something in the field of health can also be a demonstration of the functioning of the scientific method. For example, some people find it difficult to understand a "controlled experiment" when it is expressed to them as an abstract concept. However, it is much more likely to be comprehensible when it is explained in the setting of, say, an animal experiment. We can "see" controls when it is explained why litter mates are used for comparative studies (to guarantee equal age and at least some similarity of genetic background) and why the animals must be treated and fed in exactly the same way except for the one factor under study, such as a vitamin or mineral food which is included in one diet and excluded from the other.

Of course, many teachers prefer not to *tell* their pupils the answers in relation to how to do experiments. Instead, they consider it important to encourage the class to think out many of the answers for themselves by means of skillful questioning. For example, the teacher may ask "But how can we make sure that one rat isn't bigger to start with or older, or growing more rapidly because of age"? Or: "If we use just one rat, how will we be able to tell what a properly fed rat would look like after a few weeks"? "Don't we need a basis for comparison?"

The following is a description of a simple feeding experiment:

> The value of a balanced diet as well as of a specific food, such as milk, can be demonstrated by use of an experimental animal, the white rat. This demonstration is often done with kindergarten or first grade children to encourage the drinking of milk and to discourage overeating of sweet foods.
>
> Two young white rats about three weeks old, from the same litter and of the same sex are placed in separate cages or in separate compartments of a breeding rat cage. Rat A is fed on cooked cereal, milk, egg, lettuce, whole wheat bread; Rat B is fed on cooked meat, potato, white bread, cake, and candy. Be careful to exclude cake containing butter and egg yolk from the diet.
>
> In the primary grades it is not necessary to weigh the rat; the eye can observe growth differences. In the upper grades a gram-scale should be used to weigh the rats weekly. About three to five weeks are required for the demonstration. Keep Rat B on its diet until it shows definite signs of malnutrition, then give it the same diet that Rat A is receiving to show how easily proper diet will correct dietary deficiencies. The hair on Rat B should gradually become thinner, shorter and rougher looking in contrast with that of Rat A. The eyes of Rat B will have a secretion and tend to close. The animal will be nervous and irritable.*

The experiment as explained above is an effective but simple demonstration in which no effort is made to define in precise terms the effects of specific food values. It merely shows the need for a well-balanced diet in which sweets and non-essential foods are not permitted to replace essential foods. In other experiments, milk has been replaced in one rat's diet by a soft drink, so that effects might be observed in contrast to a litter mate whose diet included milk.

The effects of vitamin deficiencies upon growth can be demonstrated strikingly by carefully controlling the feeding of animals. Diets deficient in vitamins A, B, C, and D soon result in stunted or disturbed growth and thus illustrate the need to include all of them in a good diet. Two young guinea pigs or rats may be placed on identical vitamin C-free diets except that one is given a small amount of orange juice each day. Within a few weeks the animal which did not receive the vitamin C (orange juice) will be found to have had its growth stunted.

---

*Demonstration as suggested by Lois M. Shoemaker, State Teacher's College, Trenton, New Jersey.

Two cull chicks may be obtained to demonstrate the effects of sunlight (which causes the body to generate vitamin D) upon growth. If both are placed on identical vitamin D deficient diets and only one is exposed to sunlight, the one deprived of both the vitamin D foods and the sunlight will undergo marked growth failure. By a similar technique it may be shown that if vitamin D-poor food is exposed to sunlight or other ultraviolet source, the resulting "irridation" will compensate for that lack of D vitamin and prevent growth failure.

One of the most dramatic phenomena to be seen and stressed in animal feeding experiments is the usual speed of recovery of animals when the missing essential food is restored to the diet.

SOME POSSIBLE SAFETY DEMONSTRATIONS.—There are many opportunities for employing demonstrations in safety education. The following are a few examples:

1. *Safety problems at street intersections.*—Models may be used to demonstrate correct behavior at street intersections. A large piece of plywood with a street intersection painted on it may be placed upon a table, and small cars and figures can be used to represent automobiles, bicycles, and people. Various problems may be posed and worked out with this equipment.

There are advantages in suspending a board from a wall and working out traffic problems where all pupils may see them from their seats. For example, flannel board to which pieces of paper readily stick, may be used. These pieces of paper, cut to represent automobiles, bicycles, and people may be moved about on the flannel material as needed.

Another type of equipment for this demonstration involves a piece of sheet metal and small magnets to which are glued wooden or cardboard automobiles, cyclists, and pedestrians. The sheet metal may be suspended from the wall and the magnetized objects may be moved about on it as needed.

2. *Combustibility of various materials.*—A wide variety of materials may be obtained and tested for the readiness with which they will catch fire. The test materials may include: asbestos, glass, stone, water, paper, cotton cloth, wool cloth, fiber glass, large and small pieces of wood, and kerosene. Demonstrations of this kind help children to analyze their homes from the point of view of fire hazards. Great care should be taken when demonstrating the combustibility of such substances as kerosene.

3. Extinguishing Fires.—Various means of extinguishing fires may be demonstrated. By blowing gently on a burning substance, it may be shown that increasing the air supply increases the rate of burning. By dropping a vigorously burning match into a bottle and then capping the bottle, it is possible to demonstrate how quickly fire is smothered. In this way it is also possible to emphasize the fact that if a person's clothing catches fire, it is better for him to roll on the ground or wrap up in a woolen blanket than to run.

4. The Conductivity of Electricity.—If the necessary equipment is available (perhaps in a science laboratory), demonstrate that some materials conduct electricity much more readily than others. Salt, water, and metals are good conductors while wood, glass, and plastics are poor conductors. Analyze situations in and out of the home in which it is possible to be in danger of receiving electric shock because of the presence of good conductors of electricity. Emphasize the hazards of turning on a bathroom light while standing on a wet floor; similarly, indicate the danger of touching the radio when bathing.

5. Demonstrations by Dramatics.—Use pupils as actors to demonstrate correct and incorrect street crossing (use pupils as automobiles, police, etc.), In a similar way, demonstrate the principles of behavior in emergency situations.

Presentation of Demonstrations.—The presentation of demonstrations, like the showing of films, should not be regarded as single events in themselves, but as a sequence of related events. In the first place, if at all possible the presentation of a demonstration should be appropriate to the subject matter content. Thus, for example, a demonstration of visual tests or vision mechanics should be planned to fit in a unit on vision. Yet, it frequently happens that demonstrations, especially those prepared by pupils, are not completed until a considerable period of time after its unit's completion. However, even in such circumstances it can be used to advantage as review as well as for further expansion or clarification.

Special attention should be given to: (1) introducing the demonstration, (2) presenting it, and (3) doing proper follow-up. If students are to present the demonstration, they should be carefully coached on presenting and following up the demonstration.

Introducing the Demonstration.—The class should be properly oriented regarding the purpose of the demonstration. Significant related information should be provided. For example, historical backgrounds of the thing to be presented or of the experiment itself may need to be given. The demonstrator should describe the principle of the demonstration to be shown in order to encourage the pupils to give thought and attention to the demonstration. Also, pupils should be told specific things to watch for.

Presenting the Demonstration.—It was previously mentioned that teachers should pre-test their own demonstrations and that informal rehearsals are desirable if pupils are to be expected to be effective in presenting demonstrations. The demonstration rehearsal is proposed not only to be assured that the demonstration will work as expected, but also to coach the pupil in the principles of effective presentation. In practice, the teacher may accomplish his coaching by simply asking the student a series of questions, such as: "Now what do you intend to say about your demonstration?" and "How will you show it without obstructing the class's vision?". The student's language, voice, posture, and possible distracting mannerisms should be considered by the teacher. These observations should be made and mention made of them in such a way that the pupil will not become self-conscious and become unable to concentrate his attention on his demonstration. Having constructed the equipment alone or having spent considerable time studying the subject individually, the pupil is likely to consider it simple and the details obvious; consequently it may be necessary to remind him to give a full account and to proceed deliberately. The class should feel free to raise questions when details are not made clear.

The Follow-up.—The follow-up should include a review of the demonstration by way of clinching significant understandings. The class may be asked questions informally or perhaps in examination form in order to determine the extent in which the principles and applications of the demonstration are understood. The pupils may be asked to make constructive criticisms for improving the demonstration or the presentation. It sometimes happens that suggestions will be made and assistance offered which lead to major improvements. Almost invariably one good demonstration can be used to stimulate thought and to lead to other good demonstrations. Moreover, when the evaluation is completed, each pupil should have a better idea of a good demonstration. Thus, improved ability to express ideas can be achieved and imaginations stimulated for further creative work.

The follow-up phase of the demonstration provides an invaluable opportunity for both teacher and class to relate the demonstration to its various applications. For one of many possible examples, one junior high school teacher followed the presentation of an animal feeding experiment with a brief discussion of the role of animals in scientific and medical research.

PRESERVING DEMONSTRATION MATERIALS.—Materials from successful demonstrations should be stored for future use as: (1) a means of introducing or otherwise enhancing subject matter units in subsequent classes, (2) a means of stimulating future students' thought as to how demonstrations may be made or improved upon, and (3) an occasional exhibit in the health education classroom or elsewhere in the school if they are deemed suitable for this purpose. It is plainly a waste of resources if some future use is not found for good demonstration materials.

Questions for Discussion

1. Of what value are demonstrations in health education?
2. For what specific purposes can demonstrations be used in a health teaching unit?
3. How can students participate in the preparation and presentation of demonstrations?
4. What advantages are there in encouraging a maximum of student participation in demonstration work?
5. How would you evaluate individual laboratory work in health in the ordinary school situation? Compare the possibilities of demonstrations and individual laboratory work in your own school or a school with which you are familiar.
6. What are the merits of demonstrations of such things as relaxation exercises and physical examinations in contrast to verbal descriptions of these things?
7. Of what value are animal experiments?
8. How can animal feeding experiments be modified to be suitable for younger or older pupils? Give specific examples.
9. Of what three phases is the presentation of a demonstration composed? Discuss each.
10. What are possible future uses of demonstration materials?

Suggested Class Activities

1. List several demonstrations which might be used with each major unit in health education.
2. Draw up complete plans describing how a specific demonstration can be (1) introduced, (2) presented, and (3) followed up.

3. Write to a number of organizations and agencies for materials on animal feeding experiments. Make detailed plans for conducting such experiments. Take into account such factors as obtaining or building cages, obtaining animals, the care of the cages and the animals and the details of the experiment to be conducted.
4. Working in committees, prepare a number of demonstrations. Present these before the entire class.

References

1. Billett, R. O., *Fundamentals of Secondary-School Teaching*. Boston: Houghton Mifflin Co., 1940.
2. Blanc, S. S., "Vitalizing the Classroom: Laboratory and Demonstration," *School Science and Mathematics,* October 1952.
3. *Health Education.* Washington D.C.: National Education Association, 1948.
4. Humphrey, J. H., "The Place of the Demonstration in Health Education," *The Science Teacher,* October 1952.
5. Popkin, R. B., "Student Demonstrations," *Industrial Arts and Vocational Education,* December 1950.
6. Wayland, L. C. N., "Health Education Dramatized," *Health Education Journal,* December 1954.

References on Feeding Experiments

7. "Animal Experiment Shows Two Foods Better than One," *News Exchange* (General Mills, Inc., Minneapolis, Minn., 1950, free.)
8. "Care of Rats, Mice, and Guinea Pigs," (leaflet) General Biology Supply House, Inc. (761 East 69th Place, Chicago 7, Illinois, free)
9. "Food Makes the Difference in these Twin Rats," (chart) Human Nutrition and Home Economics Research, Agricultural Research Service, U.S. Dept. of Agriculture, Washington 25, D.C. Free.
10. "How to Conduct a Rat-Feeding Experiment," Wheat Flour Institute. (309 W. Jackson Blvd., Chicago 6, Illinois, free)
11. Kohout, J., "A New Type Standard Size Cage for Rats and Other Small Animals," School Science and Mathematics, October 1954.
12. "Nutrition Experiment" (leaflet), General Biology Supply House, Inc. (761 East 69th Place, Chicago 7, Illinois, free).

CHAPTER 14

FIELD TRIPS IN HEALTH EDUCATION

School health education field trips are activities designed to provide sensory experiences with individual, school and community health and safety projects, programs and phenomena which cannot be brought into the classroom. They involve detailed planning and transporting students to places and locations where the subject matter of health and safety may be observed and studied in its normal setting. The field trip is a way of teaching employed outside of the classroom and usually in the community. In most cases it is the most practical and certainly the most real of all the visual aid techniques because it brings students into direct contact with existing health and safety conditions as they affect the lives of the people within the community, state or nation.

Although field trips, tours, excursions, or journeys have been used to some extent in all phases of education in the schools, they have perhaps as yet not been fully capitalized upon as an effective means of teaching. Even though the possibilities of field trips have not as yet been fully developed in the area of general education, they are used even less in the teaching of health. Experience in the use of field trips in teaching health in both the elementary and the secondary school shows that they are far more effective in teaching certain parts of health and safety than virtually any other technique of classroom teaching.

There are a number of reasons why field trips have not been fully developed in the teaching of health. First, there has been a lack of experience with them. In order for the school health and safety field trip to be most effective there must be careful planning and organization, otherwise the visit is likely to result in wasted time other than for the entertainment of the children. There is need for the development of a body of knowledge in this area which is based upon experimentation and research as well as upon the experiences of many teachers and schools in the actual conduct of school health field trips.

A second reason why field trips in health education are not widely used is that many schools are slow to discard the rigid lines of formal education marked by inflexible programs and time schedules. Also, the feeling of both school personnel and the laymen has been to some extent, that education can take place most effectively only in the classroom. There has been a failure on the part of some people to recognize the values and potentialities of the community and surrounding area as a laboratory-type setting in the educational process.

Another reason why the school health education field trip remains undeveloped is that health, as it is recognized today, is comparatively new in the school program. A majority of the schools in America do not as yet have highly *organized* and acceptable health and safety education programs. Furthermore, in many of the schools that attempt to conduct organized health education programs many of the teachers lack the proper background and training in health and safety education which is fundamental to the most successful teaching regardless of methods used. Lack of training, background, and experience on the part of teachers is particularly handicapping in the organization and conduct of field trips in health education. Nevertheless, it is often easier for the inexperienced teacher to plan and conduct field trips in teaching certain parts of health than it is for her to attempt to impart the same information and knowledge through classroom procedures. In those schools where a definite allotment of time has not been given to health teaching in the program and in which health is taught more or less incidentally and haphazardly, the effective use of field trips is practically nil because the teachers have insufficient time to plan, organize, and conduct the visits.

Because the success and value of health field trips, the same as all school trips, depends upon the attitude of the teachers, it is highly essential that the faculty as a whole, as well as the individual teachers, give their full support to this phase of the program. Some teachers in a school may not be directly involved. Others will have to plan, organize, and conduct the trips. All teachers in the school, however, will be affected either directly or indirectly. An example of this is that in which a high school class may go on an all-day trip. The students making the trip miss their regularly scheduled classes in other school subjects as well as in health education. It is then necessary for all teachers to arrange and plan their work for the students in accordance with the program of field trips arranged by the school. In the case of most elementary schools and some junior high schools the problem of other teachers and classes is not so great as in high school.

The community must be educated to accept health field trips as a recognized, desirable, and acceptable means of education. The attitude that education takes place only in the classroom and that time is being wasted if children are on field trips during school hours must be changed if laboratory study through trips is to be most successful. The public can be enlightened as to the value of health field trips the same as to other school trips through various means including Parent-Teachers Associations, civic organizations, newspapers, and through the children.

It is also important to develop the proper attitude toward health field trips on the part of the students. In those schools where they are a common occurrence, the students are likely to have the proper attitude whether or not the trips have been made for the expressed purpose of studying health. In schools where field trips are rare, it is usually advisable to educate the students concerning the value of trips and what is expected of them. This is also highly important from the viewpoint of reaching and educating parents through the students. Children can be reached in the elementary school directly by the classroom teacher. In the high school the students can be enlightened concerning the proper attitude toward field trips through teachers of the various academic subjects, school newspapers, homerooms, assembly programs and posters.

The Purposes and Values of Field Trips in Health and Safety Education.—One main purpose of field trips in health education is to use the community and surrounding area as a laboratory. Teaching through the use of the community as a practical and working laboratory helps to create interest and provide a medium whereby students can actively participate in the instructional program.

A substantial part of health education in the schools just as in other areas is, to a certain extent, unrelated to the practical existing conditions within the community. A considerable part of the usual curricular work in the schools remains more or less formal and academic following the rigid patterns upon which education in America was originally founded. Through field trips and visitations the opportunity is provided for the subject matter of instruction to become real and meaningful to the student. Study and exploration of existing health and safety conditions outside the classroom tend to blend the school program with that of the outside world. It creates and stimulates interest in health education as it affects society as a whole. The usual type of classroom instruction in health and safety, based largely upon the use of textbooks, printed materials, and class discussions frequently results in boredom and a lack of interest on the part of the student because the reality of the situation is more or less remote from the oral and printed description. For example, the use and production of milk and milk products is included in the health teaching program at various grade levels. Textbooks in health as well as supplementary reading and study materials may give detailed descriptions and enthusiastic accounts of modern methods of sanitation and hygiene applied in the production and distribution of milk. These descriptions are often accompanied by drawings, pictures, and illustrations which are for the purpose of clarifying the descriptive material and embellishing the printed material in general. Experience in the use of textbooks and other printed and study materials of this type indicates that the children frequently have the greatest interest in the pictures and illustrations seemingly because they are the nearest thing to reality in the abstract learning situation in which they are placed. This should not be interpreted to imply that textbooks and study materials are unnecessary or undesirable in the teaching of health and hygiene for certainly they have a highly important place. The main point to be made is that the instruction phase is only partially completed if no effort is made to expand and fortify the learning process by real and existing conditions whenever it is possible to do so. When a class is studying the problems of milk and milk production for example, it is far more interesting and meaningful to the child to visit, observe, and study the dairy and milk distribution plant. The process of milk Pasteurization for example, may mean very little to a child as studied from descriptions in textbooks or other printed materials or even after watching a laboratory demonstration, yet after a visitation to a milk distributing plant or a modern dairy where the process of pasteurization can actually be observed, studied, and understood in all its ramifications, it is more likely to become real and meaningful to the child.

One of the modern trends in education is to give children the opportunity to help in planning their work on the basis of their interests. Planning health field trips may be made a joint cooperative enterprise in which both teachers, pupils, and community groups participate. Planning of visitations can be done largely by the students with the teacher assuming the role of counselor and guide. The teacher can remain in the background, yet she can stimulate initiative and self-dependence on the part of the students. In this way the school health and safety education field trip can be organized and conducted on a project and problem-solving basis which is readily adaptable to the most modern and acceptable methods and procedures in teaching.

It cannot be emphasized too strongly that health field trips be carefully planned, organized, and conducted if they are to be most effective and serve the purpose of interpreting, enriching, and properly supplementing classroom instruction. Many teachers are often somewhat reluctant to share the responsibility for planning with the students. There is no question but that the teacher alone can plan a field trip with the greatest efficiency yet, it deprives students of a rich educational experience if they do not have the opportunity to participate in the plans. Teacher-pupil cooperative planning of health field trips seems the best approach then as it capitalizes upon the interest and experiences of both the teacher and the students to provide a real and natural experience in direct connection with the classroom instruction program.

The main purposes of the health field trips may be summed up as follows.

1. As introductory activities for health units.
2. As a teaching device for developing keen and accurate observation on the part of pupils.
3. As a means of creating and developing interest in individual and community health and safety.
4. As a means of securing definite and first hand information concerning health and healthful living.
5. As a means of securing definite and first hand information concerning safety and accident prevention.
6. As a means of verifying, supplementing, and enriching information gained through the usual classroom procedures.
7. As a means of giving pupils actual practice in cooperative group planning in health and healthful living and in safety and accident prevention.

Kinds of School Health and Safety Trips.—School health and safety trips can well begin within the school plant and facilities. There are many phases of health and safety education that can be studied and surveyed in the usual facilities used by the schools. Furthermore, a study of the school plant and facilities from the viewpoint of health and safety helps to create and develop interest in the total school program. The children are more likely to regard field observation, as well as the total health and safety program, as something real and meaningful in that it directly affects their daily lives. Examples of things in and about the school that may be studied are: the heating and ventilating systems; school lighting; the water supply system; safety and potential hazards in the school buildings including shops, laboratories, halls, stairs, and classrooms; school building construction from the viewpoint of acoustics and hearing; school building construction from the viewpoint of fire safety; hygiene and sanitation in the cafeteria and lunchrooms; hygiene and sanitation in the swimming pool including purification, care and testing of the water; sanitation and general care of the buildings; nutrition as reflected through plans and provisions in the school cafeteria and lunchrooms; safety hazards on the playground and athletic fields; and traffic safety near and surrounding the school plant.

Trips to study health and safety within the confines of the school have many advantages for a number of reasons. First, they can be more readily arranged than community field trips. Second, they do not necessarily need to consume more than one class period in most cases. Third, it is relatively easy to arrange for any number of repeat visits if the study is not completed on the first trip. Fourth, surveys, experiments, and continued and extended studies of existing conditions can more readily be carried out on a visitation plan within the school building and facilities. The fact that visits within the school plant have certain advantages largely because of accessibility and comparative ease of making arrangements does not exclude the necessity for trips within the community and surrounding areas. Although the school facilities ordinarily provide a highly important source and laboratory for studying certain phases of health, hygiene, and safety, they alone are far too limited and narrow to be considered sufficient.

The trip to some point within the community or surrounding area is the usual type of "field trip". A trip to the community water purification plant or to a modern dairy are examples of the usual kinds of community field trips. The community field trip usually requires more specific and detailed arrangements. It ordinarily consumes more than one class period. Often it requires a half-day and sometimes a full day or more. Occasionally the community field trip is arranged and taken on Saturdays and holidays.

In addition to the field trip in which groups of students participate, there are those in which a student makes a trip alone. In such instances the student may be given some particular assignment in connection with a health or safety lesson or unit, or the trip is made to pursue a special interest in some phase of the program being studied or investigated. As a result of the trip the student may give a class report on the basis of his study and observations, or he may submit a written report. Regardless of the uses made by a student and class of the results of individual visitations in the study of health, hygiene and safety perhaps the greatest value is to the individual student in learning to accept responsibility in the pursuit of knowledge.

Even though pupils are eager to make individual trips in the study of health, hygiene and safety the teacher must necessarily give considerable supervision and direction in making arrangements. This is particularly true for elementary schools in which the possibilities of field trips on an individual basis are very definitely limited because of the maturity level of the children. If elementary school children are permitted to make individual trips the teacher should, in most cases, decide whether the trip in question can be made safely and profitably without supervision. Also, in many cases it is necessary to secure the help and cooperation of persons and groups outside the schools and particularly where the visit is to be made. As a general rule persons outside the schools prefer to have contact with and the approval of the teacher before permitting the students to visit. Again, this holds particularly true in the case of elementary school children. Junior and senior high school students are mature enough in most cases to take greater responsibility in organizing and arranging for individual health field trips. Sometimes, though, it is necessary for the teacher to give considerable assistance even to those more mature students.

Another type of trip is the school tour or journey. Two distinguishing characteristics between the field trip and the tour is that the tour usually takes several days, a month, or even longer periods of time and it is usually made to more distant points than in the case of community field trips. An example of this type of trip is that in which a group of students make a tour to another part of the country, a state capitol or to the national capitol. The school tour or journey seems to be growing in popularity in the schools. The development of rapid and safe means of transportation and the ease of travel have given impetus to the growth of school tours for large numbers of students.

School tours are seldom if ever made for the sole purpose of studying health, hygiene and safety. The aims are ordinarily much broader than the subject matter lines drawn in the classroom. It is to be expected and recommended that there be correlation and integration of subject matter materials on extended trips. Therefore, some time and attention should be given to a study of health and safety the same as to other phases of the curriculum. When tours or journeys are being planned for students, teachers in health and safety education should cooperate with other teachers in the school in planning the total program of study for the trip.

Correlation and Integration Through School Trips.—The aims of the community field trip, just as for tours or journeys, may be made much broader than the usual subject matter areas. A class may visit some objective within the community with a number of purposes in mind, one of which is the study of health, hygiene, and safety. The correlation and integration of subject matter through field trips is recommended when the object of study is to view the situation in its entirety, and in proper relationship to other factors involved. A main criticism of the field trip with broader aims and purposes in which many phases of the school curriculum are to be studied is that it may result in only general observation on the part of the students, without a thorough understanding of all phases. Too often on trips of this kind the health and safety phases are almost completely ignored or at best so little attention is given to them that the children fail to gain the proper understanding of them because of a lack of time to observe and properly study existing conditions. There is perhaps less justification for attempting to rigidly correlate and integrate health and safety with other school subjects on community field trips than in the case of tours and journeys, largely because in the case of community field trips any number of repeat visits can usually be made as needed, to give thorough study and attention to the problems under investigation. If the study of some phase of a health or safety problem is not completed on the first trip it is relatively easy to arrange other trips to the same point. This does not usually hold true for the tour or journey which may last several days and entail considerable expense. Nevertheless, there are times and situations when the more generalized field trip is recommended. An example of this might be that in which a science class makes a field trip to some objective largely for the purpose of studying science. Yet, because some phases of health and safety are closely related to or dependent upon the science knowledge to be gained on the trip it may be the most opportune time for the study and observation of the health and safety phases. Another example might be that in which a class in social studies is making a study of the community. As a part of the activities of the study a series of field trips may be planned to study and observe firsthand the various phases of community life. Certainly, a complete picture of community life could not be gained without study and understanding of means, methods, and steps taken to control and safeguard the health and safety of the people.

Organization for Health and Safety Field Trips.—There are a number of important factors to be considered preliminary to the immediate planning of specific trips. The teacher should survey the community to learn the extent of the possibilities for health and safety field trips which will be helpful in teaching the materials to be presented to the children in the classroom. After locating places and objectives for the trips, contact should be made with those in charge to learn whether permission can be gained for the children to visit the objective. Ordinarily the school administrator should make the original contact. In some cases he may wish to delegate this responsibility to supervisors or teachers. In this way general plans for visitations can be made ahead of time, which may be helpful to the teacher and pupils in planning units of study.

The value and success of the health or safety field trip naturally depends materially upon the efficiency of teachers and pupils in planning and carrying out the many details. Those experienced in the conduct of health and safety trips are far more likely to make the trips successful. This holds especially true for the longer and more complicated trips. It is usually thought advisable for those with limited experience in the conduct of health and safety field trips to plan short and less complicated visitations at the beginning. As experience is gained the longer and more complicated trips can be added with far greater chances of success. A logical beginning for those inexperienced in this area is in planning and conducting visits and surveys in and about the school plant and facilities.

Teachers of health education and elementary school classroom teachers who are planning a program of health and safety field trips should give consideration to the total yearly school program of field trips. As a matter of fact, it is highly recommended that the total school program of trips be considered by the entire faculty. It would perhaps be best for all faculty members within the school to participate in working out and drawing up plans for field trips for an entire school year. In addition to stimulating interest in general it would help to prevent overlapping and perhaps broaden the study horizon for many of the visits. Because schools in general have not fully recognized the potential values of field trips as an instrument of education, it is likely to be a number of years before complete faculty cooperation can be gained in most schools in planning a yearly program for the entire school. Until the faculty as a whole plans the total yearly field trip program those teachers who recognize the value of health and safety trips should proceed with whatever cooperation they can get from administrators, supervisors and other teachers who may be interested.

It is sometimes advisable for the teacher to make a preliminary visit to become familiar with the objective of the health or safety field trip. This is highly recommended especially if the teacher has not previously visited the objective. If the teacher has taken children on the same trip at other times it may not be necessary for her to make the preliminary visit. In some cases the teacher may think it advisable to send a committee of children to make the preliminary visit. In any case, one of the main objectives in the preliminary visit is to facilitate the planning particularly from the point of view of students gaining the most in the way of understanding. The information gained on the preliminary visit is helpful in preparing the group for the visit.

Plans, Procedures and Arrangements for Health and Safety Field Trips.—Final plans should be made a short time before the trip is to be taken. The teacher or committee should attempt to visualize and think through the details in the process of making arrangements.

Although details and arrangements to be made will likely vary from one trip to another, the following points are suggestive of those that should be given consideration in most instances:

1. Consent of the school administrators and other school personnel involved.
2. Final arrangements with the owners or those in charge of the objective of the trip. These arrangements should be made by the school administrator or by the person to whom he has delegated the responsibility.
3. Estimation of the amount of time necessary for the total trip with all other arrangements made accordingly.
4. Determination of the number of children to make the trip.
5. Permission of the parents of each child making the trip. Follow the policy of the school in securing parents' permission.
6. Determine whether the objective is within walking distance. The amount of time consumed in arriving at the

objective must be taken into consideration in making this decision.
7. Make arrangements for transportation. These arrangements should be cleared through the school administrative officers. Many schools have formulated a definite policy concerning the transportation of pupils. Ordinarily the transportation of pupils should be by bonded carriers. In some cases school buses may be available for field trips.
8. Determine the expense involved. If there are expenses involving the school they should be approved by the administrative officers. If there are expenses involving the children they should be approved by pupils and their parents when necessary. It is usually best if the trips can be managed without cost to the pupils.
9. Determination of the amount of supervision needed. It is often necessary for the teacher to have assistance in supervising the trip. The matter of additional supervisors should be discussed with and arranged through the administrative officers. Sometimes parents can be enlisted to help supervise.
10. Plan the route of the trip. Take into account the possibilities for observing interesting and educational phenomena along the route.
11. Determine the equipment needed by both supervisors and pupils and make certain it is ready. In most cases the pupils will need nothing more than pencils and notebooks.
12. Advise the children concerning the kinds of clothing to wear. This is especially important in the case of elementary school children when trips are taken during the winter months.
13. Be certain that students are prepared to profit most by the trip. Discussion of problems to be solved and things to look for help in making the trip most profitable to the pupils. It is sometimes advisable to have mimeographed materials of questions and problems to be answered and solved for the pupils to study before the trip is taken.
14. Discuss the standards of conduct, safety, and behavior expected of the pupils on the trip.

Evaluation and Appraisal of Health and Safety Field Trips.— One of the most important questions to be answered is the extent in which the trip served the purpose for which it was intended. In other words did the pupils profit from the trip sufficiently for it to be considered successful? The teacher can judge the value of the trip somewhat by the reaction of the students in terms of their attitude, interest, questions, and knowledge gained. The knowledge gained can be measured to some extent through written and oral tests prepared to cover the things studied and observed and through written and oral reports of the trip.

A second important question to be answered concerning the trip is whether it was justifiable on the basis of the time, expense, and effort required. Determination of the worth of the trip from the viewpoint of time, expense and effort depends greatly upon the degree in which the trip served the purpose for which it was intended. The teacher must finally decide whether it would have been possible to have used other methods less involved than trips to reach the ends desired. It is always best to consider the health or safety field trip, before it is taken, from the viewpoint of the time, effort, and expense involved. Yet, it is often impossible to determine exactly whether the trip should be taken. After a trip is once taken and it does not prove its worth in terms of time, effort, and expense it can be eliminated from the list of trips to be taken in future years.

Other points and questions to be considered in evaluating, appraising and improving health field trips are:

1. Was the supervision adequate?
2. Were there undue safety or health hazards involved?
3. Were the arrangements satisfactory with the owners or those in charge of the objective?
4. Was the transportation adequate and managed satisfactorily?
5. Were the plans for study and observation carried out efficiently and with a minimum of wasted time?
6. Were cordial relations developed and maintained with guides, managers, and other persons involved in the trip?
7. Was discipline and management of students satisfactory both from the viewpoint of the teacher, the school and those in charge of the objective?
8. Were there too many students on the trip from the viewpoint of efficiency of study and observation?

Suggestions for Field Trips in Health and Safety.—Although the possibilities and resources for health and safety field trips vary greatly from one community to another there are many objectives in any community that can be visited and studied with profit year after year. The following list of possible objectives is not intended to be complete. It is included for the purpose of suggestion and for stimulating thought in developing a program of school health and safety field trips:

HEALTH AND SAFETY TRIPS, STUDIES AND OBJECTIVES WITHIN THE SCHOOL

NOTE: Some of the following are suitable for both elementary and secondary school students.

Lunchrooms and cafeterias to study hygiene, sanitation, and care of foods
Acoustics in classrooms, auditoriums, swimming pools and other rooms and areas
Water supply system
Heating system
Ventilating system
Lighting in classrooms, laboratories, shops and other rooms
Color schemes throughout the school including classrooms, auditoriums, gymnasiums, laboratories, offices and halls
School lunchrooms to study the lunch hour from the viewpoint of time, serving, crowding and noise
Activities participated in by the children during the lunch hour
Swimming pool to study sanitation, hygiene, care, and testing of water
The school building to study from the viewpoint of sanitation and hygienic care of lavatories and washrooms
Building survey to determine the location of first-aid supplies in places such as shops, laboratories, home economics rooms, etc.
School nurses' quarters
Medical examination center
Equipment used in maintaining proper sanitary and hygienic conditions of the buildings and facilities
Survey of housekeeping throughout the school
Equipment and procedures for waste disposal
Safety hazards in school shops
Safety hazards in laboratories
Safety hazards in classrooms, halls, and corridors
Safety hazards in gymnasiums and swimming pools
Building construction from the viewpoint of fire safety
Potential fire hazards
Electrical wiring throughout the school from the viewpoint of fire safety
Safety hazards on play areas and athletic fields
Traffic hazards surrounding the school
Safety in pupil transportation and school busses
Bicycle safety and inspection at school
Survey of fire fighting equipment such as extinguishers and their locations such as in shops, laboratories, basements, engine room, and halls

Fire alarm system
Survey of the safety condition of playground apparatus and equipment
Survey and observation of the work of safety councils and traffic patrols

HEALTH AND SAFETY TRIPS, STUDIES AND OBJECTIVES IN THE COMMUNITY AND SURROUNDING AREA

NOTE: Some of the following are suitable for both elementary and secondary school students.

Modern dairy to study sanitary and hygenic methods employed in the production, care, and handling of milk
Milk distribution plant to study sanitary and hygenic methods employed and the pasteurization of milk
Health museums
Museums with special health exhibits
Ice cream manufacturing plant to study such phases as sanitary means employed
Health centers
Health clinics to study and observe phases related to health education
Hospitals
First-aid stations
Food plants to observe and study modern methods of caring for and handling foods
Packing plants
Canning factories
Frozen foods plants
Food storage plants
Municipal vegetable markets
Food plants preparing dairy products
Food plants preparing breakfast foods
Pharmaceutical manufacturing and supply houses
Municipal water filtration and purification plant
Municipal health department
Municipal sewage disposal plant
Physicians to study work and methods of physicians
Dentists to study work and methods of dentists
Pharmacy to observe work and methods of pharmacists, patent medicines, etc.
Restaurant to observe and study care, preparation and handling of foods
City departments of health
State departments of health
Truck farms
Veterinaries and animal doctors

Health laboratories
Public organizations assisting in health work
Private organizations assisting in health work
Water storage plants
Plants that manufacture waste disposal equipment
Manufacturers of heating, lighting and ventilating equipment
Factories and plants to study and observe health measures for employees
State testing laboratories
County health departments
Housing projects to observe and study from viewpoint of health and hygienic conditions
Special health exhibits in department stores
Fire stations to study from the viewpoint of fire safety
Survey and study of traffic conditions
Survey and study of traffic control methods
Survey and study of main traffic thoroughfares in the vicinity of the school
Traffic signal control systems
Municipal safety bureaus
State safety bureaus
Safety procedures, equipment, and devices in all types of factories
Safety equipment on all types of motor vehicles
Fire prevention equipment and measures used in large buildings
Manufacturers of safety devices and equipment
Fire prevention equipment and measures used in factories and plants
Study and survey of hazards on public playgrounds
Study and survey of safety hazards on municipal swimming facilities and public beaches
Study and survey of safety conditions and hazards in both public and private recreational facilities
Observation of safety conditions in homes
Traffic courts
City and state officials responsible for safety
Boys' court for bicycle offenders
Traffic control divisions and emergency units of police stations
Sanatoriums of some types
Police stations to study their responsibilities concerning health and safety in the community

Questions for Discussion

1. What are some major advantages of field trips in contrast with other class activities?
2. Why have field trips not been widely used in health education?

3. What are some important considerations to be taken into account when planning and organizing a field trip?
4. Why is it recommended that the school and community be surveyed for possible field trips?
5. Why is it important that the public be taught the value of field trips in health education?
6. What are the roles of introductory activities and of follow-up activities in relation to field trips? Give an illustration in relation to a specific field trip.

Suggested Class Activities

1. Make a list of the possible field trips in a school with which you are familiar.
2. Make a list of the possible field trips in a community with which you are familiar.
3. Prepare an outline showing how a field trip might be used effectively as an introductory activity for a unit on foods and nutrition, community health services, water purification, fire safety, and health and safety organizations in the community.
4. Draw up detailed plans for a field trip for a group of third-grade pupils. For a group of eleventh-grade pupils.
5. Take an individual field trip and prepare a study guide which might make the trip most profitable for pupils taking the trip at some later date.
6. Make a list of tours or journeys which might be planned for pupils in health classes.

References

1. Barr, A. S., W. H. Burton and L. J. Brueckner, *Supervision,* New York, 1947, Appleton-Century-Crofts, Inc.
2. Dale, Edgar, *Audio-Visual Methods in Teaching,* New York, 1946, The Dryden Press.
3. Frazier, A., "Is This School Trip Necessary?" *Educational Administration and Supervision,* March 1946.
4. Pitluga, G. E., "Science Excursions as a Teaching Technique", *School Science and Mathematics,* May 1947.
5. Smith, Julian W., "The Use of Community Resources", *The Bulletin,* Michigan Secondary School Association, May 1948.
6. Wood, Dora, "Planned Field Trips—an Integral Part of Science Units," *School Science and Mathematics,* January 1941.

CHAPTER 15

EXHIBITS AND MUSEUMS IN HEALTH EDUCATION

By definition, to exhibit is to "present to view . . . especially in order to attract notice as to what is interesting or instructive . . ." Exhibits are in such common use as a means of "attracting notice" to organizations, localities, and products that every reader is familiar with a wide range in their uses and applications. Health teachers as well as other teachers should be aware of and familiar with the uses to which exhibits may be put in health education.

Exhibits amount to an organization of subjects and materials in such a way that they convey a specific meaning, idea or set of ideas. Ordinarily, exhibits appeal to the sense of sight, as for example, in the case of an exhibit displaying the various models and demonstrations prepared by a class during a health teaching unit. On the other hand, they may be composed of objects which can be picked up, examined, and operated. However, the various elements in the exhibit should all contribute to the basic idea with which it is concerned. Thus, for example, if the point of an exhibit is to show the work of a class during a semester, all of the pupil's models, demonstrations, and other work may be displayed together, regardless of their application, merely to show what has been done. But if the purpose is to make a specific point regarding health or safety, only those items which contribute to the making of that point should be exhibited. As an example, in conveying the idea of modern public health methods such things as a demonstration of a water purification plant, a picture of a modern sewage disposal plant, a model of a country privy and a country well, and a chart showing various bacteria which are transmitted by way of polluted water, may be organized in an exhibit in such a way as to emphasize the importance of modern sanitary methods.

Since exhibits may usually be regarded as visual aids, it is obviously essential that they be displayed in easily seen locations and that they have eye appeal, (art teachers can play an important role in helping to design and locate good exhibits.) Moreover, since we know that the best of exhibits in any field soon become uninteresting and boresome, as a general rule it is also essential that they be displayed for not more than a few days at a time.

Uses of Exhibits.—There are three major ways in which health teachers may utilize exhibits: (1) as a means of conveying important health knowledge to the general student body of the school, (2) as a way of calling the attention of parents and other school visitors to specific health matters, and (3) as a tool of health education to be used in the classroom by teachers.

1. CONVEYING HEALTH KNOWLEDGE TO THE GENERAL STUDENT BODY.—There are certain basic knowledges of health, including such phases as nutrition, diet, rest, exercise, cleanliness, safety and first aid, which should be common knowledge to all educated people. Many of the vital concepts involved in these and other areas can be taught, reviewed and reemphasized by way of well-prepared exhibits displayed in prominent places in various parts of the school.

One of the functions of a school health council or committee might well be to plan a squence of exhibits to be displayed throughout the school year. Individual teachers might accept responsibility for preparing and displaying exhibits on given health topics, ranging from balanced diets to exercise, and playground safety. Health classes can do excellent work of this kind in the forms of class projects.

If there are health specialists in the school, they can assist in preparing sequences of health exhibits. Also, art and science teachers can assist very materially in the planning and preparation of school health exhibits.

In some instances certain organizations sell or lend professionally prepared exhibits for use in schools. The American Medical Association, The Cleveland Health Museum (which sells "Suitcase Exhibits" for classrooms) and several commercial concerns are examples of sources for prepared exhibits on health subjects. Exhibits available from these sources include such subjects as certain physiological functions, nutrition, the birth process, various phases of public health, outstanding medical figures and their contributions, and safety problems. Although professionally prepared work may add greatly to the school health exhibit program, it must not be forgotten that exhibit planning and designing, and the necessary research in the health field can constitute an important learning experience for pupils who prepare them as a class project.

Teachers have frequently been lax in leaving health exhibits and posters on display in schools for such long periods that they become utterly valueless. An important part of exhibit planning is to schedule take-down dates as well as display dates. Much of the exhibit's value lies in its eye-catching novelty.

2. EXHIBITS FOR PARENTS AND OTHER VISITORS.—Exhibits are among the many means used to inform parents and other persons as to what children are doing in school. Interpreting the school health program to parents is a most worthwhile activity and one that can be rewarding in terms of both parental cooperation and support. Since parents are likely to take a marked interest in the work of their own children, exhibits which have been made by pupils are likely to attract and thus, perhaps, to instruct the parents on some health concepts being given at school. As an example one school exhibit composed of colorful "cut-outs" of various wholesome breakfast foods and photographs of children at work and at play made the point that a good breakfast is important for vigorous and exacting activity during the day; some parents admitted that seeing this exhibit caused them to take their children's breakfasts more seriously.

Some schools make a practice of displaying exhibits and other materials at times when they know that parents will be visiting the school. This is sometimes done for the specific purpose of increasing the parents' health awareness and knowledge with the hope that they will pay closer attention to such things as: the eating and resting habits of their children; the importance of a good nutritious breakfast; the use of television; and cleanliness and grooming.

3. EXHIBITS IN HEALTH EDUCATION.—Exhibits have sometimes been found to be an effective way to introduce units of instruction or even entire courses. When pupils enter a room, see and examine new, attractive and meaningful things, their interest tends to be aroused. They are thus introduced to a new subject in a way that involves learning and that encourages more learning.

A recommended procedure is for teachers to collect suitable exhibits when possible from professional and commercial sources as well as from among pupil projects. The teacher should use these exhibits in introducing new material, in discussing means of educating the public on health subjects, and in planning exhibits with classes. In the case of planning exhibits, superior, fair, and inferior work may be shown and analyzed for those things which make them good, mediocre or poor.

It is essential that exhibits be factually correct. Thus it is frequently necessary for pupils to do considerable study and research concerning many health topics in order that they may present authentic information. The accuracy of the health and safety information conveyed by the exhibit may well constitute a means of appraisal and evaluation of the knowledge of the pupils involved. In the primary grades labeling the parts of an exhibit may be used as an exercise in writing and spelling.

Principles of exhibit construction and preparation.—Some principles to keep in mind regarding exhibits are: (1) ordinarily they should convey a single message, (2) they should be as simple as possible in order to be quickly understood, (3) they should involve a minimum of reading, (4) they should be eye-catching in terms of location, color and lighting. When possible, movement and sound should be included. In other words, not only the exhibit itself but also its meaning should command attention.

Perhaps the most important single principle to keep in mind when preparing an exhibit is that every part of it should contribute to making one very apparent point. A most common error is to attempt to convey too much through a single exhibit, with the result that all points may be obscured even though there may be eye-catching design, color, and motion.

School and Classroom Exhibits.—It has been mentioned previously that exhibits ordinarily should be constructed to convey a single idea in a short space of time in that most audiences who view them are moving. Examples of this are in the cases where pupils and parents are moving through the school halls and corridors where exhibits are displayed. However, exhibits used by teachers or work groups in classrooms and laboratories can be somewhat more elaborate and involved because the audience or class can have sufficient time to study the various phases of the exhibit and the teacher is present to answer questions and to make explanations.

Like all other teaching aids, the concepts and vocabulary of exhibits should be geared to the age level of the intended audience. The following example shows how an exhibit with limited vocabulary and easily understood concepts can be used in primary grades. A primary grade teacher and her class constructed a "good grooming exhibit" in the form of a railroad engine pulling cars. To each car was attached some article used in everyday good grooming such as a comb, tooth brush, toothpaste box, handkerchief, and fingernail file. The only words used were Good Grooming Train in large lettering, and the label of each car such as Comb Car, Handkerchief Car and Toothpaste Car. Each morning the children gave attention to the exhibit and the children who had made use of the articles of each car that particular morning got to ride on the Good Grooming Car. One pupil was selected as the engine and all who qualified "hooked on" behind him and made a trip around the room. The number of pupils eligible to ride increased rapidly after the idea was introduced. Although an exhibit and its use such as the Good Grooming Train is excellent, the teacher should be careful to eliminate any tendency toward competition among the children.

Other primary teachers have used a similar device in the form of a Good Foods Train to encourage a wise selection of foods. For example, the cars may be made with a slit in them. The children make colorful pictures of various types and kinds of foods. When they include certain essential foods in their diets they may slide a picture into the appropriate slit so that the food shows on the car. The train makes a colorful and changing exhibit and the children enjoy both the food study and the ensuing train ride. In using a food train exhibit of this kind care must be taken on the part of the teacher to avoid calling attention to those children who are unable to eat certain foods because of home and family circumstances.

Exhibits of food for the primary level can be composed of pictures and models of various foods. In some cases, a large number of pictures are made or cut out of magazines. A large breakfast plate and bowl, lunch plate, and supper plate are made and attached to a background piece. Each day the class helps to select food from the collected pictures which constitute a balanced diet and pin or stick them to the desired plate. In this way they learn that balanced diets can involve considerable variety. Among older pupils, this same general type of plan can be followed except that the basic values of the foods such as proteins, vitamins, and minerals can be introduced to show that these are the essential factors to be considered in the selection of a good diet.

Some primary grade teachers have had success with an exhibit which is made of a wooden wheel on a stand. On the wheel are pasted samples of the essential foods. Each day, those children whose total food intake for the previous day included the foods that are essential in a balanced diet get to spin the wheel. Since the wheel is frequently used, some teachers keep it in an easily seen spot in the room and have background materials and objects near it to complete the exhibit when it is not in use.

Intermediate grade and junior high school pupils can prepare an exhibit in which a properly laid table place setting is displayed on a shelf and pictures or models of suitable foods are added in different combinations from time to time. For unusual but effective perspective the various pieces in this exhibit may be secured to a flat board and hung from a wall in picture fashion. This exhibit is useful for teaching pupils the proper way to arrange table place settings as well as for helping to teach principles of food selection.

Some exhibits can be effective at several grade levels and even with adults. For example, one displaying the essential and desirable contents of different sizes of first-aid kits, and one showing the steps in the first aid treatment of various common injuries would be worth while from, perhaps, the sixth grade upwards. Other exhibits of this general application might include:

1. Diagramatic or pictorial representations of:
    a. The approved method of artificial respiration
    b. Poisonous and non-poisonous snakes and plants
    c. Harmful and useful bacteria.

2. A safe rifle or bow and arrow range, possibly contrasted with unsafe ones, with key precautions prominently displayed.

3. Good outside readings, samples, and pictures dealing with some special phases of health, such as fitness for sports, sports and games for the family, and the control of body weight.

4. The various public and private health resources at the disposal of young people, schools, or citizens in general. This might involve a picture of a young person in the center connected by strings to pictures of various agencies, clinics, and individuals.

5. A collection of teeth, ranging from healthy to badly decayed, to point up the question, "At what point should care or treatment begin?"

6. For high school students, a presentation of the various possible careers in the general field of health, ranging from school and public health educators to nurses, food inspectors, sanitarians, physicians, and psychiatrists. Leaflets, fliers, booklets, and books describing careers in specific areas might be made available as a part of the exhibit.

It was mentioned previously that many teachers prefer to use exhibits, demonstrations, and other devices which have been made by their pupils. Frequently they prefer to propose only a topic and leave specific planning and designing largely to their classes or to committees within classes. It is significant that invariably teachers, even teachers of primary grades, report being astonished by the ability of pupils to make plans and carry through in constructing exhibits with a minimum of assistance from the teacher.

MUSEUMS IN HEALTH EDUCATION.—There are three common ways in which museums are utilized in health education: (1) established public museums may be visited, (2) museums may serve as a source for audio-visual materials on health subjects, and (3) in some cases schools may develop their own health museums.

Visitations.—Because of the fact that increasing numbers of museums have taken an interest in and have prepared exhibits and materials on health subjects, teachers of health should explore the possibility that museums in their locality may have displays dealing with some phase of health and related fields. In some instances, visiting school groups may see ingenious models showing the human nervous system in a transparent model, a giant heart with ingenious operative devices, pictures and other displays showing new surgical techniques and the operation of artificial limbs, working models of digestive systems, food exhibits, representations of the embryonic and fetal periods of life, and the birth process.

Class trips should be planned carefully in advance. A psychological readying process should include alerting the pupils to what is to be seen and providing sufficient insight into the museum offering to insure maximum benefit from the experience. Follow-up activities might involve a review of what was seen and discussion and study of subjects suggested by the trip. Moreover, visiting natural history, medical, and art museums should stimulate ideas regarding the design and preparation of exhibits and displays.

Audio-visual materials.—In some localities teachers may find museums to be a worthwhile source of audio-visual aids that are useful in health instruction. Even though a museum may list offerings entitled "health" as such, some of its "science" offerings may include information on anatomy, physiology, neurology, medicine, medical history and various phases of health. The museum may provide booklets and other literature. Some broadcast radio programs which should be considered for possible health instruction value. In a few cases, museums constitute an audio-visual center providing materials ranging from films to records. Museums such as the Cleveland Health Museum and the Metropolitan Muesum of Natural History in New York both lend and sell effective portable exhibits. A note addressed to local and regional museums will produce listings of whatever audio-visual materials may be available to teachers.

School Museums.—In some cases it is possible to develop a school health museum. This can be done most satisfactorily if a school has a health laboratory. If the more modern type health education laboratory is not available an ordinary classroom can be set aside for health instruction and all materials used in teaching concentrated in the health room.

Exhibits, models, demonstrations, charts, objects, and other suitable materials may be accumulated over a period of time. Health class projects may include planning and building the necessary display space. Planning and setting up the entire museum layout in terms of some central theme can also be a class activity. In order to round out a complete display, it may sometimes be necessary for pupils to make new exhibits.

The available space will determine the extensiveness of the school museum display at any given time. However, it is important that the same materials not be left on display for long periods of time. Rather, they should be rotated periodically, preferably in a way to point up some significant phase of health. For example, all elements in a museum display might contribute to the central theme, "The World Health Organization and its Activities." One chart might show the basic structure of this organization. A world map might show the World Health Organization's regional offices and the location of its major activities. One exhibit might include books, pamphlets, and a supply of different issues of WHO's Newsletters. It is apparent that the several elements in the museum offering could do much to teach the nature and role of the United Nations' World Health Organization in the world today.

Where museum work of this general kind is done, school classes not involved in the project and perhaps not taking health courses at a particular time may be invited to visit the exhibits. If visitors are invited, mimeographed fliers are useful for providing orientation and commentary on the various displays, and they may be very helpful in subsequent review and discussion.

If materials are to be assembled so that sequences of museum displays may be planned for an entire school year, it is apparent that storage space will be an important consideration. In fact, this constitutes a major limiting factor in many situations where space and storage facilities are limited. Another factor which sometimes prevents school health museums from playing the role that they might in health education is the common absence of a health education room as such. The old and outmoded procedure, particularly in junior and senior high schools, of scheduling health classes in many different classrooms throughout the school building makes it next to impossible to utilize both demonstrations and exhibits which are so important in health instruction. In this respect attention should be called to the field of science. If junior and senior high school science classes were shifted from one room to another without laboratory facilities, the quality of instruction would likely be very low. Practically the same situation exists in health education. Consequently, health instruction in those schools lacking a health laboratory or at least a health room, is usually of a comparably low quality. Unfortunately a majority of the junior and senior high schools have not progressed to the point of having a health laboratory or for that matter even a health classroom as such.

Questions for Discussion

1. What are some uses of exhibits in the school health program? Consider application in the total school health program.
2. How can teachers in subject matter areas other than health be utilized in the preparation of exhibits?
3. What are some important considerations to be kept in mind when exhibits are being used to convey health or safety concepts to the general student body?
4. How can a coordinated sequence of health exhibits be planned in a school?
5. What are the major sources of health exhibits?
6. In what ways can exhibits be used as teaching devices in health education classes?

7. What are some principles which should guide the planning and preparation of exhibits?
8. In what ways can museums be utilized in health instruction? Under what conditions is a health museum in a school feasible?

Suggested Class Activities

1. Prepare a list of exhibit topics which would be suitable for use at: (1) the elementary school level, (2) the junior high level, (3) the senior high level, (4) the college level. Of what elements might each exhibit be composed?
2. Draw up a lay-out for several exhibits, showing charts, models, literature, and other elements to be incorporated. Pay particularly close attention to eye-appeal, simplicity, and unity in terms of conveying a single idea or concept.
3. Working as committees, construct several actual exhibits for presentation to the class.
4. If you are now teaching evaluate your teaching situation in terms of: (1) how exhibits might be utilized, (2) whether or not a health museum might be feasible.

References

1. Chandler, A. C., *Audio-visual Techniques for Enrichment of the Curriculum.* New York, 1948, Noble and Noble, Publisheers Inc.
2. Dale, E., *Audio-visual Methods in Teaching.* New York 1946, The Dryden Press.
3. Gebhard, B., "How Cleveland Museum Educates Its Public on Health Matters," (reprint), *Hospital Management,* Sept. 1949.
4. Grout, R. E., *Health Teaching in Schools.* Philadelphia 1948, W. B. Saunders Co.
5. Haas, K. B., *Audio-visual Education.* New York, 1950, Prentice-Hall, Inc.
6. Kinder, J. S., *Audio-visual Materials and Techniques.* New York, 1950, American Book Co.
7. Wittich, W. and C. F. Schuller, *Audio-visual Materials.* New York 1953, Harper & Co.

CHAPTER 16

DRAMATIZATION IN HEALTH EDUCATION

The Meaning of Dramatization In Health Education.—Dramatization is so comprehensive in scope that it is somewhat difficult to determine its exact place and boundaries in health education. In essence, dramatization may be described as ways and means of expressing feelings and urges through imitation, imagination and personification. But to understand the place of dramatics in health education at the present time, it is necessary to turn back to the early beginning of the child health movement in this country.

In 1918 when the child health organization was founded, a great deal was then known about the things children could do in order to keep healthy in body and mind. However, comparatively little had been done in the schools to win the cooperation of the children and their parents in the learning, use and application of this knowledge. The child health organization was founded on the basis that teachers could take the lead in improving and maintaining the health of school children by making the ways of healthful living so vivid, concrete and attractive that children would be eager to learn and follow them.

In the beginning, dramatic methods had a very important and real part in furthering and advancing the idea of health education. The picturesque, compelling presentation of health habits in the elementary schools, through fairy stories, rhymes, plays and other dramatic devices we look upon now as a way of calling attention to a new day in health education. By following up these dramatic methods with a more definite, accurate and comprehensive approach and with the development of careful, sound principles of pedagogy, health education has now become an integral part of the program of the modern school.

In the present day we are inclined to change or discontinue entirely some of the early ways of teaching, including the dramatic method, nevertheless, there remains a need and place for dramatics in health education, even though most teachers place little or no emphasis on it. It should be remembered that judicial use of the dramatic method is one way of capitalizing on the interest of children through their normal and natural tendencies to make-believe.

Although dramatizations were used largely with elementary school children, they were employed in a limited way with junior and senior high school students. In the secondary schools such things as radio programs, panel discussions and round table discussions of a dramatic nature were used with limited degrees of success in health education.

Characteristics of Children As a Basis for Dramatics.—One of the chief reasons for the use of the dramatic method of teaching may be found in certain characteristic traits of children which are related to dramatization. It has often been said that "play is the business of childhood." It might also be added that a large part of all play, particularly during the very early years, is dramatic in nature. In fact dramatic play seems to be one of the child's primary methods of expressing himself in relation to his environment.

Although much variation is likely to occur, children seem to follow a more or less general pattern as far as dramatic play and interest are concerned. For example, pre-school children appear to derive much satisfaction from imitative types of play.

For children of kindergarten and early elementary school age, it is not uncommon to see boys and girls acting as doctors and nurses in caring for dolls or even younger children in a "make-believe" world. As children advance through the elementary school there seems to be a diminishing interest in the element of make-believe. At the same time there is an increasing interest in projecting one's self into someone else in a "pretend" kind of characterization. Through the process of development, children gradually become interested in higher forms of dramatization either by direct participation or through vicarious experiences.

Of course all children and youth do not fall categorically into a rigid pattern of development as far as dramatic play and interest are concerned, nevertheless, extensive observation of children indicates that a general pattern has been established which can serve as a standard to guide teachers in the use of the dramatic method.

General Characteristics of the Dramatic Method.—Before discussing some of the different forms of dramatization it is necessary to consider certain essential characteristics of the dramatic method which pertain primarily to its advantages and limitations. The fact that dramatization can take so many varied forms in health teaching makes it difficult to evaluate as a teaching method. The frequent criticisms of the dramatic method are often unjustifiable in that the weaknesses are due to the way dramatics are used rather than to the method.

ADVANTAGES.—The very fact that dramatic play has an appeal for children, indicates that the dramatic method offers certain more or less unique advantages. Some of these advantages may be listed as follows:

1. Dramatization affords pupils an opportunity to engage in life-like activity as a way of learning.
2. Dramatization provides another way of varying the learning activity.
3. Dramatization can route the "make-believe" and "pretend" urges of pupils into suitable channels for learning.
4. Dramatization capitalizes on the imagination of pupils.
5. Dramatization presents a good opportunity for the development of proper health attitudes.
6. Dramatization holds the interest of pupils.

LIMITATIONS.—Teachers should be aware of some of the following limitations of the dramatic method as it pertains to health teaching.

1. Unless the "cast" is frequently changed, all pupils will not receive benefit of direct participation.
2. It is possible that entertainment will be substituted for education.
3. Certain forms of dramatization may not warrant the expenditure of time that it takes to prepare and present them.
4. Literary values may be over-stressed with little or no value in health and safety.
5. The lines may be largely "preachment" of health facts.
6. The dialogue might develop into the mere memorization of health facts.
7. There might be an insufficient amount of action and an over abundance of dialogue.
8. There is the possibility that the pupils may be considered only as DRAMATIS PERSONNAE. Despite Shakespeare's immortal words, the play is *NOT* the thing; the learner should receive the greatest consideration when the dramatic method is used.

The forms of dramatization which are presented in the following discussions have been used with varying degrees of success in diverse health teaching situations. For this reason they appear alphabetically because it would perhaps be futile to attempt to present them in order of importance. It will also be noted that some overlapping occurs in the content and scope of some of the various forms of dramatization. This is due largely to differences in terminology used to define certain kinds of dramatization. It is highly recommended that the reader keep in mind the advantages and limitations of the dramatic method when evaluating the forms of dramatization for direct application in teaching-learning situations.

Amateur Shows.—Some teachers have used the amateur show idea with certain degrees of success. The term "amateur show" is used in preference to the term "amateur contest" because it does not seem advisable to have pupils "contest" against each other in matters pertaining to their individual health. Contests in the form of health songs, original poems and the like are recommended for this type of dramatization, provided that the preparation of them does not consume an unwarranted amount of time.

Teachers should exercise caution in the use of contests that pit pupil against pupil with regard to such things as "best posture," "cleanest handkerchief," and other matters pertaining to individual health and healthful living. The inequity of this procedure is obvious when it is considered that there may be certain phases of individual health over which some pupils have little or no control.

HEALTH PLAYS.—If used wisely health plays may serve as a satisfactory supplement to the health learning situation. In considering the health play as a medium for learning, the teacher should take into consideration two very important factors. First, the time spent on the preparation and presentation of the health play must be justified. If the play is of such length that other desirable learning experiences might have to be curtailed, it is doubtful that it should be used. A second factor that must be considered is the number of class members who will take part in the play. If the teacher must spend a great deal of time with a few pupils to the neglect of the majority, the play could not be considered a desirable health learning medium.

There are two general sources of health plays: those that are developed by the pupils themselves, and those that are published by official and voluntary health groups and by some commercial organizations. Health plays devised by pupils perhaps have more merit in that they draw upon the creative ability of pupils who have a special aptitude for this type of activity. A health unit may include the writing of a short health play as an optional activity. With the help of the teacher, one or more pupils may work on this optional activity to produce a short health play for class presentation. This procedure has proved successful in practical situations as another way of taking into account the individual differences of pupils.

Although health plays that appear in published form may not be as effective as those developed by pupils, they have been used successfully in many situations. When using the published health play it is extremely important that the teacher give utmost consideration to its limitations. One of the difficulties encountered in the use of the ready-made health play comes in the selection of a play that is commensurate with current class projects and interests. If the play is not in exact accord with the health concepts that are being developed with regard to a specific health topic, it is possible that confusion might result.

Experimentation with health plays as a part of teaching units indicates that this type of activity has three rather specific applications. One of these, the optional activity, has been discussed previously. A second way that a health play may be used in teaching units is in the form of an introductory activity. The teacher may employ this approach by selecting and working with a few class members prior to the time the unit is to be introduced. It is advisable that the cast be few in number and that the play be brief. Experience has shown that the genuine enthusiasm of pupils for play acting enhances its potentiality as an approach to the unit. In considering the health play as an introductory activity for a unit, the reader should review the purpose of the unit introduction set forth in a previous chapter.

A third way in which the health play may be used as part of a teaching unit is in the form of an evaluation technique. Pupils can create a health play in order to dramatize those things which were learned in the study of the unit. This procedure is of particular importance in the evaluation of health attitudes.

Pageants.—A pageant may be defined as a story portrayed in dramatic sequence. Its use as a health learning medium is perhaps limited due to such factors as the amount of time for preparation and the need for elaborate pageantry costumes. Moreover, the pageant sometimes borders on the spectacular to the extent that portrayal of the health story may be lost. In other words, pupils who should receive a vicarious type of experience from viewing a pageant may lose sight of the health concepts and become engrossed in the pageantry.

Materials for health pageants may be selected from various sources. Two that are perhaps used more frequently than others are the historical pageant and the seasonal pageant. A specific example of the historical health pageant is one called "Breakfast Through the Ages."*

The historical pageant may also take the form of an original study of a certain aspect of the life of persons who have contributed to the improvement of the health of mankind. In this connection, material might be drawn from a study of the lives of such people as, Louis Pasteur, Clara Barton, Florence Nightingale and others.

The seasonal pageant has been used in conjunction with the study of different kinds of wearing apparel suitable for the changing seasons in various geographical areas.

Pantomime.—In health pantomime, action rather than words, is used to convey meaning. This medium of expression is a popular activity with children at the lower elementary school grade levels. Also, this type of dramatization may be used successfully with pupils who may experience difficulty in verbal expression.

Through the use of the dramatized guessing games known as "Charades," pupils can act out in pantomime such desirable health practices as brushing the teeth, washing the hands, proper ways of crossing the street and many others. This procedure can be used successfully as a means of estimating educative growth that takes place as a result of the study of a specific health topic.

Puppets.—One of the outstanding media of dramatic expression in health teaching in the lower elementary grades is the puppet. There are many different kinds of puppets, some of which include hand and finger puppets, string puppets, rubber hose puppets, clothes pin puppets, spool puppets, and shadow or silhouette puppets. Perhaps the most useful type for health teaching purposes is the hand or finger puppet. This type is easy to construct, and with a minimum of practice, it can be satisfactorily manipulated by children. The hand puppet consists of a head, arms and a piece of colored cloth for a costume. A rubber ball

---

*Published by Cereal Institute, Inc., and edited by Laura Oftedal, Laboratory Schools, University of Chicago.

can serve as the head and the thumb and third finger under the cloth are used for the arms.

Through the use of hand puppets, stories from health readers can be acted out. This process helps pupils to "see" health stories that have been told to them. Another successful way in which puppets can be used is in the introduction of a health unit. In this case the teacher manipulates the puppet and the dialogue usually consists of questions and answers. This procedure is a very satisfactory way to stimulate the interest of primary grade children in a specific health topic.

Quiz Programs. Radio and television quiz programs have gained phenomenal popularity in recent years. Some teachers have capitalized on this by utilizing the health class quiz program as a medium for learning. Like its antecedent, the old fashioned "spelling bee," the health quiz program can be applied in a game or contest. Experience has shown that best results are obtained when the class members produce their own programs with the consultation and help of the teacher.

It is recommended that the quiz program be carried on in such a way that pupils are not eliminated if they fail to give a correct answer. Rather than use the process of elimination, some sort of point system should be devised so that a majority of the class members are active participants at all times.

Radio Broadcasts. The use of "radio broadcasts" may take a variety of forms when used as a means of providing learning experiences in health. Two examples are given here.

In the classroom situation a health radio program may be planned and presented by the class members. A homemade microphone and sufficient other simple equipment may be provided for proper atmosphere. Such materials as book reviews on health, original health stories, original health skits and the like may be made more interesting through this medium. All pupils should have the opportunity to be a part of the radio program as well as members of the listening audience.

The public address system is fast becoming standard equipment in the modern school. This medium has been used to advantage in health dramatization in some situations. This is done by channeling the program directly to the room in which the health class is taking place. The class members become the listening audience for other class members who have prepared the program. Alternating pupils on the program is recommended unless the radio broadcast is optional activity that a few pupils have selected.

Role-Playing and Socio-drama. The terms "role-playing" and "socio-drama" for purposes of this discussion are synonymous and they may be used interchangeably. Role-playing is a type of dramatization that is not rehearsed. This procedure in health teaching is most effective when the dramatization centers on a central theme in the form of a health problem.

Essentially, the socio-drama technique consists of having one or more pupils assume a role in a situation involving a health problem. Other supporting role players can be selected from the class if necessary. Those participating directly may be given limited amounts of information regarding the health problem while the other class members are given complete information about the health problem. With the information available the members of the cast carry on for a specified period of time in an attempt to arrive at a satisfactory solution of the health problem.

There are numerous ways in which the technique of socio-drama can be used in health teaching. One concrete example of the use of this technique concerns its application as a method of appraising learning in a high school unit on first aid. This was done in one situation by having a pupil in the class take the part of a person who had sustained a type of injury requiring first aid. All class members with the exception of one stayed in the room. One pupil was required to remain out of the room until such time as he was called in by the teacher to examine the first aid "case." As a means of putting into practice the material that had been studied in the unit, the pupil had the problem of deciding upon the type of "injury" that had occurred and then applying appropriate first aid. Clues were given in the form of "symptoms" and actions of the "injured" pupil. All class members had an opportunity to follow this procedure in determining the type of injury and rendering first aid. Each member of the class also served as an injured victim in the socia-dramatic situation.

Another practical way of using the technique of role-playing is by means of the panel discussion and the round-table discussion. In the panel discussion each member of the panel sets forth his views on an aspect of the health problem under discussion. After the views of all panel members are presented they are summarized by the chairman and opened to discussion by the remaining members of the class who act as the audience. The round-table differs slightly from the panel discussion procedure in that any member of the round-table group may interject a comment or question by seeking recognition of the chairman for permission to do so. The role-playing technique can be applied in these two methods of discussion by having pupils assume the role of certain school officials, community officials, professional personnel, or laymen who might be members of the specific discussion group. For example, in a panel or round-table discussion for a "Classroom Parent Teachers Association Meeting" one pupil could assume the role of the school principal, another pupil could take the part of the school nurse and another could be a teacher. The rest of the class would make up the P.T.A. audience as the panel or round-table group discussed an important school health problem.

The round-table procedure is particularly well-adapted to the problem solving approach at the secondary school level. Another of its chief values lies in the fact that it gives pupils a better understanding of health problems facing adults, and at the same time it provides for a more favorable influence on health attitudes.

Story Telling and Story Playing. In most cases dramatization is centered around a story. This medium of providing health learning experiences is particularly useful with children of early elementary school age because it is a way in which they can participate in the experiences of others. The fact that practically all children receive a great deal of satisfaction and enjoyment from listening to stories makes this procedure a very desirable way for the teacher to capitalize on a natural interest.

Health stories may be related to children by reading or through story telling. Of the two, story telling seems to be far more effective. Some teachers find it necessary to read stories because of the time element involved in learning the content of them. However, if at all possible, stories should be told so that the reading material does not act as a barrier between the teacher and the pupils. In telling the story it is not necessary to commit it to memory. On the other hand, if the teacher has an outline of it in mind, she should experience ease in relating it to pupils.

After a health story has been told to the pupils, a group evaluation should take place with regard to such factors as the meaning of the story, the reason why it was interesting, and its most important points. Among other things, this short evaluation period serves the purpose of the next logical learning procedure which consists of story-playing or acting out the story. Children can select the characters that they would like to portray and if time allows, all class members should be given an opportunity to participate. With large classes, stories should be short so that more than one story can be told, thus, giving more pupils the opportunity for direct participation without too much overlapping in casting.

Story telling is a desirable way to initiate a health unit at the early elementary level because of its possibilities in arousing interest in a health problem. When story telling is followed by story playing, pupils have a better opportunity to find purposeful goals in relation to the specific health topic under consideration. It should be recalled that this is one of the fundamental purposes of the introductory phase of the health teaching unit.

It is not necessary for all health stories to originate with the teacher. Pupils should be given the opportunity to relate stories of their own past experiences which pertain to the area of health which is being studied. Experience has shown that pupils enjoy telling of their experiences, and that they profit greatly from it.

Grade Placement of Health Dramatic Activities.—Because of a lack of objective evidence, the grade placement of health dramatic activities is difficult to determine satisfactorily. Moreover, it is doubtful that sufficient experimentation with the various forms of health dramatization has been done by teachers to justify resolute recommendations with regard to the specific grade level where best results can be obtained. Also, individual differences in teachers may be such that one teacher might have a high degree of success with one form of health dramatization at a certain grade level while another teacher might experience failure at the same grade level with the same form of health dramatization.

Perhaps the characteristics of children pertaining to dramatization, discussed earlier in this chapter, can be considered as valid criteria for the grade placement of the various forms of dramatization. In the absence of scientific evidence, child characteristics along with successful experiences of teachers in the use of health dramatization may serve as a guide for the application of this medium of learning at the various grade levels.

Questions for Discussion
1. What is meant by the dramatic method in health teaching?
2. What are some of the characteristics of children which might serve as criteria for the use of the dramatic method in health teaching?

3. What are some advantages of the dramatic method in health teaching?
4. What are some limitations of the dramatic method in health teaching?
5. In health teaching, why should the term "amateur show" be preferred to the term "amateur contest?"
6. What are two sources of health plays? Which source is better? How do you support your answer?
7. What are some of the specific applications of health plays in health teaching units?
8. How can pageants be used effectively in health teaching?
9. What are some of the precautions that should be taken in the use of the health quiz program?
10. How can the school public address system be used in health education?

Suggested Class Activities

1. Form a group for a round-table discussion to consider certain characteristics of children which would indicate that dramatization should be a "natural" health teaching method at certain grade levels.
2. Consult the advantages and limitations of the dramatic method of health teaching presented in this chapter. See if you can add three more advantages and three more limitations to the lists.
3. With some other members of the group write an original health play for class presentation.
4. Give a pantomime before the group which portrays a valid health concept.
5. Construct a hand puppet that might be used in a health teaching situation at the primary level.
6. Prepare a health quiz program with some other members of the group.
7. Form a group to prepare a socio-drama for presentation to the class.
8. Tell a health story to the class and then have them engage in story-playing.

References

1. Chandler, Anna Curtis and Irene F. Cypher, *Audio-Visual Techniques,* New York, 1948, Noble and Noble Publishers, Inc.
2. Grout, Ruth, *Health Teaching in Schools,* Philadelphia, 1953, W. B. Saunders Company.
3. Kepler, Hazel, *The Child and His Play,* New York, 1952, Funk & Wagnalls Company.
4. "Role-Playing in the Classroom," Portfolio of Teaching Techniques, Washington, D. C., Educator's Washington Dispatch, 1950.
5. Wayland, L., "Health Education Dramatized," Health Education Journal, Volume IX, December, 1945.

CHAPTER 17

SOURCES OF HEALTH EDUCATION MATERIALS AND INFORMATION

There are two main types of source materials available in the field of health education. These types are printed materials such as textbooks, workbooks and pamphlets, and audio-visual aids including motion pictures, film strips, photographs, still picture, slides, models, maps, posters, specimens, diagrams, graphs, museum exhibits, anatomical charts and others. There are perhaps more teaching material in health and safety education available to teachers from all types of organizations throughout the country, than in any other area of the school program. One of the main reasons for this is that there are so many different types of organizations interested in the health and safety of the school population. A great deal of the material available to teachers and students from organizations of all types throughout the country, are free and inexpensive. Therefore, just the very fact that so many groups are attempting to prepare study materials for the school child means that there is likely to be a great variation in the worth of the material in terms of modern educational standards.

In the case of health and safety textbooks and workbooks, the same as other types of reading and textbooks used in the schools, there are usually criteria by which to judge suitability. In some instances, local communities as well as state groups, have set up special criteria by which all textbooks, workbooks and printed materials used in the school, are judged in order to make certain that desirable reading and study materials are finally selected. Although the criteria for all types of visual aids have not been as extensively developed and applied as in the case of textbooks and workbooks, nevertheless, there is a great need in the field of health and safety education to apply certain criteria to the materials prepared and distributed by most of the organizations offering these to the schools.

Some of the criteria to keep in mind in selecting health and safety materials, both printed matter and visual aids, are:
1. They should be free from bias.
2. All factual materials should be accurate.
3. The vocabulary should be appropriate for the grade level.
4. Study materials should not be sensational.
5. Health and safety materials should be free from fear psychology.
6. All health and safety materials used should make a contribution in the areas with which they deal.
7. The type used in printed matter should be appropriate for the particular grade level.
8. The ideas expressed in both visual aids and printed matter should be appropriate for the grade level.
9. Health and safety materials should be designed to stimulate thought.
10. Health and safety study materials should reflect present day knowledge and scientific accuracy.
11. All materials used should be attractive.

The many questions from teachers concerning the sources of available satisfactory health education materials indicate that many, and especially, elementary school classroom teachers are not aware of the extensive amount of health and safety material available free or at very little cost. Because, there are so many inquiries from time to time concerning the sources of materials, this chapter has been devoted largely to a listing of those sources and, to giving some indication of the kinds of material available from each. It is hoped that in this way teachers can obtain and make use of some of these study materials by directly contacting those organizations likely to have the kinds of material they want.

Textbooks.—Textbooks on health, hygiene and safety are available for all grade levels in the schools and for the college level. Several publishers offer series of textbooks which range from grades one through grade eight. Also, there are many health and hygiene texts available for high school and college use. Numerous schools throughout the country now provide one or more of the health series in order to encourage systematic progression of learning, beginning with the primary grades in the elementary school and progressing through the upper elementary, junior and senior high school.

In that textbooks are an exceedingly valuable teaching tool which places at the disposal of any teacher the experience, research, and careful planning of specialists in the field, they should be regarded as basic in the health teaching program. Those teachers who do not have access to health texts for use in their classes are very markedly handicapped.

The following is a list of publishers of health and safety textbooks series.

Elementary School Health and Safety Textbooks:
American Book Company, New York
Bobbs-Merrill Company, Inc., Indianapolis
Ginn and Company, New York
D. C. Heath and Company, Boston
Laidlaw Brothers, Chicago
Lyons and Carnahan, Chicago
The Macmillan Company, New York
Scott, Foresman and Company, New York
John C. Winston Company, Philadelphia

Junior High School:
Bobbs-Merrill Company, Inc., Indianapolis
Blakiston Company, New York
Ginn and Company, New York
Lyons and Carnahan, Chicago
The Macmillan Company, New York

Senior High School:
American Book Company, New York
Chartwell House, Inc., New York
Ginn and Company, New York
Harcourt, Brace and Company, Inc., New York
Houghton Mifflin Company, New York
D. C. Heath and Company, New York
J. B. Lippincott Company, Philadelphia
Lyons and Carnahan, Chicago
The Macmillan Company, New York
D. Van Nostrand Company, New York

Some of the publishers of these health and safety texts for the elementary, junior high and senior high school provide some free and some inexpensive health materials, including charts which show health concepts to be taught at the various grade levels.

Library Sources.—Numerous library sources are available which supply health teaching materials and information for older students and teachers. These sources include:

1. Library books on a wide range of topics.
2. Standard encyclopedias and other reference works.
3. The periodical literature, including popular articles, such as those found in *Today's Health* and sometimes in *The*

Reader's Digest, Time, Fortune, and others. Also, there are more technical articles such as those found in the professional literature, some of which are suitable for the teacher's personal use and for more advanced students. The various guides to periodical literature should be utilized.
4. Newspapers, some of which carry regular articles by reputable health authorities in addition to reporting new developments and controversies.

In many cases the school library is used as a place for concentrating books, charts, leaflets, bulletins and other health materials of a similar nature. In this way all persons who teach health are able to benefit from all that is acquired.

A major advantage of utilizing the various current materials in health education is that, from an early age, students may be taught to become discriminating and careful in their evaluation of sensational, unsubstantiated, and inadequately documented reports.

The Departments of Education and Health.—Both education and health departments are included in this category because of their close relationship in matters of school health. In many cases, education and health departments at city, county and state levels constitute a major source of health teaching materials and information. A primary function of both groups is to provide information, audio-visual aids, and other materials for educational purposes. Pamphlets, film strips, motion picture films, study guides, reference lists and audio-visual handbooks or guides are only a part of the usual offering.

Certain of the personnel and programs of health departments may be regarded as especially valuable sources for health materials and information. The resource person closest to the teacher is the school nurse. She is usually able to be of great assistance in bringing the offerings of the health department within reach of the teacher. Moreover, in some instances the nurse is qualified to make competent presentations to classes and parent-teachers groups on certain subjects. Some teachers have found nurses to be especially valuable for teaching some of the functions and problems of public health work in their own cities.

It is sometimes possible to arrange for other health department personnel to assist in health instruction in the classroom. For example, physicians may be invited to talk about their specialty, answer questions, or to demonstrate and teach the meaning of the physical examination. They, along with dentists, mental health workers, and statisticians, may also serve as consultants on current health information.

The Federal Government.—Various branches of the federal government provide a considerable amount of worthwhile health materials. Outstanding among these are the Office of Education, the Public Health Service, and the Children's Bureau under the Department of Health, Education and Welfare. The Office of Education has consultation services in health education. The individuals in charge of this program will provide information as to desired source materials and current practices in the nation. The Public Health Service's various organizations, including the National Institutes of Health, will provide a great deal of valuable information regarding research on the major diseases; the U. S. Public Health program in general; the relationship of the national public health service with local health departments; and statistics on various aspects of public health. (The National Office of Vital Statistics is a division of the Public Health Service.)

Other governmental organizations which are important in this connection include, the Library of Congress, the Bureau of Human Nutrition and Home Economics of the Department of Agriculture, the National Housing Agency of the Federal Public Housing Authority, and indirectly, the United Nations' World Health Organization.

Professional Organizations.—A large number of professional organizations are excellent sources for materials and information on many health topics. They may be utilized as major sources for a wide variety of audio-visual aids, including charts, models, slides, exhibits, film strips and motion pictures. Some furnish free and/or inexpensive literature on a wide variety of health topics, and in some cases, teaching plans to aid the teacher. Many professional organizations may be called upon to furnish speakers and demonstrators who can add materially to the success of teaching units and citizens' gatherings.

Many professional organizations are included among the sources of free and inexpensive materials listed later in this chapter. However, some of the organizations which are most useful in providing information and guidance to teachers are as follows:

>The American Association for Health, Physical Education, and Recreation, Health Education Division. 1201 16th Street, NW, Washington 6, D. C.
>The American Cancer Society. 47 Beaver Street, New York 4.
>The American Dental Association. 222 E. Superior Street, Chicago 11.
>The American Hearing Society. 1537 35th Street, NW, Washington 7, D. C.

The American Heart Association. 1790 Broadway, New York 19.
The American Medical Association. 535 N. Dearborn Street, Chicago 10.
The American Public Health Association. 1790 Broadway, New York 19.
The American Red Cross. 18th and E Streets, Washington 16, D. C.
The American School Health Association. Room 617, 228 No. LaSalle St., Chicago.
The American Social Hygiene Association. 1790 Broadway, New York 19.
The National Committee for Mental Hygiene. 1790 Broadway, New York 19.
The National Foundation for Infantile Paralysis. 120 Broadway, New York 5.
The National Safety Council. 425 N. Michigan Ave, Chicago.
The National Society for the Prevention of Blindness. 1790 Broadway, New York 19.
The National Tuberculosis Association. 1790 Broadway, New York 19.

Teachers of health should be aware of the many services and materials available from these sources.

Business and Commercial Groups.—Although it is true that health materials distributed for public relations and advertising purposes by business and commercial groups must be scrutinized carefully for bias and distortion (frequently teachers are required to submit films and certain other audio-visual aids to some school authority for approval), many of these groups distribute materials of excellent quality, sometimes free and sometimes at a very low price. In many instances, advertising is restricted to a single identifying label or statement. Some concerns have banded together to promote the sales of all presenting a particular product. For example, the Cereal Institute (135 So. LaSalle Street, Chicago 3), the Florida Citrus Commission (Lakeland, Florida), and the Athletic Institute (209 S. State Street, Chicago), do not advertise particular brands, but rather, devote their efforts to improving the general market involved. Thus, the Cereal Institute identifies itself as "A Research and Educational Endeavor Devoted to the Betterment of National Nutrition," and has a number of individual cereal companies as its supporting membership. Similarly, much of the health information provided by the large life insurance companies is only indirectly related to their business interest. Organizations of these kinds usually do not deal in objectionable advertising, and on the contrary, they sometimes go to considerable expense for personnel and research to provide factually sound and colorful supplementary materials.

FREE AND INEXPENSIVE MATERIALS.—There is evidence that carefully selected, free, health materials on such subjects as diabetes, nutrition, venereal diseases, tuberculosis, cancer and heart disease can raise the level of knowledge of individuals who receive them in the mail even though they receive no other instruction on these subjects.

When properly integrated, many of the free and inexpensive materials provided by professional and governmental groups, public and private agencies, and business and commercial groups unquestionably contribute to the effectiveness of learning.

Some Major Sources of Free and Inexpensive Materials.—Below are listed several sources which many teachers of health have found to be very valuable. It is customary for the various sources to add new materials to their offering and occasionally to drop some; consequently, it is to be expected that examples indicated below may or may not be available at a given time and that prices are subject to change.

American Association for Health, Physical Education, and Recreation. 1201 16th Street, N. W. Washington 6, D. C. Samples of current offerings:

"Health, Physical Education and Recreation in Small Schools," 1948, 67pp., 50c.

"The Doctor Answers Some Practical Questions on Menstruation," 1955, 11pp., 35c.

"National Section for Girl's and Women's Sports," Free.

"The Physical Educator Asks About Health," 18 pp., 50c, 1951.

"Physical Education for Children of Elementary School Age," 1951, 47pp., 50c.

"Desirable Athletic Competition for Children," (A statement on highly competitive athletics for children based on the judgment of outstanding medical doctors, physiologists, and sociologists." 46pp., 50c.

American Medical Association. 535 North Dearborn St., Chicago 10. Samples of current offering:

"First Aid Manual," pocket-size booklet, instructions and illustrations., 32pp., 10c.
"Nursing in the home," 6pp., 5c.
"Our Youth and Narcotics," 4pp., 10c.
"How to Choose a Doctor," 8pp., 15c.
"Visual Efficiency," 10pp., 5c.
A series on the Human Body, including. "The Framework" (the bones), "The Engine" (the heart), "The Electric System" (the nerves), "Safety Devices" (sense organs). 15c each, $1.25 for the set of ten.
"They're Beating the Devil out of Epilepsy," (Paul de Kruif), 4pp., 10c.
"Outstanding Medical Advances," 25pp., 15c.
"The Teacher's Role in Mental Hygiene," 12pp., 15c.
"Mental Hygiene in the Classroom—How Would You Help a Child Like This?" 70pp., 15c.
Health Posters, 11x14 inches, in color, set of 8 posters for 25c; topics include. "Colds," "Healthy Hearts," "Food," "Sleep," "Eating Between Meals," "Vacation," and "Early Health," "Radio Handbook," and "TV Handbook."
Teachers may request current listings of all A.M.A. publications about: "Your Health."

American Heart Association. 1790 Broadway, New York 19 (If possible, requests should be made via the particular state association, e.g., Heart Association of Maryland.) Samples of current offering:

Posters: "Your Heart and How it Works," either large 16x22 inches, or small 8x11 inches for individual use. Diagram of the heart. Free.
"What You Should Know About Rheumatic Fever," and others in the Know Your Heart Series of booklets. Free.
"5 Facts You Should Know About Heart Disease," illustrated leaflet. Free.

American Dental Association, 222 E. Superior Street, Chicago 11.
This organization supplies a variety of excellent free and inexpensive materials for all school levels. The current offering includes:

"Dental Health Facts for Teachers," booklet dealing with the structure and function of teeth, dental problems, diet and dental health, etc., 28pp. Free.

Pamphlets: "Frank Visits the Dentist," (for lower elementary grades). Free. "Everybody Smile," (for upper elementary grades). Free.

Charts and Posters: Toothbrushing chart, "How to Brush the Teeth," 21x25 inches, 50c. Primary posters, 22x28 inches, set of four, $1.50.

Films (may be rented from the association for $2.50, but some of these are available through many education and health departments), and Film strips (may be rented for $1.00). Samples:

"Winky the Watchman," animated cartoon for elementary school.

"Teeth Are to Keep," for primary and intermediate grades.

"It's Your Health," a dramatic presentation for upper grade pupils.

This association will provide a catalogue showing its current offerings.

American Institute of Baking, 400 East Ontario Street, Chicago, 11.

This organization provides materials for various grade levels; and they are free in reasonably large quantities. However, the following poster has been exceptionally popular especially at the elementary school level:

"The Wheel of Good Eating: Eat Foods From Each Group Daily, Keep It Balanced—Make It Spin." A colorful guide to food selection.

Department of Health, Education, and Welfare, Washington 25, D. C.

Copies of the following publications may be obtained from the Superintendent of Documents, U. S. Government Printing Office, Washington, D. C.: The current list includes:

"Teachers Contribute to Child Health," a very useful guide to the elementary school teacher's role in the school health program. 44pp., 20c.

"Better Health for School-Age Children," 6pp., 10c.

"Physical Education in the School Child's Day," 94pp., 30c.

"The School Lunch—Its Educational Contribution," 28pp., 25c.

General Mills, Inc., Minneapolis 1. This is one of the very rich sources of free materials of wide variety. The current offering includes:

"What do children eat?" A booklet on food facts and problems: a survey of 59,727 school children shows (1) that nutrition is one of America's most pressing problems, and (2) that eating habits can be improved through education.

"The Story of the Cereal Grains." Booklet.

"A Nutrition Guide." A colorful booklet on the relationship of the basic seven foods to health.

"Teacher's Activity Book." (For a Program in Nutrition and Health).

"Teacher's Guidebook." (A Digest of Basic Nutrition and Health Information).

Elementary school readers: "Dick Davis, Food Detective," "Working and Playing," "Letters to Tony."

Large (24x36 inches) charts, including: "Health Is Not Just Luck," for elementary school use, and "Conserving Minerals and Vitamins," for older groups and adults.

Smaller chart: "Basic 7 Food Chart for Meal Planning," especially for home use in meal planning.

Metropolitan Life Insurance Company, 1 Madison Ave., New York 10.

This is one of the richest sources of free materials designed for school use. The company provides a large packet of materials, some of which are included in the following listing:

"About Us and Our Friends," booklet for elementary school children, ages 5 to 8. Contains verses, pictures, etc. Free.

"First Steps in Health Education," a guide for elementary school teachers. Free.

"Health Bulletin for Teachers," furnishes up-to-date information on the field of health. On request, teachers will be placed on the mailing list to receive this publication regularly.

"The School Health Program," a series of discussions of ways in which school, home and community may cooperate in the interests of child health.

"The School Administrator, Physician, and Nurse in the School Health Program—Functions and Education."

"Absent from School Today . . ." booklet for elementary school teachers.

"What Teachers See," a booklet showing common deviations from health; in color.

"Common Childhood Diseases," booklet.

"Health Heroes," booklets. A 35mm sound film strip in color may also be obtained on Florence Nightingale, free of charge.

"For Good Teeth," booklet.

A listing of many other free materials may be obtained by writing to this company. Metropolitan also prepares and distributes the famous "Statistical Bulletin."

National Dairy Council, 111 North Canal St., Chicago 6.

This group's booklet which lists its health education materials, folders, booklets, posters, charts, and other aids, should be examined carefully for suitable items. Dairy products play a very prominent role. Consider the following packets:

"Lower Grade Packet"
"Intermediate Grade Packet"
"Upper Grade Packet"
"College Level Packet"
"School Lunch Packet"

National Foundation for Infantile Paralysis, 120 Broadway, New York 5.

This is another of the organizations that are very active in health education work; it provides materials on polio and on other phases of the health field. Its current offering includes: (free unless otherwise indicated).

"Polio: Questions and Answers," booklet.

"Polio Pointers," leaflet that can serve as a small poster, and a flier, "Polio Pointers for Parents."

"Poliomyelitis," a source book for high school students.

"Your National Foundation for Infantile Paralysis: Here's What It Does," flier on progress to date: "Victory in Sight."

"This Is Johnny," a film strip for primary grades designed to reduce the fear often associated with polio by following the experiences of a boy who gets it. Loaned free of charge, or may be purchased at the cost of $1.00.

"Health in Your Town . . . A teaching unit on Community Health," booklet which may be used with a film strip of the same title, furnished on free loan. (Booklet free).

On request this foundation will provide a listing of all its posters, publications, films and exhibits. Its electrical table exhibits are effective in citizens' meetings as well as in classes.

National Society for the Prevention of Blindness, Inc., 1790 Broadway, New York 19.

The low-cost offerings of this society are valuable both as teaching aids and as information sources for the teacher. The current offering includes:

"Causes and Prevention of Blindness in Children of School Age," 12pp., 10c.

"Signs of Eye Trouble in Children," 75c per 100. (2 color), suitable for distribution to groups, e.g. PTA's.

"Classroom Lighting," 16pp., 15c.

"Eye Cues for Eye Health," deals with eyeglasses, good lighting, eyestrain, eyes in mid-life. Free.

"A Guide for Eye Inspection and Testing Visual Activity," 8pp., 5c.

"Study of Procedure Used for Screening Elementary School Children for Visual Defects," 16pp., 10c.

Vision testing charts are also provided at low cost (35c to 40c).

Medium-sized Posters are provided for from 15c to 35c: "Seeing Through Life," "See Better—Play Better," and "The Missing Piece Can Never Be Replaced."

Other offerings: films and a 15-minute talk on parents' responsibilities.

National Tuberculosis Association, 1790 Broadway, New York 19. (Communications should be addressed to county or state association.)

A packet of booklets and other materials may be obtained from this source; it includes:

A listing of all films, charts, exhibits, pamphlets and posters, provided free of charge by the association.

"Help Fight Tuberculosis," and elementary reader, 16pp., illustrated.

"Facts About TB."

"Chest Surgery in TB," booklet with diagrams.

"I Went to the Sanatorium," a booklet on early identification and treatment of TB.

"Crusade of the Christmas Seal," the story behind the double-barred cross.

"Tuberculosis: Basic Facts in Basic English," attractive and simple booklet outlining the nature and scope of the problem.

"What You Need to Know About TB."

In addition to material on tuberculosis, this association distributes excellent booklets, (such as "Why Sleep?") and attractive posters ("Good Food Helps You Keep Fit," and "For Vim and Vigor") on other aspects of health. In many localities, the association is prepared to send representatives to classrooms to teach units on tuberculosis and other health subjects, show films, and do knowledge testing.

Survey of Sources.—Late in 1954, a nation-wide survey of organizations, (public and private), was conducted in order to determine the extent of their activity in this field.* These organizations were asked whether their materials are free or for sale, for what school level or age group their materials are intended, the kinds of materials that they provide, and the quantities that they make available.

The following list, which reflects the findings of that survey, does not purport to be a complete representation of sources which provide good supplementary materials. However, in combination with the major sources listed in the preceding pages, it should help to meet most of the teacher's needs for supplementary materials.

Teachers are urged to examine these sources carefully, to write for descriptive literature and catalogues of materials, and to begin accumulating items that are suitable and that will contribute to the richness of their health education programs.

Aetna Life Affiliated Companies. Education Department. 151 Farmington Avenue, Hartford 15, Connecticut. Health and safety: Pamphlets and motion picture films. Intended for all school levels and lay groups. For individual teachers and groups. Free.

Agricultural Marketing Service, U.S. Dept. of Agriculture, Washington 25, D.C. Pamphlets: "Egg Buying Guides for Consumers," "U.S. Grades of Beef," . . . Suitable for senior high school, college, and lay groups. Limit of 50 copies to an individual or organization. Free.

American Cancer Society. Requests for materials should be directed to the local office of the society; if this address is unknown, requests can be sent to Cancer, c/o the local Post Office. Pamphlets, fliers, and motion picture films. Intended for senior high school, college, teacher training classes, and lay groups. Quantities for distribution to groups. Free.

American Dietetic Association. 620 N. Michigan Avenue, Chicago 11. Some pamphlets and numerous reprints of articles on problems related to diet. Some materials suitable for pupil use, much for older persons and teachers. Some free, most inexpensive.

American Hearing Society, 817 14th Street, N. W., Washington 5, D. C. Fliers, posters, and leaflets. Intended for all grade levels, college, and lay groups. Available for individual teachers and for groups (in limited quantity). Some free, some inexpensive.

---

*Johnson, W. R., et al, "A Survey of Some Sources of Free and Inexpensive Health Instruction Materials," unpub., Univ. of Maryland, 1954.

American Institute of Family Relations, 5287 Sunset Blvd., Los Angeles 27. Pamphlets and sample copies of monthly bulletin, "Family Life," for junior high, senior high, college and lay groups. Quantity for group distribution. Some free, some inexpensive.

American National Red Cross, Office of Publications, 17th and D Streets, N. W., Washington 13, D. C. Health and safety: charts, pamphlets, motion pictures. Intended for junior and senior high school and lay groups. For individual teachers and groups. Some inexpensive, some free.

American Seating Company, Advertising Department, 9th and Broadway, Grand Rapids 2, Michigan. Posture posters. For primary and intermediate grades. Free.

Ar-Ex Cosmetics, Inc., Chicago 7. Booklet: "Beauty Hygiene Syllabus," available for teachers only. Intended for senior high school, college, lay groups. Free.

Association for Childhood Education International, 1200 15th Street, NW, Washington 5, D. C. Pamphlets and bulletins on child growth and health. For teachers. Inexpensive.

Association for Family Living, 28 East Jackson Blvd., Chicago 4. Pamphlets on emotional health, sex education, child development. For teachers. Inexpensive.

Bausch and Lomb Optical Company, 635 St. Paul Street, Rochester 2. Charts, pamphlets, motion picture films. Sent to individual teachers. Some free, some inexpensive.

Better Vision Institute, Inc., 630 Fifth Avenue, New York, 20. Pamphlets, film strips, motion picture films, such as: "Wonderland of Vision," "The Magic Lens," "The Life of Helen Keller," "The House of Vision." Quantities up to 25 copies free. Films loaned free.

Bicycle Institute of America, Inc. Safety charts, pamphlets, posters, motion picture films. Designed for all school levels. Booklets for program directors; others in quantity. Free.

Borden Company, Public Relations Dept., 350 Madison Avenue, New York 17. Charts, pamphlets, fliers. Intended for all school levels and lay groups. Distribution to teachers and groups. Free.

Boy Scouts of America, Health and Safety Service, New Brunswick, New Jersey. Charts, posters, film strips and motion picture films

Sources of Materials and Information

on health and safety. Intended for primary grades to all school levels. Sample posters: "Bike Boners Kill!" "Have You a Plan for Escape From Fire?" "Water Rescue, Bring 'em Back" (on artificial respiration). Some inexpensive, some free.

Bristol-Myers Company, Educational Service Dept., 45 Rockefeller Plaza, New York 20. Charts, pamphlets and film strips on health and grooming. For all school levels. Distributed to individual teachers, and groups. Some free, some inexpensive.

Cereal Institute, Inc., 135 South LaSalle Street, Chicago 3. Many charts, pamphlets, Teacher's Source Books, Teacher's Manuals. Teaching units: "A Classroom Breakfast Party" (primary), "Two Better Breakfast Plays" (intermediate), "A Basic Breakfast Pattern" (high school). Available on request. Free.

Chicago Schools Journal, Chicago Teachers College, 6800 Stewart Street, Chicago 21. Reprints (pamphlets). For teachers.

Child Study Association of America, 132 East 74th Street, New York 21. Pamphlets on health in relation to family life, e.g.: "Understanding Children's Fears," "When Children Ask About Sex," "Getting Along With Brothers and Sisters." For teachers, parents and children. Some free, most inexpensive.

Church and Dwight Company, Inc., 70 Pine Street, New York 5. Pamphlets. Intended for primary and intermediate grades. Available to groups. Free.

Cleveland Health Museum. 8911 Euclid Avenue, Cleveland 6. Charts, pamphlets, film strips, exhibits. For teacher training classes and lay groups. Some inexpensive.

Continental Baking Company, 630 Fifth Avenue, New York 20. Charts, pamphlets, film strips. Intended for primary and intermediate grades. Teaching kit available to all—free. Bulk material also free in some areas.

Employers Mutual of Wausau, 115 West Wausau Avenue, Wausau, Wisconsin. Pamphlets on health and safety. For intermediate grades, junior high school, and teachers training classes. Available to individual teachers. Free.

Fleischmann Division, Standard Brands, Inc., 595 Madison Avenue, New York 22. Motion picture films. From junior high up. Free.

Florida Citrus Commission, Lakeland, Florida. Colorful posters on the importance of citrus fruits to health. Elementary school level. Free.

Food and Nutrition Board, National Research Council, 2101 Constitution Avenue, N. W., Washington 25, D. C. Pamphlets for individual teachers and groups. Some free, some inexpensive.

General Biological Supply House, Inc., 761 E. 69th Place, Chicago 37. Turtox Service Leaflets, including: "Nutrition Experiments" (rats), "Lantern Slides any Teacher Can Make," "The Care of Rats, Mice and Guinea Pigs," "Demonstration and Display Materials." Junior and senior high school, but mainly for teachers. 2c per leaflet in quantity. Single copies free.

Human Nutrition and Home Economics Research, Agricultural Research Service, U. S. Department of Agriculture, Washington 25, D. C. Charts and pamphlets. Examples: nutrition chart titles, "Growth," "Food Makes the Difference in These Twin Rats," "Protein Builds Muscles . . ." (Set of 10 charts, $1.00). Pamphlets: "Food for the Family With Young Children," (free), "Nutrition Up to Date Up to You," (10c). Available to teachers and adult groups. Free and inexpensive.

International Cellucotton Products Company, 919 N. Michigan Avenue, Chicago 11. Charts, pamphlets, motion picture films. Among the most attractive posters: Walt Disney's "How to Catch Cold," and "The Story of Menstruation." Materials suited to all grade levels and adults. Available to teachers and groups. Free.

International Council for Exceptional Children. 1201 16th Street, N. W., Washington 6, D. C. Pamphlets and fliers. Materials are devoted to education, primarily, of exceptional children. Intended for teacher training classes, and teachers of elementary and high schools. Free and inexpensive.

John Hancock Mutual Life Insurance Company, Health Education Service, 200 Berkeley Street, Boston 17. Pamphlets for senior high and up. Both health and safety. Set of booklets includes: "Pain That is Good for You," "Caring for the Sick in the Home," "Concerning Diabetes." Free.

Johnson & Johnson, New Brunswick, New Jersey. Charts, pamphlets, motion picture films. A film on first aid. For junior high school and up. Distributed to individual teachers and groups. Free.

Sources of Materials and Information

Lever Brothers Company, Public Relations Division, Cambridge, Mass. Charts. Primary grades. Individual teachers only. Free.

Liberty Mutual Insurance Company, Home Office Loss Prevention Dept., 175 Berkeley Street, Boston 17. Pamphlets on health and safety. Senior high, college and lay groups. Up to 50 copies free.

Maltex Company, Burlington, Vermont. Charts, pamphlets, posters. Intended for all school levels, college and adults. For individual teachers and groups. Mostly free.

Maternity Center Association, 48 East 92nd Street, New York 28. Charts, pamphlets. For senior high and up. Distributed to individual teachers and to groups. Free and inexpensive.

McKnight & McKnight Publishing Company, Market and Center Streets, Bloomington, Illinois. Pamphlets. For junior high, senior high and college. Individual teachers and groups. Inexpensive.

Modern Talking Picture Service, Inc., 45 Rockefeller Plaza, New York 20. Motion picture films, including: "Health—and the Cycle of Water," "A Better Start in Life," "Your Doctor," "The Clean Look," "Wonderland of Vision." Suitable for junior high and up. Pay postage only, or pick up at local office, free.

National Academy of Sciences, National Research Council, 2101 Constitution Avenue, Washington 25, D. C. Pamphlets, fliers. "Control of Tooth Decay," "Safe Use of Chemical Additives in Foods," "Flour and Bread Enrichment." High School and college level use. Some inexpensive, many free.

National Association for Mental Health, 1790 Broadway, New York 19. Pamphlets, fliers, film strips, motion picture films. Intended for teacher training classes and lay groups. For individual teachers and distribution to groups. Free list of materials available. Some inexpensive, some free.

National Biscuit Company, 449 West 14th Street, New York 14. Pamphlets: 6 page brochure and three student work sheets on breakfast, "Make Mine Breakfast." Free.

National Board of Fire Underwriters, 85 John Street, New York 38. Att. Public Relations Dept. Pamphlets, motion picture films. Pamphlets: "Your Fire Safe Home." Poster: "Danger." Leaflet: "Home Fire Safety Check List." Booklet about the busy fire chief. Intermediate grades. Free.

National Commission on Safety Education, National Education Association, 1201 16th Street, N. W. Washington 6, D. C. Safety teaching aids and materials. Booklets, film strips etc. For all school levels, teachers, lay groups. Inexpensive.

National Epilepsy League, Inc., 130 N. Wells Street, Chicago 6, Illinois. Pamphlets. For junior high and up. For individual teachers and groups. Some free, some inexpensive.

National Foot Health Council, P. O. Box 57, Rockland, Mass. Charts, pamphlets, reprints and posters. Intended for all school levels and lay groups. For individual teachers; small leaflets for groups. Some inexpensive, some free.

National Health Council, 1790 Broadway, New York 19. Materials for senior high and up. For sale.

National Multiple Sclerosis Society, 270 Park Avenue, New York 17. Charts, pamphlets, fliers. Intended for adults. Free.

National Rehabilitation Association, 1025 Vermont Avenue, N. W., Washington 5, D. C. Pamphlets, fliers. For college level. Some inexpensive, some free.

National Safety Council, School and College Division, 425 North Michigan Avenue, Chicago 11. Safety pamphlets, fliers. For all school levels and lay groups. For teachers and groups. For sale.

National Science Teachers Association, 1201 16th Street, N. W., Washington 6, D. C. Pamphlets. Intended for all school levels, but main emphasis on science teaching aids. For individual teachers and groups. Free.

National Society for Crippled Children and Adults, 11 S. LaSalle Street, Chicago 3. Health and safety: pamphlets, fliers, motion picture films, magazine reprints, bibliographies and reading lists. For senior high and up. Distributed to individual teachers only. Single copies of most materials free.

National Society for the Prevention of Blindness, Inc., 1790 Broadway, New York 19. Health and Safety: Pamphlets, fliers, motion picture films, vision testing charts. Intended for all school levels and lay groups. Nominal charge for materials in quantity; single copies free.

Prudential Insurance Company of America, Newark, New Jersey. Att. Public Relations and Advertising Department. Pamphlets. For teachers and lay groups. Samples: "Common Diseases of Children," "It's Fun to Be Healthy," "Safety—Your Child's Heritage." Free.

Quarterly Journal of Studies on Alcohol, 52 Hillhouse Avenue, Yale Station, New Haven, Connecticut. Health and Safety: Pamphlets. For senior high and up. Supply individual teachers only. Some free, some inexpensive.

Ralston Purina Company, Nutrition Service, Checkerboard Square, St. Louis 2. Charts, pamphlets. For primary through senior high grades. Distributed to groups. Free.

Scott, Foresman and Company, 120 East 23rd Street, New York. Health and Safety: charts, pamphlets, fliers. Primary through senior high grades. For individual teachers and groups. Some free, some inexpensive.

Society for Visual Education, Inc., 1345 Diversey Parkway, Chicago 14. Film strips and 2″ x 2″ slides on health and safety. Samples: "Susan and Peter Go to Market" (proper nutrition), "Susan and Peter Dress to Match the Weather" (proper dress), "Home Safety," "In Case of Fire." From elementary grades to college and lay groups. For sale.

Sunkist Growers, Consumer Service Division, Box 2706 Terminal Annex, Los Angeles 54. Pamphlets and other materials. Intended for intermediate grades, college, teachers training classes especially. For individual teachers, some for distribution to groups. Free.

Traffic Safety Dept., D. C. Division, American Automobile Association, 1712 G. Street, N. W., Washington 6, D. C. Safety: pamphlets, motion picture films. For all school levels, including teacher training. Intended for individual teachers and groups. Cooperates with any student or group in any traffic safety project. Free.

United Fruit Company, Educational Service Dept., Pier 3 North River, New York 6. Charts, pamphlets, film strips, motion picture films. Intended for primary grades and intermediate grades. For individuals and groups. Free.

Wheat Flour Institute, 309 West Jackson Blvd., Chicago 6. Charts, pamphlets, film strips. Intended for intermediate grades and up. Publications free to professional people, and free in limited quantities for class use.

Questions for Discussion

1. In order of their importance, what are the main sources of health instruction materials and information available to you?
2. Why are textbooks of great importance in health education? How should other materials and information be used in relationship to the text books?
3. In what ways can your library be most fully utilized as a source of health materials and information?
4. What are some cautions to be taken into account when considering materials provided by commercial and industrial sources?

Suggested Class Activities

1. Prepare a list of the various materials provided by your education and health departments.
2. Examine the lists of sources presented in this chapter. Select those that seem to offer most useful materials for your particular needs, and write to them for their catalogues and sample materials.
3. Select a unit in health education which you may be teaching in the near future (e.g., the health of the teeth). Make a list of sources of materials and information on this subject. Send for free and inexpensive materials and evaluate them for possible use in teaching.
4. Go through the same procedure for other units to be taught.

References

1. American Public Health Association: "How to Find What Health Education Materials You are Looking For."
2. Konheim, B. G. and D. N. Naiman: "Free Health Literature—How Effective Is It?" Research Quarterly, March, 1951.
3. Milwaukee, Wis., Public Schools: "A List of Free and Inexpensive Health Instruction Materials for Primary, Intermediate and Junior High School Grades."

CHAPTER 18

EVALUATION AND APPRAISAL IN HEALTH EDUCATION

The Meaning of Evaluation in Health Education.—The term "evaluation", in a purely literal sense means, "to estimate or place a value on." Evaluation in health education is concerned ultimately with the extent to which learning has occurred. In other words, it is a means of estimating the educative growth of pupils with respect to health learning experiences.

It has been stated previously that learning is concerned with changes in behavior and that teaching involves guidance, direction and supervision of learning. Therefore, evaluation in health education invokes a determination of behavior changes as a result of learning. A valid estimate of the educative growth of pupils is considered an essential phase of the teaching-learning cycle. Therefore, evaluation and appraisal of learning in health must be considered in terms of specific objectives as well as methods of achieving these objectives. For example, in a health unit the objectives may take the form of health concepts declaratively stated. Various methods of teaching are employed for the purpose of helping pupils gain insight with respect to health concepts which will influence their attitudes and behavior. There remains, then, the problem of determining whether or not health learning experiences have been provided in such a way that the desired objectives have been achieved with respect to expected outcomes. It will be the purpose of this chapter to consider numerous ways and means of evaluating and appraising learning in health education through the use of certain techniques which have been applied successfully in practical situations.

Why Evaluation is Necessary in Health Education.—The fundamental purpose of evaluation in health education is to make an appraisal of the nature, amount, kind and extent of learning that has taken place. Attempts should be made to find out if pupils are educated in health to the extent that they have accumulated sufficient knowledge of health to influence present as well as future living. If this is not done there is no way of knowing whether or not health teaching has had an influence, either positively or negatively, on pupils. When steps are taken to estimate educative growth as far as health knowledge, attitudes and practices are concerned it follows then that the effectiveness of teaching methods is also being evaluated. Although an appraisal of teaching methods may not be a primary purpose of evaluation in health education, it nevertheless occurs as a concomitant. This is particularly important because health teaching methods are, in most cases, directly related to the extent and nature of learning that occurs. In other words, if estimates of educative growth indicate that pupils are not learning satisfactorily, measures can and should be taken to improve health teaching methods. Consequently, as far as teaching methods are concerned, evaluation results can serve as a guide in the perpetuation or modification of some practices, and the elimination of others.

General and Specific Evaluation in Health Education.—There are two rather broad aspects that should be considered in evaluation and appraisal of learning in health teaching. For purpose of discussion here, these aspects will be referred to arbitrarily as GENERAL and SPECIFIC evaluation. General evaluation is concerned with an appraisal of a school's entire health teaching program, while specific evaluation refers to the appraisal of learning by classes and individual pupils.

GENERAL EVALUATION.—A general evaluation of a health teaching program may be carried on in a number of ways. A committee within the school system may be charged with the responsibility for evaluation. This group may consist of a sub-committee of an over-all curriculum committee, or it may be made up of faculty members appointed directly by an administrator or supervisor who has major charge of the health education program.

Some state courses of study and curriculum guides set forth recommendations in the form of a check list to be used in evaluating the school health teaching program. The following example of such a check list has been published by the Ohio Department of Education.[10]

A CHECK LIST FOR EVALUATING THE SCHOOL HEALTH INSTRUCTION PROGRAM

Preparation for the School Day
> Are more children coming to school better groomed, such as, hands washed, teeth brushed, and hair combed?

Proper Use of Equipment and Environment
> Are more children using the drinking fountain and lavatories in a sanitary way?
> Do the majority of students make the necessary adjustments for conserving their eyesight?
> Do pupils use soap and paper towels when washing their hands?

Correction of Defects
> Are more students securing correction of physical defects?
> Do students seek advice of school staff members regarding the correction of defects?
> Do most students visit a dentist regularly for a periodic checkup?

Protection Against Disease
> Is the number of students immunized against disease increasing?
> Are there fewer cases of absence due to illness?
> Is the number who wash their hands before eating, after playing, and after toilet increasing?
> Do pupils help keep the building clean and sanitary?

Nutrition
> Is the consumption of soft drinks and sweets decreasing, and of milk and fruit increasing?
> Are more pupils eating breakfast regularly?
> Are increasing numbers of pupils choosing nutritious lunches in the school lunchroom or cafeteria?

Safety
> Do fewer accidents occur on the playground and in the school building?
> Do pupils use playground equipment in a safe manner?
> Do pupils play in safe places?
> Do pupils practice safe pedestrian habits?
> Are pupils reasonably cautious around safety hazards?
> Do pupils obey traffic regulations?

Clothing
> Do pupils wear suitable clothing for the weather?
> Do pupils remove wraps and wet clothing when necessary?

Sleep and Rest
> Do the majority of students get sufficient rest and sleep?
> Do any of the pupils look sleepy, yawn, and rub their eyes frequently?

Mental and Emotional Health
> Are the pupils courteous, and interested in school?
> Do pupils participate in playground activities?
> Do pupils play fair and wait turns?
> Do pupils respect those in authority?
> Are pupils considerate toward younger and smaller children?
> Do pupils accept criticism cheerfully?
> Do pupils assume responsibility in the care of school equipment and in work and play activities?
> Do pupils alibi for shortcomings on the playground and in the classroom?
> Do pupils control their tempers?

On some occasions the services of outside evaluating committees may be obtained. When this is done at the secondary school level the evaluating committee frequently uses the evaluative criteria developed in the Cooperative Study of Secondary School Standards[3] although this is not entirely adequate. All of the methods of general evaluation presented here have been used with varying degrees of success. When properly applied, any of them can be useful in the evaluation of the school health teaching program. However, it is sometimes advisable for a school to develop ways, methods and instruments for general evaluation of health education.

SPECIFIC EVALUATION.—As mentioned previously specific evaluation is concerned with the appraisal of learning and estimate of educative growth of health classes and individual pupils. This procedure necessitates not only a valid estimate of health knowledge but of health attitudes and health practices as well.

Various techniques for estimating educative growth in knowledge, attitudes and practices will be presented and discussed later. At this point, attention is called to the important relationship between health knowledge, attitudes and practices.

Although a pupil may have accumulated a certain amount of knowledge regarding a given health topic, there still remains the important consideration of his assuming a proper attitude which will influence the development of proper health practice. It is obvious that "knowing is not doing." Empirical evidence bears this out in cases where people are fully aware of the importance of certain health practices but fail to observe them. In this connection one is reminded of a physician who says "Do as I say, not as I do." Nevertheless, if learning experiences are not provided whereby pupils may acquire knowledge they will have little desirable knowledge to use as a basis for the establishment of proper attitudes. Consequently, it is unlikely that favorable health practices will be developed.

It should be mentioned also that the health knowledge accumulated may not be put to immediate use. This is to say that pupils may not gain full insight into the values to be derived from certain health practice even though they may have a fairly complete knowledge of it. However, it is possible that the knowledge may eventually be reflected in desirable behavior. Therefore, when evaluating for attitudes and practices, results may be discouraging in situations where pupils show satisfactory growth in factual knowledge, but are not inclined to immediately formulate health practices commensurate with their health knowledge.

In substance, the point of importance is, although the ultimate goal is in the direction of desirable health practices, that pupils must acquire certain knowledge which will favorably influence health practices. Therefore, there are numerous inherent values in placing an estimate on the pupils' educative growth regarding health knowledge. Among others, these values include: (1) opportunity for discovery of needs of pupils, (2) possibility of diagnosing pupil attitudes from knowledge test results, and (3) means of measuring class achievements regarding certain necessary basic health knowledge.

Some Evaluative Techniques for Health Education.—Evaluative techniques for health education may be arbitrarily placed in several different classifications. Some of these classifications include: (1) data gathering devices originating with the teacher, (2) standardized tests, (3) pupil records, and (4) pupil evaluation. It may be noted that a certain amount of overlapping occurs in these classifications. However, delineation of the evaluative techniques in this manner is proposed for the purpose of giving a clearer understanding and insight into the procedure of estimating growth of pupils with regard to those factors which influence their health.

DATA GATHERING DEVICES ORIGINATING WITH THE TEACHER.—Teachers in health education may use various ways of collecting evidence of pupil growth. Such factors as individual ability, resourcefulness and ingenuity of teachers will influence, to a large extent, the successful application of these techniques. The following generalized list indicates some of these data gathering devices that have met with varying degrees of success:

1. Teacher prepared objective tests.
2. Teacher prepared written essay-type tests.
3. Oral questioning.
4. Dramatization.
5. Demonstrations.
6. Flash cards.
7. Teacher observations.

STANDARDIZED TESTS.—There are a number of standardized tests that may be used to gather information regarding health knowledge, attitudes, and practices. The standardized test is one that has been previously administered to large numbers of pupils for the purpose of establishing norms for specific grade levels or combinations of grade levels. When this type of measuring device is used it is generally recommended that the test be given before and after health teaching takes place so that specific changes in health knowledge, attitudes and practices may be noted.

PUPIL RECORDS.—In arriving at a valid estimate of educative growth of pupils, teachers of health should attempt to use all of the materials that are available. In this respect pupil records of all kinds may be explored with the idea in mind of gathering evidence of changes in behavior. For example, anecdotal accounts, case study outlines and behavior records have been found to be very useful for this purpose.

PUPIL EVALUATION.—One very important aspect in the appraisal of learning concerns the procedure which gives pupils an opportunity to determine those things which were learned through the study of a certain health topic. This procedure not only serves as a means of estimating educative growth but it helps the teacher to determine the extent in which a health teaching unit needs revision for use in a subsequent teaching situation.

One satisfactory method of effecting pupil evaluation is through the use of anonymous reports by pupils. As an example, one eighth-grade teacher conducted a survey among her pupils after the group had studied a unit on Dental Hygiene. The anonymous report by her class revealed the following information:

1. Through our experiment we learned which toothpastes may be harmful to our teeth.
2. We learned how to brush our teeth and how to care for them.
3. We learned about some of the diseases of the teeth and mouth.
4. We learned about the kinds of teeth, construction, uses of teeth, and how they grow.
5. We learned that good balanced diets are needed for healthy teeth.
6. We learned about how dentists can help us.
7. We learned how our teeth may affect our health and how they might cause us to lose our job.
8. We learned the history of dental hygiene.
9. We are giving better care to our teeth.
10. We enjoyed the study of dental hygiene because it was different, interesting and it was for our personal benefit.

No attempt has been made in this discussion to show how the various evaluative techniques can be applied. On the contrary the purpose here has been merely to point out some of the techniques that can be used. The remainder of this chapter will be devoted to a more detailed application of some of these techniques in evaluating for knowledge, attitudes and practices.

Evaluating for Health Knowledge.—Estimating the educative growth of pupils in terms of health knowledge may take place in a number of ways. The discussion that follows includes some of the commonly used methods as well as others that have been successfully applied in practical situations.

TEACHER-PREPARED PAPER AND PENCIL TESTS.— The teacher-prepared test is by far the most universal means of collecting evidence related to health knowledge. This is perhaps due partially to the fact that paper and pencil testing has been one of the most traditional methods of appraising learning in virtually all of the subject matter areas.

The two kinds of paper and pencil tests, perhaps most often prepared by teachers, include the objective test and the written-essay or subjective-type test. In general, the objective type test items may be placed in the two broad categories of RECOGNITION and RECALL. The recognition type of test item requires that the pupil recognize and select the correct answer which occurs among other answers in the test item. The recall type test item requires that the pupil supply the correct answer which has been omitted in the test item.

There are several variations of the recognition type of test item. Some of these include: (1) true-false, (2) multiple-choice, and (3) matching. In testing for health knowledge it is recommended that the teacher use a variety of the recognition type test items rather than relying on one type. The purpose of this is to help to off-set some of the limitations involved in the various kinds of recognition type items. For example, the true-false test item may have little diagnostic value since the correct response may be merely an indication that the pupil guessed correctly in selecting the answer. When true-false items are used, extreme care should be taken in constructing the false items so that they will not leave a fixed false idea with the pupils, particularly the slow-learning pupils. False ideas in this way may develop into erroneous concepts. For instance, it has been shown that statements such as the following frequently fix them as misconceptions in the minds of some children in that they eventually remember only the false statement:

1. A good way to give first aid for a burn is to put iodine on it.
2. If your clothing catches fire you should run for water.
3. Oil, grease, and rag fires should be put out with plenty of water.
4. Everyone with weak feet should wear arch supports.
5. Most colds can be prevented by taking vitamin pills.
6. Milk is pasteurized to make it easy to digest.
7. A pain in your right side usually means you have appendicitis.
8. Spring water that is clear and cold is always safe for drinking.
9. Most fat people are very healthy.

The multiple-choice type of recognition test item is not widely used due to the amount of time and difficulty involved in its construction. When carefully prepared, the multiple-choice item can be very thought provoking and it is an excellent way of determining whether pupils have achieved the desired health knowledge and information which the test covers. In the multiple-choice test item there are usually from

Evaluation and Appraisal   341

three to five possible responses. Five responses are preferred because as the number of possible answers is increased the possibility for guessing the correct answer is reduced. Some samples of multiple-choice items in health knowledge testing follow:

INSTRUCTIONS: Place the letter of the best answer in the space provided.

1. _____Persons who do not perspire readily may be especially subject to: (a) colds (b) heat stroke (c) sun tan (d) tonsillitis (e) sinusitis.
2. _____Volume of blood in the body may be reduced by: (a) dehydration (b) anemia (c) hemorrhage (d) all of the above (e) none of the above.
3. _____The greatest amount of digestion takes place in the: (a) large intestine (b) small intestine (c) stomach (d) rectum (e) mouth.
4. _____The span of life expectancy today is approximately: (a) 48 years (b) 58 years (c) 68 years (d) 78 years (e) 88 years.
5. _____The leading cause of death for all ages in the United States is: (a) tuberculosis (b) heart disease (c) accidents (d) infantile paralysis (e) pneumonia.

Matching test items have the obvious limitation of being the type of items used for the collection of mere factual information. However, when properly constructed this type of test item can be useful in measuring achievement and educative growth. The following is a sample of matching test items in health knowledge testing. It will be noted that the two columns present an unequal number of items. The purpose of this is to prevent the possibility of getting a "free" answer through the process of elimination.

INSTRUCTIONS: Match the following items by placing the letter of the correct answer in the space provided.

1. _____liver   (a) cancer
2. _____protein   (b) citrus juice
3. _____calcium   (c) gonorrhea
4. _____Vitamin B 1   (d) narcotic
5. _____heat unit   (e) milk
6. _____iodine   (f) hypertension
7. _____food tube   (g) glycogen

8. _____high blood pressure (h) thiamin
9. _____communicable   (i) esophagus
10. _____heroin   (j) nitrogen
                                    (k) thyroxin
                                    (l) calorie

The recall type of test item which requires the pupil to supply the correct answer takes the form of a completion or fill-in type of item. One of the chief disadvantages of this type of test item is that it may place a premium on mere rote memorization of health facts. Another possible limitation is that the test item may be such that more than one correct answer can be given. For example, in a recall test item such as "Exercise generally shows an increase in.........development" a correct answer might be either "muscular" or "organic." On the contrary a recall item such as ".........makes up the greatest part of the body" has only one possible correct answer which is "water." When there is a possibility of more than one correct answer the teacher should include each one in the test scoring key.

The written essay or subjective-type test of health knowledge, although somewhat lacking in objectivity, may help the teacher determine evidence of achievement and educative growth that frequently cannot be measured through the purely objective test. For example, the teacher can formulate questions in such a way as to provide for better problem-solving situations than is usually possible in straight objective type tests. Also, the teacher may ask pupils to write a summary of what has been learned through the study of a certain health unit. If this procedure is undertaken the teacher should analyze the summaries to determine how closely they are related to the objectives of the unit. In this way the teacher should be able to ascertain to a reasonable degree whether or not pupils have gained insight into the understandings and concepts that formed the basis for the unit objectives.

ORAL QUESTIONING.—One satisfactory means of accumulating evidence of pupil progress in health knowledge and understanding is through oral questioning. When this method is used the teacher should devise a technique suitable for keeping satisfactory records. Otherwise, there will be no documentary evidence of growth when final evaluation and appraisal is made. Some teachers find it desirable and helpful to keep a log where results of oral questioning can be quickly recorded.

Oral questioning may be formal or informal in nature. In any event questions should be such that the teacher can actually tell whether pupils are accumulating satisfactory health knowledge. In this respect, certain types of questions usually should be avoided. For example, questions that require only a "yes" or "no" answer may have little value in that the pupil has a 50% chance of guessing the correct answer. On the other hand, the type of questions that necessitate critical thinking and judgment can be phrased in such a way that the teacher should be able to immediately detect evidence of correct and accurate health knowledge. Perhaps one of the main disadvantages that teachers have found in using the oral questioning technique, is that it may be difficult to appraise the achievement of all pupils if classes are large. The chief advantage in this means of evaluation, however, lies in the fact that the teacher may get a more valid estimate of the individual who expresses himself best through the spoken word.

DEMONSTRATIONS.—Evaluation of health knowledge through demonstrations can be carried out by either teacher-demonstrations, or pupil-demonstrations. When the teacher demonstrates, the pupils are required to identify those things that are demonstrated. When pupils perform a demonstration, they are expected to show the health knowledge that has been attained. An example of the use of teacher-demonstration for purposes of evaluating health knowledge is one that took place in a high school class in first aid. One of the health knowledge tests consisted of the teacher demonstrating various kinds of bandages and the pupils were required to identify the bandages by writing down the correct name of the bandage on the test paper. Another example was one in which the teacher demonstrated classifications of foods by placing certain kinds of foods together. The pupils were required to indicate whether each food was classified correctly by writing down the words "right" or "wrong" when asked to do so. For example, if the teacher had milk and butter in one group and added cheese to this group, the correct answer would be "right." However, if the teacher had added a citrus fruit to this group, the correct answer would be "wrong." The efficacy of this plan of health knowledge evaluation is obvious because it tests pupil knowledge in a real and life-like situation which could be carried over and applied in a practical way, such as in the selection of proper foods when doing the shopping for the family.

Asking pupils to demonstrate certain procedures that were developed in a health unit is a valid way of evaluating health knowledge. The chief disadvantage of this is in the amount of time required for such an evaluation procedure. As in the case of oral questioning, evaluation of health knowledge through pupil-demonstration may provide for a better estimate of educative growth in cases where pupils do not express themselves well on written tests.

FLASH CARDS.—Flash cards can be used in much the same way as demonstrations as an evaluative technique. As mentioned in a previous chapter, flash cards can be used rather than written test items to show certain objects that pupils should be able to identify. For example, the teacher can use the card to test pupils health knowledge in the recognition of certain harmful agents such as poison ivy or poison sumac in evaluating knowledge in a unit on Summer safety. This procedure would be considered as one of pure identification.

More than one flash card may be used at a time so that pupils can select the correct answer in much the same way as the written multiple-choice test item.

EXAMINATION OF WORK DONE BY PUPILS.—Appraisal of learning in terms of health knowledge need not always take the form of testing. For example, the teacher can evaluate scrapbooks, notebooks and other materials prepared by pupils. This can be done for the purpose of determining whether pupils have gained insight into certain health concepts necessary for the satisfactory preparation of these materials.

DRAMATIZATION.—Another suitable means of appraising health knowledge is through dramatization. The use of socio-drama in evaluating health knowledge in a high school unit on first aid was described in a previous chapter. Original health plays and skits, particularly for elementary school pupils, provide another form of dramatization which is useful in evaluating health knowledge. When pupils write a health play or skit, evidence of health knowledge is shown in terms of the degree of validity of the dialogue of the play. That is, the teacher should determine whether the dialogue written by the pupils shows that they understand the health concepts that the original health play intended to convey.

Still another possibility of health knowledge evaluation through dramatization consists of having pupils act out some of the understandings that were developed during the study of a health unit. This procedure is most useful at the elementary school level and can be accomplished through pantomime or play acting. With regard to pantomime the teacher might ask pupils to show the correct way of brushing the teeth. An example of a play acting situation would be one in which pupils show the correct procedure to take in crossing a street bearing heavy traffic. In this type of evaluation the teacher can actually see the extent to which educative growth has taken place with regard to health and safety knowledge.

Evaluating for Health Attitudes.—Although it is highly important that measures be taken to determine changes in pupils' attitudes toward health, it is difficult to measure and appraise objectively. The principal reason for this lies in the fact that attitudes are concerned predominantly with one's feelings and emotions. Consequently, the teacher is confronted with the problem of evaluating in an area that is more or less intangible. In other words, it may be relatively easy to determine, what an individual knows about health, but it is a much more difficult matter to arrive at valid conclusions concerning his feelings toward the subject even though knowledge and attitudes may be related to a certain extent. A pupil may display an undesirable attitude about certain phases of health because of past experiences, invalid concepts, or environment. In some cases a lack of knowledge can contribute to this condition. This is to say that it is possible that an indifferent or negative attitude may be "synonymous with ignorance." For example, a child may display a negative attitude toward a certain kind of food simply because he has been in a family environment where parents have had a dislike for that particular kind of food. If proper learning experiences are provided, the child's attitude toward the food may be reflected in various ways. It is the concern of this discussion to explore ways in which the teacher can make an appraisal in terms of change of attitude.

Some of the methods of evaluating health knowledge might also be used to measure health attitudes. However, the limitations of these techniques should be recognized. In the use of the teacher-prepared paper and pencil test the obvious disadvantage is that the pupil has the opportunity to write down the answers that are correct, but may not portray his true feelings. In the use of the paper and pencil test for health attitudes it may be less difficult to secure an entire class attitude than health attitudes of individuals. This can be done by administering a test without requiring pupils to place their names on the test paper in a public opinion type of procedure. In this way it is more likely that a valid estimate of health attitudes will result.

The limitations indicated in the written test as a health attitude measuring device necessitates a consideration of other methods that will yield more valid results. In this connection, teachers will perhaps be likely to arrive at a more accurate measurement of health attitudes by using procedures that involve casual actions and expressions of pupils.

Techniques such as dramatizations, individual conferences, and observation have been used with varying degrees of success as aids to teachers in determining attitudes toward health. The zeal that some children show in dramatizing health situations can furnish the teacher with clues indicating the differences in attitude that some pupils might have. Informal conferences and conversations with pupils likewise reflect their health attitudes. Observation on the part of the teacher is another desirable instrument in determining attitudes. For example, the eating habits of pupils in the school cafeteria may be observed in order to find how they feel about certain kinds of foods.

Although these techniques are necessarily subjective in nature, they seem to contain a certain degree of validity as health attitude measuring devices. They can be reduced to a more or less objective basis when the teacher keeps an anecdotal record of the actions and expressions of pupils. Periodically, these records can be analyzed to see if favorable changes in attitudes have taken place as a result of health teaching.

Evaluating for Health Practices.—One of the most important factors to consider in evaluation of health learning experiences concerns the extent to which pupils put health knowledge into actual practice. In other words, are they doing those things which have been accepted as valid procedures for the maintenance and improvement of health?

Some of the techniques used to evaluate health knowledge and health attitudes may be employed to a limited extent in making a valid appraisal of health practices. However, many of the methods previously mentioned for the appraisal of health attitudes have similar limitations when used to evaluate health practices. For example, in the case of the paper and pencil test, as a possible means for evaluation of health practices, there arises the problem of whether the pupil actually practices what he had indicated as the correct answers on the test.

Perhaps one of the most effective ways of determining those favorable health practices in which pupils should engage is through the technique of observation. The following examples that occurred in practical situations give some support to the possibilities of the technique of observation as a means of determining health practices.

In observing her group of third graders during and after the study of a unit on "The Common Cold," one teacher observed the following:

1. No child had been reported for not washing his hands before lunch since studying the unit.
2. As a result of an experiment involving coughing on paper to see how far droplets of moisture travel, no child had been seen coughing or sneezing without covering his mouth or nose.
3. On the day the unit was introduced, one boy had a handkerchief and two girls had a package of paper handkerchief tissues. Six days later when an inquiry was made, nine boys had handkerchiefs and four girls had paper handkerchief tissues.

In another application of the observation technique a teacher noted that the milk-drinking practices of her 33 fourth-grade pupils showed that: (1) sixteen took platters with milk, (2) nine drank no milk, and (3) eight gave away their milk. As a result of a class discussion, she found that the following reasons were given for not drinking milk.

1. Grassy taste in the spring makes it unpalatable.
2. Some children had grown accustomed to pasteurized milk and did not like it homogenized.
3. The heating process in pasteurized milk caused it to have a different taste from raw milk.
4. Some children would not drink milk without chocolate in it.

After teaching a unit on "Milk" the following observations were made:

1. Twenty-one children took platters with milk.
2. Five drank no milk.
3. Three gave away their milk.

Although the technique of observation may be subjective in nature it can, as indicated in the above examples, be reduced to a more or less objective basis. As such, observation becomes a fairly reliable instrument for the evaluation of health practices.

Necessary Abilities for Successful Evaluation and Appraisal of Learning in Health Education.—Because evaluation and appraisal of learning is an essential phase of a valid teaching-learning cycle, teachers should develop certain competencies necessary for successful evaluation. Some of these basic abilities include:

1. The ability to construct and use the results of objective-type health tests suitable for use at the particular grade level.
2. The ability to select and use those standardized tests which are best adapted to the local situation.
3. The ability to use oral questioning in such a way that it becomes an effective means of evaluation.
4. The ability to construct written essay-type questions that are of a problem-solving nature.
5. The ability to interview pupils through conferences and casual conversations in order to appraise learning that has accrued.
6. The ability to employ the technique of observation in matters which concern pupil-health so as to make the best possible valid estimate of growth in health attitudes and health practices.

Questions for Discussion

1. Why is evaluation important in health education?
2. What is meant by general evaluation in health education?
3. What is meant by specific evaluation in health education?
4. What procedures would you recommend for having pupils evaluate a health teaching unit?
5. What are some of the factors to consider in the use of oral questioning in the appraisal of learning in health education?
6. How can individual conferences with pupils be useful in the appraisal of learning in health education?
7. How can sociodrama be used in the appraisal of learning in health education?

Suggested Class Activities

1. Prepare a check list for evaluating a school health education program with which you are familiar.
2. Form a round-table discussion group for the purpose of discussing the relationship between health knowledge, health attitudes, and health practices.
3. Write a report indicating how pupil records could be used for evaluation in health education.
4. Prepare five true-false test items on a specific health topic.
5. Prepare five multiple-choice test items on a specific health topic.
6. Prepare eight matching test items on a specific health topic.
7. Prepare five completion or fill-in questions on a specific health topic.
8. Prepare two written-essay type questions for the purpose of appraising learning in a unit on "Cleanliness" for any grade level in which you are interested.

9. Prepare a check list for the purpose of evaluating the attitudes of a sixth-grade group of pupils, toward sleep and rest.
10. Using magazine pictures, prepare several flash cards for the purpose of appraising learning in a unit on "Summer Safety."
11. Observe a member of the class anonomously for a period of one week for violation of certain health practices. Record these violations and report them to the class without divulging the name of the person observed.

References

1. Byrd, Oliver C.: *Byrd Health Attitude Scale,* Stanford University Press, Stanford University, 1940.
2. Conrad, Howard L.: "The Construction of Health Knowledge Tests," *The Journal of Health and Physical Education,* December, 1938.
3. Evaluative Criteria 1950 edition, Cooperative Study of Secondary School Standards, Washington, D. C., Section D-7.
4. Grout, Ruth E.: *Health Teaching in Schools,* 2nd edition, Philadelphia, 1953, W. B. Saunders Company.
5. Johns, Edward B., and Warren L. Juhnke: "Health Practice Inventory," Board of Trustees of the Leland Stanford Junior University, 1952.
6. Neher, Gerwin: "Health Inventory for High School Students," California Test Bureau, Los Angeles, California.
7. Oberteuffer, Delbert: *School Health Education,* 2nd edition, New York, 1954, Harper & Brothers.
8. Rash, J. Keogh: "Refining the Health Education Test," *The Journal of School Health,* Volume XXIII, January and February, 1953.
9. Southworth, W. H., Jean V. Latimer, and C. E. Turner: "A Study of Health Practices, Knowledges, Attitudes, and Interests of Senior High School Pupils," *Research Quarterly of the American Association for Health, Physical Education and Recreation,* Volume XV, May, 1944.
10. State of Ohio, Department of Education, "A Guide for the Teaching of Healthful and Happy Living for Children in the Elementary Grades," Columbus, Ohio, 1952.

CHAPTER 19

IN-SERVICE EDUCATION IN HEALTH EDUCATION

It is generally recognized that there are no terminal points in education and that it is a continuous process. It is readily evident then, that teacher education and training does not end with the customary number of semester hours required at the undergraduate pre-service level nor does it end even after a master's or doctorate degree has been completed. Constant study on the part of teachers is necessary if they are to keep abreast of the results of scientific discoveries, new development, improved methods of teaching and the ever-expanding knowledge in all areas of education.

Need for In-Service Education in Health and Safety Education.—The growing importance of health education in the schools is such that many more qualified teachers are needed than are currently available in this area. Furthermore, it is likely to be many years before a sufficient number of teachers are properly prepared in this area. This means that school health education will be dependent, to a certain extent, upon in-service education and training programs for whatever degree of success it is likely to attain.

Even in those teacher-training institutions where students may specialize in health education, it is doubtful that they can be expected to become little more than generalists upon completion of the prescribed course. Consequently, there is a very great need for in-service education programs for teachers who must do advanced study while teaching.

Another thing that clearly shows the need for in-service education in health education is the ever-increasing knowledge related to mental, physical and emotional health and healthful living. The rapid progress that is constantly being made in research concerned with health places strong emphasis on the need for a continuous appraisal and evaluation, and in some cases, modification of health concepts. Therefore, teachers of health should keep abreast of the latest findings concerned with all phases of health and healthful living.

The following list delineates some of the reasons why there is a need for continuous in-service education in health and safety education.

1. The curriculums of many teacher-education institutions are or were inadequate to prepare the teachers at the time they were preparing to be teachers.
2. There is usually a loss of knowledge caused by the lapse of time between learning and teaching.
3. Continual scientific developments, changing concepts, facilities, and resources necessitate constant study.
4. The teacher can be helped while in service to make adaptations of health education to meet the immediate, continuing, and shifting needs of communities and children.
5. Teachers as individuals seldom concern themselves with health conditions until faced with specific problems.
6. Teachers with limited training and experience in health education need special help.
7. In-service education helps to improve and maintain mental, physical, and emotional health of teachers, pupils, and the community, as well as to develop wider understanding and convictions.

Scope of In-Service Education in Health.—There is a wide scope of possibilities for in-service education in health education. In fact almost anything that a teacher does might be considered as in-service education provided that she benefits by the experience. Perhaps all in-service education could be placed in one of two categories. That is, in-service education methods, whereby provision is made to help the teacher, and in-service education in which the teacher accepts the responsibility for helping herself. In the establishment of an in-service education program, teachers should be encouraged to effect self-improvement in whatever ways seem most desirable.

The following list indicates a few of the possibilities of in-service education for health that have been used with relative degrees of success in practical situations throughout the country.

1. Supervision
2. Workshops
3. School-system in-service courses

4. Advanced study
5. Professional literature
6. Professional Associations

Supervision in Health Education.—One of the most satisfactory ways of improving the health education program is through supervision. This seems to indicate that direct assistance should be given to teachers by persons qualified to render this special service. The specialist in health education may be referred to as a health supervisor, coordinator, consultant, or a school health educator. Along with making source materials available to teachers, the health supervisor, through a variety of accepted supervisory techniques can do a great deal to improve the teacher-pupil learning situation.

The extent to which specific supervisory techniques are applied for the improvement of the teacher-pupil learning situation in health depends upon a number of conditions. Factors involving the qualifications of the person in charge of supervision, training and experience of teachers, plan of organization of health education, and school enrollment will govern to a large extent how, when, and where specific supervisory techniques may be successfully employed. The following discussion of some of the regular supervision techniques suggest ways in which the teacher may benefit from supervision.

VISITATION.—There seems to be no adequate substitute for visitation, for it is through this technique that the supervisor gets a first hand understanding of certain problems that may be confronting the teacher. By visiting the teaching in the classroom and observing her teaching, the supervisor has a very good opportunity to render assistance that may be needed. In addition to visits by the supervisor, other members of the school health education staff may be utilized for visitation. For example, the health supervisor might arrange for visits by the school physician, nurses, or others as resource persons to aid the teacher.

MEETINGS AND CONFERENCES.—Group meetings with supervisors and health specialists for the purpose of discussing desirable health learning experiences and the availability of health materials are most profitable to teachers.

Individual conferences with the supervisor may be supplemented with conferences between the teacher and other health specialists. In this regard teacher-nurse conferences offer excellent opportunities for the teacher to gain a more extensive knowledge about certain school health problems. Consequently, the teacher can plan accordingly with pupils in attempting to solve some of these problems.

BULLETINS.—Notices of new health materials may be channeled to teachers by means of bulletins. Also, information pertaining to health examinations, supplements to curriculum materials, and notices of a routine nature may be transmitted to teachers through this medium.

DEMONSTRATIONS.—Because of the rapidly changing concepts concerning teaching methods in health and safety, demonstration teaching holds great promise as a supervisory technique. The supervisor or a superior teacher can demonstrate a new health teaching technique, or the use of certain types of health education materials. Furthermore, group demonstrations of screening devices such as for hearing and vision may be presented to teachers by the supervisor or health specialists. This training is particularly useful for teachers who anticipate the use of health teaching units on aspects of hearing and vision. Demonstrations of physical examinations by physicians also offer an opportunity for teachers to become familiar with a practical health procedure. A demonstration, such as this, should furnish the teacher with a suitable background for the proper education of pupils in terms of preparing them for the physical examination. Preparing children for a physical examination is particularly important at the early elementary school level where pupils may sometimes suffer unnecessary apprehension and mental anguish prior to and sometimes during the examination.

Health Education Workshops.—Since the origin of the modern workshop idea some two decades ago, this plan for teacher growth and improvement in service has had almost universal acceptance. Some of the desirable characteristics of the workshop in health and safety education are:

1. The workshop is a democratic method of learning in which individual participation in group discussion is encouraged.
2. It provides an opportunity for the individual to work, study, and associate with professional personnel in the same or related fields and thereby, promotes good relations and cooperation.
3. It provides an opportunity to deal with actual and practical school and community health and safety problems.
4. Workshops usually provide a wide range of resources including special health consultants.

Health education workshops may be carried on in a number of ways. Teacher education institutions are making more widespread use of them as time progresses.

State Departments of Education and Health sometimes assume the responsibility for health education workshops, and in many instances they cooperate in lending their assistance to teacher-training institutions in the promotion and conduct of workshops.

Another way in which health education workshops are carried on is through the efforts of various commercial organizations that have a specific interest in some phase of healthful living.

The current interest manifested in school health has stimulated some local communities to establsh their own school-system workshops in an effort to more definitely meet the needs of local teachers. There are a variety of ways in which school-system workshops in health education may be effectively carried on. Some schools make a practice of holding a workshop before the school year starts, while others may divide the time for a session at the close of the school year, as well as at the beginning of the school year. There are still other school systems that hold short workshop sessions periodically throughout the school year.

While many different procedures may be used in carrying on local school-system workshops in health education, each school is likely to have certain problems that may be manifested in a variety of ways. For this reason it is doubtful that a general recommendation can be made for all schools in the development of local workshop procedures. Such factors as available time, personnel, finances, and local needs materially influence the organization of health education workshops at the local level. The following suggested procedures are submitted as a guide for the development of workshops in health education.

1. Workshops seem to be most effective when the need originates with local teachers under the leadership of the school administrator or the county or community health officer.
2. Flexibility in program planning should prevail so that participants are not made to feel obligated to follow a rigid schedule.
3. Continuity of sessions should be preserved so far as possible.
4. Cooperation of the local board of education and board of health should be obtained with respect to use of facilities and personnel.
5. Personnel of colleges and universities and other agencies in the near-by areas should be invited to participate as consultants.

The practice of organizing workshops for the in-service education of teachers has become so widespread in a relatively short time that it may be difficult to identify certain trends and to adequately appraise their full potential. However, there appear to be certain developments in some cases that could place a limitation on the workshop as an in-service education device. In some situations the term "workshop" has been used to refer to a variety of meetings that may not conform to the basic idea underlying the true spirit of the workshop program. For example, when a series of all-day lectures comprises a program, it should not be misconstrued as a workshop. The term "workshop" might be interpreted in a combined literal and figurative sense.

Teachers and others convene to "work" and "shop"; to work with others in the solution of health problems of mutual interest, and to shop for new ideas that may be adapted and applied to local situations. A workshop carried out on this basis would appear to hold much promise as a means for eventual improvement of teachers in service who have certain responsibilities in the area of health education.

School System In-Service Courses.—In-service education classes in health teaching are useful in helping teachers acquire knowledge in an area in which they may have had little or no previous training. Also, these courses serve the purpose of helping the teacher keep abreast of recent discoveries related to healthful living. Courses in which various kinds of screening devices are demonstrated for teachers have proved useful in assisting teachers in gaining a clearer insight into the use and application of these techniques. These classes may be taught by the person who has major charge of health education in the school system, or by a superior teacher who has had training and experience in health education.

There are a number of ways in which in-service classes in health education may be carried on. Sometimes these classes occur during the school day, but generally they are likely to be held in the late afternoon after the school day is completed. In some cases they may take place in the evening or on Saturdays. The time that such classes convene will depend largely upon when the greatest number of interested teachers are available, because release-time of teachers is a very important problem in conducting classes of this nature.

In order to determine those teachers who are interested in certain kinds of health activities, it is advisable for the health coordinator or supervisor to survey the teaching staff. In this way, the need for such instruction originates with the teacher. When a sufficient number of teachers indicate an interest, a class can be organized on the basis of the information obtained from the survey.

In some instances where health education in-service classes are taught, the participants are given credit for this work in the way of salary schedule increments. Although this practice appears to be concerned with extrinsic motivation, it seems justifiable in this case. It seems advisable also, to give some sort of credit or compensation to those individuals who teach in-service courses, particularly if the courses take place after school hours. If it is a policy of the local school system to allow extra remuneration for extra-class activities, teachers of in-service courses should be considered for this additional compensation.

Advanced Study.—Educators generally agree that education is a continuous process. While the teachers may carry on advanced study in a number of ways, this means of professional growth can perhaps be placed in the two broad categories of institutional education and independent study.

INSTITUTIONAL EDUCATION.—Numerous institutions of higher learning offer summer courses in an attempt to help meet the needs of school personnel. Also, some colleges and universities offer late afternoon and evening courses as well as off-campus extension service and correspondence courses to serve individuals in the adjacent and outlying areas. Teachers in service sometimes criticize such courses as being too theoretical in nature and too far removed from their practical needs. However, it should be mentioned here that the content of any course which is not applicable, at least in part, to a practical situation is also devoid and lacking in its theoretical approach; or the fault may lie in the implementation of the theory. Blanket criticism of these offerings is not entirely justified when it is considered that the courses must be more or less generalized to meet the many different needs of the class members. Teachers attending such classes should perhaps do so with the idea in mind that only a portion of the course content may be applied to their local situation. The teachers must make application of principles themselves. Furthermore, a greater effort should be made on the part of those persons teaching these courses to bridge the gap between theory and practice. In this regard, the EXTENSION type of course can be of considerable value in that it can be geared to the needs of teachers in a specific school. This is particularly true in the case of health and safety education courses because teachers have an opportunity to study the health and safety problems that exist in their own school and then formulate plans for the use of methods and materials accordingly. An additional feature of the extension course is that it is economical for teachers because they have little or no traveling to do.

Extension type courses in health education are sometimes arranged through the cooperation of the person who has major charge of health education in the local school system and the teacher-education institution that is to offer the course. In some cases the local board of education assumes a part of tuition expenses for teachers, although this is not a general practice. However, in some school systems, teachers are elevated to a higher salary level when they have completed a specified number of credit hours at an approved institution.

INDEPENDENT STUDY.—Teachers whose attitudes are characterized by high professional standards frequently like to engage in independent study. This may take the form of professional study groups or, in many cases, individual study for professional improvement. The former is practiced in some school systems where staff members may engage in committee work, particularly for the purpose of the advancement of the health education curriculum. The value of any type of independent study is enhanced when it takes place on a voluntary basis. That is, when the teacher feels the need for self-improvement, perhaps a greater contribution will be made toward the teacher-pupil learning situation.

Professional Literature.—The extent to which the professional literature in health and safety education is consulted will rest largely with individual teachers. It is frequently mentioned by some teachers that they do not have sufficient time to engage in any type of professional reading. However, in view of the fact that there are many changing concepts with regard to physical, mental and emotional health and healthful living, such reading is considered as virtually indispensable to growth in service if a teacher is to maintain a reasonably high professional standard.

The following partial list of periodicals includes several which may serve as desirable references for teachers in terms of keeping abreast of the most valid health concepts. Some of these periodicals may be found in the local school library.

1. *American Journal of Hygiene*
2. *American Journal of Public Health*
3. *Child Development*
4. *Child Study*
5. *Childhood Education*
6. *Journal of Exceptional Children*
7. *Journal of Health, Physical Education and Recreation*
8. *Journal of School Health*
9. *Public Safety*
10. *Safety Education*
11. *Today's Health*

In addition to the above list, most State Departments of Health issue a periodic bulletin on health conditions, and frequently by request, teachers may be placed on the mailing list if they wish to receive current editions of such materials.

Professional Associations.—Membership in professional associations provides a desirable medium for in-service education. Professional organization membership should instill in the teacher the feeling that she is a component part of a movement consecrated to the progress of a profession which is dedicated to the service of society.

Two examples of professional associations concerned with school health are the American School Health Association and the American Association for Health, Physical Education and Recreation. The American School Health Association is "devoted to the interests and advancements of those engaged in school health activities and the service rendered by them." The official organ of this Association, the JOURNAL OF SCHOOL HEALTH, is published ten times annually and is distributed to those persons holding membership. The American School Health Association is affiliated with the American Public Health Association.

The American Association for Health, Physical Education and Recreation contains a Health Education Division devoted primarily to interests in this area. This Association is divided into six district associations and each state maintains its own association. The official publication of the National Association is the JOURNAL OF HEALTH, PHYSICAL EDUCATION AND RECREATION. It is published monthly, September through April, and bi-monthly in May and June. There are three types of membership: regular, professional, and student. Regular membership includes subscription to the JOURNAL while professional members also receive the RESEARCH QUARTERLY of the Association. This association is affiliated with the National Education Association.

In addition to these two national professional associations most states maintain local state teachers associations, which generally have sections devoted to the specific interest of teachers and other school personnel engaged in school health activities.

When feasible, teachers should be encouraged to attend professional meetings and conventions, especially when such activities are held in a near-by area. Attendance at these affairs enables teachers to learn first hand new developments in the field of health. Naturally, it would be next to impossible for every staff member of a school to attend all professional meetings. Consequently, some plan of rotation should perhaps be devised for attendance at such meetings. When provision is made for a limited number of teachers to attend educational conferences and conventions, those attending should be prepared to report the proceedings to the entire staff.

Questions for Discussion

1. Why is in-service education necessary in health and safety education?
2. How can bulletins be used for in-service education in health?
3. What is the value of school system in-service courses in health education?
4. What are some of the problems involved in inaugurating a school system in-service course for health education?
5. How would you arrange for a plan of individual independent study to improve yourself as a teacher of health?

Suggested Class Activities

1. Form a panel discussion group for the purpose of discussing the need for in-service education for health teachers.
2. Write a brief report on the scope of in-service education in health.
3. Prepare an agenda for a one-day workshop in health education for a school with which you are familiar.
4. Prepare a bibliography of references for teachers charged with the responsibility of teaching health in the elementary school, the junior high school, the senior high school.
5. Make a list of five professional journals or magazines, in addition to those listed in this chapter, that might be useful professional reading for health teachers.

References

1. Anderson, W. A., "Modern Supervision Is In-Service Education," *Education*, Volume 67, December 1946.
2. Illinois Joint Committee on School Health, "A Basic Plan for Student Health Education in Teacher-Training" Institutions, State of Illinois, 1944.
3. Irwin, Leslie W., and James H. Humphrey, *Principles and Techniques of Supervision in Physical Education,* St. Louis, 1954, The C. V. Mosby Company, Chapters X, XVI.
4. Joint Committee on Health Problems in Education of the National Education Association and the American Medical Association, Health Education, 4th edition, Washington, D. C., 1948, The National Education Association, Chapters VI, XV.
5. Prall, C. E., and L. C. Cushman, "Teacher Education in Service," Washington, D. C., 1944, American Council on Education.
6. "Teacher Education for the Improvement of School Health Programs," Bulletin, 1948, Number 14, Federal Security Agency, Office of Education, Washington, D. C.

INDEX

A

Accidents, 110-130
  causes of, to children, 117
  classification of, 113-114
  deaths and injuries from, 110-112
  home, 120-123
  motor vehicle, 123-125
  occupational, 125
  public non-motor vehicle, 126
  risks and exposure to, 114-115
  school, 126-128
    liability and responsibility for, 128-130
Administration of school health program:
  policies and procedures, 37-38
  under official community health organization, 26-31
  within the school, 36-37
Advanced study, 356
Alberty, Harold B., 193
Amateur shows, 305
American Association of School Administrators, 68
American Public Health Association, 332
Anderson, C. L., 52
Anderson, W. A., 360
"Animal Experiment Shows Two Foods Better Than One", 275
Animal experiments, 267
Audio-Visual Aids:
  adequate preparation in use of, 231
  basic factors involved in use of, 230
  evaluation of, 235
  contribution to motivation and interest, 229
  place of, 226
  program of sensory aids, 234
  purpose of, 227 ff
  scope of, 226
  selection of, 230
Audio-Visual Aids Handbook for Teachers, 236, 253

B

Barg, B., 254
Barr, A. S., 291
Bauer, W. W., 254
Bell, R., 253
Billett, Roy O., 174, 193, 275
Blanc, S. S., 275
Board of Education:
  administration of school health program, 31-34
Body efficiency, 263
Bogert, L. J., 205
Braun, E. C., 254
Breckenridge, M. E., 52
Brown, C. Adele, 39
Brubacher, J. S., 193
Bulletin boards, 209
Bulletins, 353
Burton, W. H., 169
Business and commercial groups, 318
Butts, R. F., 193
Byrd Health Attitude Scale, 349
Byrd, O. C., 349

C

Campbell, D. S., 193
"Care of Rats, Mice and Guinea Pigs", 275
Cartoons, 210
Caswell, H. L., 193
Chandler, A. C., 301, 312
Charts, 210-213
  data, 210
  diagrammatic, 211
  flow, 211
  genealogical, 212
Check List for Evaluating the School Health Instruction Program, 335
Chenoweth, L. B., 39
Concepts:
  changes in teaching method, 155-156
  as teachers' goals, 160, 177
  as unit objectives, 177
Conrad, H. L., 349
"Construction of Health Knowledge Tests", 349
Corey, S. M., 169
Correlation in health teaching, 105-106
Courses of study, use of, 105
Cowell, Charles C., 68

Creer, R. P., 253
Cromwell, G. E., 52
Cross, E., 236, 253
Curriculum guides, use of, 105
Cushman, Wesley P., 169

D

Daily health observations, 40-41
Dale, E., 236, 253, 291
Data gathering devices, 338
Definitions, 21-23
  health counseling, 23
  healthful school environment, 22-23
  healthful school living, 22
  school health appraisal, 23
  school health education, 22
  school health program, 21-22
  school health service, 22
Demonstration in health education, 255 ff.
  activities to improve bodily efficiency, 263
  animal experiments, 267
    feeding, 268
    inheritance, 268
  assigning of, 261
  dairy, 258
  disease control, 263
  examples of, 262
  feet and their care, 264
  first aid, 264
  food tests as, 262
    fat, 262
    minerals, 262
    protein, 262
    starch, 262
    water, 263
  laboratory work vs. demonstrations, 255
  lighting, 265
  lung action, 265
  medicine and first aid kit, 263
  physical examination, 266
  pupil demonstrations, 258
  preparation for, 259
  presentation of, 272
    introducing, 272
    presenting, 273
    following up, 273
  preserving demonstration materials, 274
  pupil ingenuity, 260
  relaxation, 263
  reproduction with insects, 266
  role of, 257
  safety demonstrations, 271
    combustibility of materials, 271
    conductivity of electricity, 272
    dramatics, 272

Demonstration in health education—Cont'd
    extinguishing fires, 272
    safety at street intersections, 271
  sewage disposal plant, 259
  teacher demonstrations, 257
  tooth decay, 264
  vision, 265
  water purification, 258
Department of audio-visual instructions, 224
Departments of Education and Health, 316
Disease control, 263
Douglass, Harl R., 169
Dramatization, 302, ff.
  advantages of, 302
  amateur shows, 305
  characteristics of children as a basis for, 303
  general characteristics of the dramatic method, 303
  grade placement of, 311
  health plays, 305
  limitations of, 394
  meaning of, in health education, 302
  pageants, 306
  pantomime, 307
  puppets, 307
  quiz programs, 308
  radio broadcasts, 308
  role playing and socio-drama, 309
  story telling and story playing, 310
Duker, S., 205
Dunham, F., 254
Dzenowagis, Joseph G., 108, 152, 205

E

Ears, 47-48
Education, responsibility of, through schools, 24-25
Edwards, N., 224
Elementary school,
  health teaching in, 96-98
  safety teaching in, 132-140
Elkow, J. Duke, 152
Evaluation, 333 ff.
  check list for, 335
  data gathering devices, 338
  demonstrations, 343
  dramatization, 344
  flash cards, 345
  for health attitudes, 345
  for health knowledge, 339
  for health practices, 346
  general and specific, 334
  in unit method, 182-183, 189-190
  meaning of, 333
  necessary ability for, 347
  need for, in health education, 333

Evaluation—Cont'd
  of health guidance program, 67
  oral questioning, 342
  paper and pencil tests, 339
    matching items, 341
    multiple choice items, 340
    true-false items, 340
  pupil evaluation, 338
  pupil records, 338
  specific evaluation, 336
  standardized tests, 338
  techniques for health education, 337
"Evaluative Criteria", 1950 edition, 349
Examination of work done by pupils, 344
Exhibits and museums, 292 ff.
  definition of, 292
  exhibit construction and preparation, 295
  examples of, 297 ff.
  in health education, 298 ff.
    audio-visual materials, 299
    school museums, 299
    visitations, 298
  school and classroom
    use of, 293
      conveying health knowledge, 293
      for parents and visitors, 294
Extra class sponsors, 64-65
Eyes, 46-47

F

Feet and their care, 264
Field trips in health education, 276, ff.
  correlation and integration through, 283
  evaluation and appraisal of, 286
  in the community and surrounding area, 289
  kinds of, 280
  organization of, 284
  orientation to use of, 276
  plans, procedures and arrangements for, 285
  purposes and values of, 278
  suggestions for, 287
  within the school, 288
Film evaluation report, 244
First aid, 264
First aid kit, 263
Flash cards, 344
"Food Makes the Difference in These Twin Rats", 275
Food tests as demonstrations, 262
Fraley, L. M., 52
Frazier, A., 291
Free and inexpensive materials, 319

G

Gebhard, B., 301
General evaluation, 334

Graphs, 214 ff.
  area, 214
  bar, 215
  pictorial, 216
Group health guidance, 66-67
Grout, R. E., 301
Guidance personnel, 63

H

Hass, K. B., 236, 301
Hallock, Grace T., 53, 69
Havel, Richard C., 68
Hazard, P. P., 253
Health attitudes
  evaluating for, 345
Health coordinator, 63
Health counseling, 65-66
Health guidance, 54-67
  and health appraisal, 58-59
  and health counseling, 65-66
  and health teaching, 54
  and school records, 59
  and teacher observation, 59
  appraisal of, 67
  definition of, 54
  evaluation of, 67
  group, 66-67
  meaning of, 54-55
  media for, 62
  methods of, 65-67
  need for, 55-56
  organization and administration of, 60-61
  principles of operation, 61
  problems of children, 57
    basis for determining, 58
  purpose of, 56-57
  responsibilities of personnel, 62-65
    elementary school teachers, 64
    extra-class sponsors, 64-65
    guidance personnel, 63
    health coordinator, 63
    health service personnel, 63
    school administrative officers, 62
    school psychologist, 63-64
    secondary school teachers, 64
    special teachers, 64
  techniques of, 65-67
Health interests
  surveys of, 60
Health misconceptions, 73-88
Health observations
  by teachers, 40-51
Health of children, 40-51
  and heredity, 44-45
  bases of good health, 43
  common signs of poor health, 45-51
  detecting illness, 41-43
  general appearance, 40

Health of children—Cont'd
  in relation to growth, 43-44
  symptoms of deviation from normal, 41-43, 45-51
    ears, 47-48
    eyes, 46-47
    facial appearance, 46
    hair and scalp, 49
    mental and emotional health, 50-51
    neck, 48
    posture, 49-50
    respiratory system, 46
    speech difficulties, 50
    teeth, 48-49
  teacher observation of, 40-51
Health deviations, 45-51
Health plays, 305
Health practices,
  evaluating for, 346
Health record card, 45
Health teaching, 70-108
  in elementary school, 96-98
  in high school, 101-105
  in junior high school, 98-101
  methods, 153-169
  need for, 70-73
  place of in schools, 88-91
  plans for, 93-96
  scope of, 92-93
  through correlation, 105-106
  through integration, 106-107
  units, 170-193
  value of, 91-92
Heredity, 44-45
Hicks, Dora A., 108
High School:
  health teaching in, 101-105
  safety teaching in, 145-149
Hill, Patricia J., 108
"How to Conduct a Rat-Feeding Experiment", 275
Humphrey, James H., 68, 152, 275
Huseby, H., 236

I

Independent Study, 357
In-Service Education, 350
  advanced study, 356
    independent study, 357
    institutional education, 356
  need for, 350
  professional associations, 358
  professional literature, 357
  school system in-service courses, 355
  scope of, 351
  supervision in health education, 352
    bulletins, 353
    demonstrations, 353

In-Service Education—Cont'd
    meetings and conferences, 352
    visitations, 352
    workshops, 353
Institutional education, 356
Integration in health teaching, 106-107
Irwin, Leslie W., 39, 53, 108, 152, 360

J

Jacobs, L., 52
Johns, Edward B., 173, 193, 349
Johnson, Warren R., 68
Joint administration of school health program, 34
Journal of Health, Physical Education and Recreation, 358
Journal of School Health, 358
Junior high school health teaching, 98
Junior high school safety teaching, 140

K

Kelley, G., 236, 253
Kepler, H., 312
Kinder, J. S., 236, 253
Knight, S. S., 169
Kohout, J., 275
Konheim, B. G., 332
Koon, C. M., 225

L

Laboratory work, 255
Lejoie, J. K., 225
Langton, C. V., 52
Lantagne, J. E., 68
Larrick, N., 225
Laurent, L., 254
Lawler, M. R., 225
Lesson planning, 184
  criteria for, 184
Levenson, W., 254
Library sources, 315
Lighting, 265
"List of Free and Inexpensive Health Instruction Materials," 332
Lottick, K. V., 253
Lung action, 265

M

McPherson, P. V., 108
Matching test items, 341
Material Aids to Learning, 206
  bulletin boards, 209
  cartoons as, 210
  charts as, 210
  definitions of, 206
  evaluation of, 223
  flash cards as, 212
  flat or still pictures in, 213

Material Aids to Learning—Cont'd
  graphs as, 214
  maps as, 217
  nature, purpose and use of, 207
  objects, specimens and models as, 217
  posters, 219
  scrapbooks, 219
  study and activity guides, 220
    sample study and activity guides, 220
    workbooks, 222
Materials for the unit, 103
Medicine kit, 263
Meetings and conferences, 352
Mental and emotional health, 50
Methodology in health education, 153
Methods of teaching, 155
  changing concepts in, 155
  concepts of, 153
  early methods in health education, 154
  facts affecting, 156
    classification of pupils, 157
    equipment and materials, 157
    individual teacher, 156
    time allotment, 157
  general, 163
  importance of, 153
  individual, 167
  lecture, 164
  and principles of learning, 158
  problem solving, 167
  recitation, 166
  small groups, 167
  sources of selection of, 158
  textbook, 165
  unit, 170
Miskelson, J. M., 169
Miller, H. H., 169
Models, 217
Morehead, J., 53
Moriarty, M. J., 53
Motion pictures, radio and television in health education, 237, 239
  basic problems in, 237
  criteria for using motion pictures, 240
  film evaluation reports, 243
  film sources, 240
  previewing and scheduling films, 245
  radio as a teaching aid, 247
  showing the film, 246
  silent and sound pictures, 239
  standards for selecting films, 243
  television in health and safety education, 249
  using films, 244

Moss, B., 109
Munroe, W. S., 169
Multiple-choice test items, 340
Museums in health education, 298
Musial, J. S., 225

N

Needs, techniques for discovering, 178
Neher, G., 349
Nichtenhauser, A., 254
"Nutrition Experiment," 275

O

Oberteuffer, D., 169, 349
Objects, Specimens and Models, 217
Official Health Agencies, administration of school health program under, 28
Oral Presentation, 194
  as an introductory activity, 198
  by students, 199
  critical listening, 203
  discussion in, 199
  discussion leaders, 200
  evaluation in, 204
  lecturing in, 194, 202
  oral comprehension, 203
  questions and answers in, 195
  role of, 194
  types of questions to avoid, 197
  typical class discussion, 201
Oral questioning, 342

P

Pageants, 306
Pantomime, 307
Paper and pencil tests, 339
Physical examination, 266
Pitluga, G. E., 291
Podolsky, E., 53
Poole, L., 254
Popkin, R. B., 275
Posters, 219
Posture, 49
Prall, C. E., 360
Previewing and scheduling films, 245
Principles of learning applied to health education, 158
Professional literature, 357
Professional organizations, 317
Pupil evaluation, 338
Pupil records, 338
Puppets, 307

Q

Quiz programs, 308

R

Radio as a teaching aid, 247
Radio broadcasts, 308
Rash, J. K., 109, 174, 193
Rasmussen, C., 205
Referrals on child health status, 41
References for units, 183
"Refining the Health Education Test," 349
Relaxation, 263
Remmers, H. H., 68
Reproduction, 266
Respiratory system, 46
Research Quarterly of the American Assoc. for Health, Physical Education and Recreation, 359
Robertson, W., 225
Rogers, J. F., 169
Role playing and socio-drama, 309
"Role-Playing in the Classroom," 312
Rones, B., 254

S

Safety
  habit formation in, 118
  misconceptions, 73
  prior to modern times, 112
  in the world today, 112
Safety education
  in the elementary school, 132
  in the high school, 145
  in the junior high school, 140
  probable value of, 118
  relationship to health, 110
  responsibility for in school program, 130
Sample study and activity guide, 220
School committee
  administration of school health program, 31
School health education
  development of, 17
  orientation in, 17
  administration of, under official community agency, 26
  administration, under board of education, 31
  organization and administration of, 24
  fundamental policies, 37
  procedures, 37
  within the school, 36
School psychologist, 63
School safety programs:
  community cooperation, 149
  organization of, 119
  supervision of, 119
Schuller, C. F., 253

Schreiber, R. E., 225
Scrapbooks, 219
Selkirk, T. K., 39
Sensory aids in health education, 234
Siebrecht, E., 152
Silent and sound pictures, 239
Simpson, A. P., 225
Smith, J. W., 291
Sources of health education materials, 313
  business and commercial groups, 318
  criteria for selection of, 314
  education and health departments, 316
  federal government, 317
  free and inexpensive materials, 319
  library sources, 315
  professional organizations, 317
  survey of sources, 324
  textbooks, 314
Southworth, W. H., 349
Special teachers, 64
Specific evaluation, 336
Specimens, 217
Speech difficulties, 50
Spencer, L. M., 68
Stack, H. J., 152
Standardized tests, 338
Starr, H. M., 109
Starr, I., 68
Stiles, L. J., 169
Stonecipher, J. E., 225
Story telling and story plays, 310
Streit, W. K., 109
Study and activity guides, 220
Survey of sources of free and inexpensive materials, 324
Survey of student health interests, 60

T

"Teacher Education in Service," 360
Teacher observation and health guidance, 59
Teacher observation of health of school children, 40
"Teaching of Healthful and Happy Living for Children in the Elementary Grades," 349
Teeth, 48
Television in health and safety education, 249
Textbooks, 314
Tooth decay, 264
Trice, R. A., 185
Trips, studies and objectives in the community and surrounding area, 289

Trips, studies and objectives within the school, 288
Turner, C. E., 39, 169

U

Unit
  approach, 186
  construction of, 176
  development of, 170
  evaluation, 182, 189
  in health education, 170
  introduction, 180
  learning activities and experiences, 181, 186
  length of, 183
  materials for, 183
  meaning of, 170
  objectives, 177
  overview, 176
  patterns, 173
  references for, 183
  teacher-pupil planning, 186
  types of, 172

Unit—Cont'd
  resources, 172
  teaching, 172

V

Vincent, E. L., 52
Vision, 265
Visitations, 352

W

Wayland, L. C. N., 275
Wheatley, G. M., 53, 69
Wittich, W. A., 253
Woelfel, N., 225
Wood, D., 291
Workbooks, 222
Workshops, 353

Y

Yeo, J. W., 174, 193

Z

Zankan, L., 254

RET'D DEC 16 1988

NOV 21 1988